D1547722

Adaptive Environmental Assessment and Management

Wiley IIASA International Series on Applied Systems Analysis

1 **CONFLICTING OBJECTIVES IN DECISIONS**
Edited by David E. Bell, *University of Cambridge*,
Ralph L. Keeney, *Woodward-Clyde Consultants*, *San Francisco*,
and Howard Raiffa, *Harvard University*.

2 **MATERIAL ACCOUNTABILITY**
Rudolf Avenhaus, *Nuclear Research Center Karlsruhe*,
and University of Mannheim.

3 **ADAPTIVE ENVIRONMENTAL ASSESSMENT AND MANAGEMENT**
Edited by C. S. Holling, *University of British Columbia*.

3 **International Series on Applied Systems Analysis**

Adaptive Environmental Assessment and Management

Edited by

C.S. Holling
Institute of Animal Resource Ecology
University of British Columbia

Sponsored by the United Nations Environmental Program

A Wiley–Interscience Publication
International Institute for Applied Systems Analysis

JOHN WILEY & SONS
Chichester–New York–Brisbane–Toronto

Reprinted January 1980

Library of Congress Cataloging in Publication Data:
Main entry under title:

Adaptive environmental assessment and management.

(Wiley IIASA international series on applied systems analysis; 3)
'A Wiley–Interscience publication.'
Bibliography: p.
Includes index.
1. Environmental impact analysis. 2. Economic development. 3. Environmental protection. 4. Ecology.
I. Holling, C. S.
TD194.6.A33 333.7 78–8523
ISBN 0 471 99632 7
Typeset at the Alden Press, Oxford, London and Northampton and printed by The Pitman Press, Bath.

The Authors

C. S. HOLLING
Institute of Animal Resource Ecology
University of British Columbia
Vancouver

ALEXANDER BAZYKIN
Research Computing Center
Pushchino, Moscow Region

PILLE BUNNELL
Institute of Animal Resource Ecology
University of British Columbia
Vancouver

WILLIAM C. CLARK
Institute of Animal Resource Ecology
University of British Columbia
Vancouver

GILBERTO C. GALLOPIN
Fundacion Bariloche, Argentina

JACK GROSS
U.S. Fish and Wildlife Service
Fort Collins, Colorado

RAY HILBORN
Institute of Animal Resource Ecology
University of British Columbia
Vancouver

DIXON D. JONES
Institute of Animal Resource Ecology
University of British Columbia
Vancouver

RANDALL M. PETERMAN
Canadian Department of the
Environment and
Institute of Animal Resource Ecology
University of British Columbia
Vancouver

JORGE E. RABINOVICH
Instituto Venezolano de Investigaciones
Cientificas
Caracas

JOHN H. STEELE
Marine Laboratory, Department of
Agriculture and Fisheries for
Scotland
Aberdeen

CARL J. WALTERS
Institute of Animal Resource Ecology
University of British Columbia
Vancouver

Dedicated to Dixon Douglas Jones,
whose spirit and intellect enriched
both his colleagues and this book

Foreword

Throughout the long history of man, people have altered the environment on which we all continue to depend. Generally this alteration was undertaken in order to make the environment what was conceived as a better place to live in – more productive of food, shelter, water, mineral resources, or other useful products. Such alteration is now commonly termed "development."

In the past, development was generally based on intuition, although that in turn rested on experience, some of it learned painfully through mistakes that wasted natural resources. In recent years, confronted with the evidence of past mistakes and the realization that we can no longer move to new lands to escape from those we have damaged, there has been a welcome trend toward a more careful and formalized approach to decisions about the development and management of the environment.

In developed countries one component of this trend has been the use of various methods of environmental impact assessment as a guide to the design of new environmental development and management projects. This process has usually begun with the survey of features of the environment likely to be affected by the particular developments under scrutiny. Analysis of the information collected in such surveys has led on to attempts at the prediction of the impact of the suggested developments and to the laying down of guidelines or rules for their management. Because these analyses have been based on large amounts of data, it has been assumed that they will be inherently more reliable than the intuition of our forebears. But because the world is so complex a place, it is quite impossible to record all its observable features. Abstraction and simplification are necessary, and in this process important, but often inconspicuous, components may be overlooked. Moreover, the world is in a state of constant change. Most plants and animals exhibit annual cycles of growth and reproduction, and many species exhibit regular or irregular fluctuations in numbers. Even in the absence of human interference, some of these fluctuations are sudden and dramatic and result in permanent change. Static surveys taking "snapshots" of the world at particular times are therefore not likely to document all the important features. Perhaps the most important constraints are imposed by the fact that development arises from the interplay of environmental and social systems, and the essential features of the latter are difficult to define; there is the added difficulty of reconciling the one with the other.

The uncertainties intrinsic in environmental systems are not always manifest in the statements of environmental scientists or managers. The ecologist has been too prone to behave as a latter-day prophet, seated remotely in his laboratory and functioning in a fashion reminiscent of the Delphic oracle. His predictions, often shorn of the qualifications that should be attached to them, have received more trust than they deserved, and when they have not been borne out by experience, the real value of scientific method as an aid to planning has tended to be discredited.

This book is therefore timely. It has grown out of concern with practical problems – how to guide developments in the high mountains and in the far north of Canada; how to manage salmon and other fisheries and land being opened up for recreation; and how to control an insect pest capable of devastating forests. The team that wrote it sought to apply a general understanding of environmental systems in methods that worked in the real world with its many uncertanties. It does not reject the concept of environmental impact analysis but restates its approach. It stresses the need for fundamental understanding of the structure and dynamics of ecosystems as entities. It sweeps away some of the exaggerations of popular ecology – for example, that ecosystems are universally fragile and that, because everything in nature is ultimately linked to everything else, it is necessary to study all components of the environment before one can evaluate the impact of a development project or the behavior of a system under management. As the following chapters point out, both these tenets are of limited truth.

Ecosystems by definition are bounded: they are complexes of plants and animals interacting with one another and with their immediate habitat. While links exist between ecosystems, it is by no means always necessary or possible to trace these to their ultimate terminations in order to understand the functionings of the systems. Moreover, ecosystems, like species, have resilience. They are in a state of dynamic equilibrium: the "balance of nature" is the result of continuing change. They have evolved in such a manner as to be able to withstand considerable stress before their structure and integrity are damaged. Indeed, controlled stress can enhance the useful productivity of some systems. The need is not to abstain from management because of a fear of the fragility of ecosystems, but to engage in studies that document the relationship between stress and resilience. Man operates as a manager of complex systems whose behavior is the outcome of many variables. Measurement of those variables, so that man's activities can be placed within the context of the system, including its uncertainties, is an integral part of the management process.

However, this book is not primarily about ecology. It is rather about how ecological understanding can be used to improve management and to guide development. Its point is that some of the ideas about ecosystems and their methods of characterization have led us astray, because they have not been based on sound understanding. In consequence, much effort has been devoted to the wrong kind of analysis and to collection of unnecessarily large quantities of data that have given rise to undue expectations and unsatisfactory predictions. Bigger data systems, founded on the uncritical collection of information, are not necessarily better data systems if the purpose is to contribute to decision making.

Understanding of environmental systems can only be gained by a careful sampling of carefully selected elements and processes, proceeding in parallel with the building of a model (ideally an analytical or mathematical simulation model). The building of the model is an integral part of the study, for it helps to structure the processes of both sampling and evaluation. The approach in this book places emphasis on the dynamics of ecological systems and the need to recognize on the one hand those elements that are sensitive to management and on the other, those that are robust. In nature there are some variables that are best treated as random, and both for this reason and because the models we build are abstractions of the real world, there must be uncertainty in the predictions they help us to make. One of the most telling points in the text is the statement that one cannot validate a model, but only invalidate it by exploring the implications of its assumptions and testing how far its predictions diverge from reality. We also have to remember to differentiate between the descriptive and scientific nature of the model and the prescriptive advice on policy we may choose to give as a result of our understanding of the results of modeling and of other elements in the assessment and management processes.

Because of uncertainties, environmental science can be used to guide the development and management of natural resources only if there is a continuing interaction between the scientist and the manager. Dialogue is needed at the outset to identify the key questions posed by a new development or management program – what might be done where and on what timescale? Such a preliminary dialogue guides field study, analysis, and modeling and the consequent judgement about the likely impact of new development or alternative possible management methods. It is often desirable to explore a number of alternative methodologies, and one important task of the scientist in such a dialogue is to explain new approaches to potential users. The dialogue must continue throughout the development process because of the uncertainty of predicting impacts at the beginning; for this reason also development plans need to be designed in a manner that admits of some flexibility so that they may be adjusted to make the best use of the environment. Similarly, management methods need continual monitoring and adaptation, feeding back to fresh work designed to improve the methods available. Such dialogue between developer or manager and environmental scientist can often be helped by a series of workshops at which the whole range of environmental and social variables and the alternative options and methods for development are discussed; the even more intimate association of manager and scientist in a small multidisciplinary team may provide for a still more effective interchange of ideas.

The value of this book is in its illustration of how these dynamic concepts, and the principle of continual adaptation of development and management to make the wisest use of the environment, can be operated in practice. It must be stressed that the accounts of case studies are an integral part of this volume, for they provide much of the supporting scientific information on which the general thesis is based and they illuminate how the arguments in the introductory chapters were arrived at. This volume is not a "cookbook." It does not provide a model for responding to all the many environmental problems of the world. What it does is show how the process of adaptive management can work.

The approaches to adaptive resource management discussed in Chapters 4 and 5 pose a special challenge to scientists and environmental managers in the developing countries, but at the same time offer them a particular opportunity. For these are the regions of the world in which the need for development is most pressing and the untapped resources are greatest. Technology is well able to create massive change, bringing with it the prospect of increased material wealth, but at the same time, because of the large number of people at subsistence level many are potentially vulnerable to a wrong move. At the same time, in these areas scientific and managerial skills to deal with such issues are in shortest supply. It would be quite impossible to catalogue all the environmental features of these regions in any comprehensive manner. Their ecosystems would require decades of study if they were to be understood at the level of detail that we understand the ecosystems that have been examined for centuries in developed countries. At the same time, development cannot wait. The methods proposed, emphasizing as they do selectivity and simplification of models so that the data gathering and analysis exercises are related to essential questions, offer the chance of effective action within the resources that developing countries have at their disposal: they permit an economy of approach that is vital under such circumstances. In developing, as in developed, countries, the emphasis on a partnership between environmental scientists and environmental managers remains of the first importance. The characterization of the social constraints and priorities within which development must take place is also particularly important in the Third World. A close and continuing dialogue extending through the whole process of development and monitoring its outcome is essential. The dynamic properties of both environmental and human social systems need to be reflected in a continuous interaction between them.

To meet all these requirements for a sensitive and adaptive environmental management process, scientists thus need to work alongside planners and administrators, whose constructive role in assessment is often not sufficiently recognized. This boon breaks new ground, going beyond existing analyses of environmental impact assessment, but it should be regarded only as a beginning. Although it grew from practical management problems, not many administrators and planners have been involved in its production. It is hoped that it will stimulate a response which will lead on to the development of new methods and the further clarification of the most efficient ways of deploying our limited resources and limited scientific manpower, so that we may learn how to work with (rather than against) nature in combining essential development with wise resource management.

MARTIN HOLDGATE
Director-General of Research
Department of the Environment
United Kingdom

Preface

This book is a report on our efforts to develop an adaptive approach to environmental impact assessment and management. It is written for policy makers and managers who are dissatisfied with the traditional procedures and principles and who seek some effective and realistic alternatives.

The study was initiated by a workshop convened in early 1974 by SCOPE (Scientific Committee on Problems of the Environment). The workshop was attended by individuals with an often bewildering range of experience, concerns, and styles – precisely those ingredients that are so useful at the very start of an analysis for defining the full range of issues and possibilities. Three particularly relevant questions emerged (Munn, 1975):

1. What, if anything, does our understanding of the nature and behavior of ecological systems have to say about the issues, limitations, and potential of environmental assessment?
2. What can be done to bridge the abyss presently separating technical impact assessment studies from actual environmental planning and decision making?
3. To what extent, and under what circumstances, do present methods provide useful predictions of impacts?

With those issues identified, a core group comprising the authors of this book was formed to test and evaluate the concepts, procedures, and techniques available, adding others where necessary and feasible. It drew upon an international network of expertise developed at the International Institute for Applied Systems Analysis (IIASA) in Laxenburg, Austria, combining this with the experience of a Canadian group at the Institute of Resource Ecology, University of British Columbia, and Canada's Department of the Environment.

The complexion of a core group is critical. With coherence and synthesis as the goal, the individuals had to be chosen for defined and focused biases. In this case the biases took the following form:

1. There was a bias that, however broad the issues, some things must explicitly be left out. In this instance no one was chosen with formal expertise in institutional analysis. Criticisms of environmental assessment and policy often identify institutional problems as central. But even the most ideal institutional organization (if such exists) is specific to nation or situation. Concepts and methods at least have some generality and can be subjected to useful review, testing, and evaluation by a group.
2. There was a bias toward experience and competence in ecology, in mathematics, and in dealing with government management agencies: in short, a simultaneous emphasis on relevance of concepts, rigor of analysis, and usefulness of technique.
3. There was a bias that both theoretical and applied techniques had gone far beyond the state of the art as it is practiced in environmental assessment and management.
4. There was a bias that process and product are inextricably linked; the sequence and design of workshops, the emphasis on adaptive approaches, and the design of different modes of communication are as important as models and the analysis.
5. Finally, there was a bias that alternative views of the way systems respond to disturbance are an essential step in identifying, classifying, and living with the unexpected.

Equally important for the motivation of the group was the opportunity to bring together some kindred spirits to form a kind of institute-without-walls – a project in which a major feature was our own learning and that of our students and colleagues in seven different nations. The United Nations Environmental Program (UNEP) expressed its willingness to support such a venture, and the present book is the very personal, very biased result.

The project itself spread over a two-year period. It was structured around a set of three intense five-day working sessions, in which all core-group members were brought together with a small number of outsiders to counteract inevitable tendencies towards self-satisfaction and parochialism. As in the adaptive procedures described in this book, such workshops were designed to provide a programmed series of sequential targets and to maintain integration while minimizing organizational and emotional overhead. Each session reviewed past work and writing, initiated and explored new proposals, and defined the activities and responsibilites for the next step. These were consolidated between the sessions by individuals cooperating with others in their home institutions. The result was a revolving series of position and briefing papers that were gradually refined and modified into material appropriate for the book. A draft prepared immediately after the third session set the stage for the final workshop. This last session, hosted by IIASA, again opened the project to as broad a range of perspective as encompassed by the initial SCOPE exercise.

Twenty-two participants were invited, each with a senior policy or administrative post in national or international organizations, operational responsibility for environmental research and management, or broad experience as a consequence of backgrounds in universities and foundations (Appendix B). Each received the draft volume several weeks before the meeting and was asked to subject the book to the kind of detailed critique expected of an outside reviewer. In addition, participants were asked to participate in an intense five-day discussion to share their views of issues and provide the authors with both a broader perspective and detailed recommendations for change in the manuscript. That meeting was a remarkable experience. Again, by bringing well-prepared, broadly experienced people together for a shared purpose, recommendations emerged that were more than the sum of each individual's contribution. The manuscript was fundamentally reoriented as a result of that experience, and the present book is the consequence. We believe it has been qualitatively improved, and we are indebted to the participants.

It is a pleasure to thank as well the other individuals and institutions who made the work both possible and enjoyable. Prior to this study and during it, Canada's Department of the Environment, through the good offices of Evan Armstrong, provided continuing access to people, projects, and resources. Without that sustained support, the effort would have been hopelessly irrelevant and utopian. The University of British Columbia's Institute of Resource Ecology (IRE), the International Institute for Applied Systems Analysis and the Venezuelan Institute for Scientific Research (IVIC), with generous support from UNESCO's Man and the Biosphere program, hosted the series of delightful workshops during which the book was conceived, planned, and edited. Numerous colleagues at the Fundacion Bariloche (Argentina), IRE, and IVIC labored through evaluating the usefulness of different techniques. M. P. Austin, W. Greeve, W. Matthews, R. E. Munn, Y. Shimazu, and N. Sonntag provided valuable suggestions and contributions. Joan Anderson, Ulrike Bigelow, Wendy Courtice, and Cathi Lowe contrived to produce and edit the manuscript. Finally, Howard Raiffa and Roger Levien of the International Institute for Applied Systems Analysis once more performed their unique roles as catalysts and supporters. To all, many thanks.

I will close with a personal and deeply serious observation. This effort represents a truly corporate activity of a group whose extraordinary individual talents blended in a way that resulted in a work qualitatively superior to any one individual's contribution. How, with traditional reward systems, can we give due recognition to the individuals of such groups? After all, the problems we address in modern society need the kind of group scholarship that can cross disciplinary, institutional, cultural, and even ideological barriers and still maintain excellence.

We originally intended to at least make a step in that direction by having the senior authorship of this book ascribed to the fictitious cover name Ralf Yorque, with all the others following in alphabetical order. The name was born as a product of the sometimes indelicate, perhaps naive, but always joyful, creative spirit of the group. Against great resistance we persisted to the eleventh hour. And then, in the face of the myopic pragmatism of tradition and publishing, we succumbed to the present inadequate compromise. As the one ultimately responsible, I repeat the original question. How can we properly recognize, reward, and hence encourage individuals to form such groups for the purpose of creative scholarship?

In having been totally unable to resolve that question, I can only end by apologizing to my colleagues and friends for my failure. Their talents and dedication deserved better.

C. S. HOLLING

Contents

1 Overview and Conclusions

Although the focus of this book is environmental assessment, its central message is that the process itself should be replaced. Environmental concerns are now often dealt with in a fixed review of an independently designed policy. We argue that this reactive approach will inhibit laudable economic enterprises as well as violate critical environmental constraints. We offer, as an alternative, the process of adaptive environmental management and policy design, which integrates environmental with economic and social understanding at the very beginning of the design process, in a sequence of steps during the design phase and after implementation. This argument is directed to senior administrators and policymakers who are responsible for the design of mechanisms and processes for dealing with developmental issues.

At the same time, however, we recognize that in many countries environmental assessment is practiced as a reactive review process. Even in that mode, the goal of environmental protection can be more validly and effectively achieved by the application of concepts, procedures, and techniques different from those commonly used. We describe these methods in some detail, directing our analysis to those persons with operational responsibility for doing environmental assessment and for communicating the results to senior administrators.

Because we are speaking to these two audiences, not all chapters will be of equal interest to all readers. Some concentrate on broad conceptual issues, some on fundamental procedures, and some on nontechnical but still detailed descriptions of techniques. The final chapters provide specific examples of five case studies.

This first chapter is designed for both audiences. It presents a broad overview and summary of the book – the issues, concepts, procedures, and techniques. Since it is written as an extended executive summary meant to stand largely alone, the themes and framework of analysis presented here will be repeated throughout the remaining chapters in greater detail.

In this summary we will treat five themes. The first is a brief encapsulation of present practice, presented in a rather exaggerated way for emphasis. The second provides a background that describes how present assessment practices have evolved. The third concerns the issue of uncertainty and the problem it now presents. The fourth offers a view of stability and resilience of systems, pointing to resilient or robust policy design criteria that differ from the traditional. The fifth and final topic reviews the processes and techniques that have emerged from our experience in dealing with specific problems of environmental policy design and assessment. Together, this set of issues, concepts, and techniques defines our approach.

MYTHS OF ENVIRONMENTAL MANAGEMENT AND ASSESSMENT

Perhaps the best way to introduce what adaptive environmental management and assessment is, is to indicate what it is not. Below we discuss twelve "myths" of present management and assessment. However much these appear to be straw men, they are still inherent in present practice. Most of us have subscribed to at least one or two at some time or another.

MYTHS OF ENVIRONMENTAL MANAGEMENT

The first set of myths concerns policy design and decisions.

Myth 1 The central goal for design is to produce policies and developments that result in stable social, economic, and environmental behavior.

Stability is a two-edged sword. If our knowledge of objectives and structure is complete, then design should indeed minimize the chance of the unexpected. But what we know of social, economic, and environmental behavior is much less than what we do not know. Therefore, the opportunity to benefit from change and the unexpected should be part of the design goal.

Myth 2 Development programs are fixed sets of actions that will not involve extensive modification, revision, or additional investment after the development occurs.

Program goals change, and unexpected impacts trigger corrective actions that result in progressively greater economic and political commitments to make further corrections if the initial ones are not successful. Thus, present decisions have *future decision consequences* as well as direct environmental ones, and these subsequent induced decisions often generate greater environmental impacts than seemed possible originally.

Myth 3 Policies should be designed on the basis of economic and social goals with environmental concerns added subsequently as constraints during a review process.

We must ride with ecological forces as much as with social and economic ones. Unless all are incorporated at the very beginning of the design, opportunities to achieve social goals are lost and subverted. The design will be more costly and the benefits too sensitive to the unexpected.

Myth 4 Environmental concerns can be dealt with appropriately only by changing institutional constraints.

This might ultimately be necessary, but constraints are more often perceived than real. Often, for example, one agency will have policy and management responsibility, and another, research or assessment responsibility. But the latter agency can hardly fulfill its research role without a policy perspective. That perspective can be developed internally if the goal is to design a number of alternative, but possible, policies. Each of these implies distinct or shared priorities for research that can be a powerful guide for research planning. At the same time, they provide an interface of communication between those responsible for the research and those responsible for decisions and management.

MYTHS OF ENVIRONMENTAL ASSESSMENT

This second set of myths concerns the details of how assessments are done.

Myth 5 Environmental assessment should consider *all* possible impacts of the proposed development.

The interesting question is rather: What does the fact that it is impossible to foresee all (or even most) of the impacts imply for the structure of the basic development plan and assessment research?

Myth 6 Each new assessment is unique. There are few relevant background principles, information, or even comparable past cases.

It is true that each environmental situation has some unique features (e.g., rare animal species, geological formations, settlement patterns). But most ecological systems face a variety of natural disturbances, and all organisms face some common problems. The field of ecology has accumulated a rich descriptive and functional literature that makes at least some kinds of studies redundant and some predictions possible. The same is true for economic, social, and physical aspects of the assessment.

Myth 7 Comprehensive "state of the system" surveys (species lists, soil conditions, and the like) are a necessary step in environmental assessment.

Survey studies are often extremely expensive yet produce nothing but masses of uninterpreted and descriptive data. Also, they seldom give any clues to natural changes that may be about to occur independently of development impacts. Environmental systems are not static entities, and they cannot be understood by simply finding out what is where over a short survey period.

Myth 8 Detailed descriptive studies of the present condition of system parts can be integrated by systems analysis to provide overall understanding and predictions of systems impacts.

The predictions from systems analysis are built up from an understanding of causal relationships between changing variables. Descriptive studies seldom give more than one point along each of the many curves that would normally be used to express such critical relationships. In short, what a complex system *is doing* seldom gives any indication of what it *would do* under changed conditions. Again, the interesting question is: What are the assessment, monitoring, and policy implications of the fact that even comprehensive systems models can make predictions only in sharply delimited situations?

Myth 9 Any good scientific study contributes to better decision making.

The interests of scientists are usually quite narrow and reflect the particular history of a discipline. There is thus no guarantee that in a scientific study the appropriate variables or processes will be measured, or that information will be collected on the proper spatial and temporal scales to address management questions. The research necessary for adaptive assessment and design must be focused through policy concerns.

Myth 10 Physical boundaries based on watershed areas or political jurisdictions can provide sensible limits for impact investigations.

Modern transportation systems alone produce environmental impacts in unexpected places. Transfers of impacts across political boundaries lead to a wide range of political and economic reactions from the other side. A narrow study that fails to recognize at least some of these impacts and reactions will provide inadequate and misleading information for the decision maker.

Myth 11 Systems analysis will allow effective selection of the best alternative from several proposed plans and programs.

This assertion would be incorrect even if systems models could produce reliable predictions. Comparison of alternative policies can occur only if someone places values on the results of each alternative. Rarely is this an explicit part of environmental assessment.

Myth 12 Ecological evaluation and impact assessment aim to eliminate uncertainty regarding the consequences of proposed developments.

Attempts to eliminate uncertainty are delusory and often counterproductive. The appropriate concept for both assessment and policy design is a recognition of the inevitability of uncertainties and the consequent selective risk-taking.

These shortcomings of present assessment practice are in part the consequence of the sudden and recent broad perception that environmental issues are important to the health of societies. The shortcomings reflect an urgent response to apparent crises, and before providing suggestions for an alternative, it is useful to explore this historical background.

DEVELOPMENT OF CONTEMPORARY ASSESSMENT PRACTICES

It is commonplace now to perceive limits – limits to growth, to resources, to climatic and environmental stability. Although the general perception of the importance of those limits is relatively new, mankind has always been confronted by them. There have always been problems of resource depletion, environmental contamination, and poverty. Moreover, industrial man's history, by and large, has been one of successful resolution of these problems, at least in the short term. In recent years, however, they seem to have taken the shape of crises, perhaps because the problems are ours and not our fathers'; more likely because our perceptions and methods, having once helped, now hinder.

The current approach to environmental concerns has been very much colored by a sudden shift of public awareness in the industrialized nations. What was once the concern of a minority became the concern of the public at large. The problems were not that qualitatively different from those of the past, but in the past they were largely local and often transient. Solutions were often found by simply waiting – next year's weather for crop production could well be better. And when this was not the case, there was often "somewhere else" that provided a way out – an unexploited resource, an unsettled piece of land, a new river to dam. In seeking elsewhere for solutions, the knowledge and technological devices needed could evolve at an easy pace. It required more innovation of spirit than innovation of technique for the Young Man To Go West.

With the "elsewheres" gradually becoming scarcer, however, alternatives had to be sought in new knowledge and technology rather than in new places. In seeking them, the scale and intensity of impact inevitably grew, eventually triggering that sharp shift of public awareness.

The past solutions however, provided little experience with ways of dealing with the environment. In most instances the goals of economic and social advance were most promptly achieved by subduing nature. The present protective response was therefore natural. In the face of limits now so suddenly perceived, time at least could be bought by protection of the environment and regulation of its use. The response is, therefore, largely reactive. Regional developments or policies are still designed within an economic context and reviewed only after the fact for their environmental consequences.

There has now been enough experience with this approach to suggest two major difficulties. First, the fundamental properties of any development or policy are set very early in the design stage. If problems arise because the original context was too narrow, any fundamental redesign is extremely difficult unless there is extraordinary pressure. Confrontation is guaranteed as different groups identify clear conflicts with their own interests. Confrontation and public debate are essential dimensions of the development of policies, but if the issues emerge only because the design phase was unnecessarily limited, economic enterprises offering legitimate social benefits can be halted and opportunities for husbanding and enhancing man's natural endowment can be subverted.

The second major difficulty with the present protective and reactive response is that it makes the practice of environmental assessment arbitrary, inflexible, and unfocused. Each issue is often dealt with as if it were unique, as if the environmental consequences could be separated from the social and economic ones. And yet the major environmental impact of a pipeline, for example, often occurs not along the route itself but at sites remote from it, as human settlements experience an acceleration of economic and population pressures. Such environmental effects induced through social forces are rarely considered. And the reverse is true. Deleterious social and economic impacts can be induced through ecological forces that, if recognized early, could at times be turned to man's benefit rather than simply suppressed and ignored.

The result of simple reactive assessment is therefore intolerable. How can we know what to measure for base-line information or assessment if the detailed character of the policy or development is not revealed until it has largely crystallized? The tendency is to measure everything, hence producing the indigestible tomes typical of many environmental impact statements. More time and effort are spent in measuring what is, rather than in projecting what is likely to be or could be made to be. Static and confused description replaces anticipation and clear prescription of alternatives.

But enough experience has now accumulated to allow a start to be made in developing and implementing an alternative approach. Systems ecology, in partnership with the physical sciences, has now matured enough to be capable of producing succinct representations of key elements of ecological and environmental systems. The resulting models mimic not simply static properties, but the dynamic ones that shift and change because of natural and man-induced influences. They can serve, alone or combined with similar economic representations, as a kind of laboratory world for the development of alternative policies and for the exploration of their impact.

The systems sciences have evolved methods of optimization that, if used with care, can point toward general policies that better achieve objectives by working with, rather than against, the rhythm of ecological and economic forces. There are techniques to deal with uncertain information, with mobilizing available data on partially known processes, and with the formulation of objectives that are less sensitive to the unexpected. All these lie at the heart of developing policies that recognize and benefit from both economic and environmental realities. Finally, decision theory provides a few theoretical hints and some practical experience in ways to explore decisions in the face of uncertainty and conflicting objectives.

This set of descriptive and prescriptive techniques provides the skeleton for policy design that can integrate economic, ecological, and environmental understanding. What's more, this integration can commence at the very beginning of the design process. But techniques alone are not enough. The best of techniques, unless guided by a clear vision of the fundamental issues and by a concept that gives them form, can turn solutions into larger problems. We argue that the fundamental challenge is not simply to better mobilize known information. Rather, it is to cope with the uncertain and the unexpected. How, in short, to plan in the face of the unknown. It is to that generic issue that we now turn.

THE ISSUE OF UNCERTAINTY

The design of policies or economic developments implies knowledge – knowledge to develop alternative policies, and knowledge to evaluate their respective consequences. And indeed a significant part of the contents of this book is concerned with how to deal with qualitative and quantitative data, how to use this knowledge of fundamental processes to construct models that can serve as "laboratory worlds" for the testing and evaluation of intrusions, developments, and policies. How, in short, to better reduce uncertainty. But however intensively and extensively data are collected, however much we know of how the system functions, the domain of our knowledge of specific ecological and social systems is small when compared to that of our ignorance.

Thus, one key issue for design and evaluation of policies is how to cope with the uncertain, the unexpected, and the unknown. It seems a common plea that too little is known of the structure and behavior of ecological systems. That can lead to the syndromes of living dangerously ("who cares how birds and bugs are affected – jobs and income are more important") or living safely (" nothing must be done until we know more"). But man has always molded the environment and been molded by it, and we will argue that more is known of ecological systems than is generally appreciated or used. Nevertheless, there is still uncertainty.

At the same time, there is growing unease about the economic systems with which ecological systems are linked. The unexpected increases in oil prices that have touched so many aspects of national economies have the same flavor as the unexpected appearance of a new crop pest after successful control of the original pests with insecticide. There is sufficient knowledge to anticipate both events, but both come as surprises. And, being unexpected, they are ignored in the original design of policies.

Even the ultimate objectives of environmental policies and developments are uncertain. A renewable-resource industry might have as an initial high-priority objective stabilized employment over the short term, which then shifts to a major concern for environmental standards, then to diversity of opportunity, and then to simple economic objectives. A design that assumes that objectives are immutable can rapidly foreclose options if those objectives shift.

Man has always lived in a sea of the unknown and yet has prospered. His customary method of dealing with the unknown has been trial-and-error. Existing information is used to set up a trial. Any errors provide additional information to modify subsequent efforts. Such "failures" create the experience and information upon which new knowledge is built. Both prehistoric man's exploration of fire and the modern scientist's development of hypotheses and experiments are in this tradition. The success of this time-honored method, however, depends on some minimum conditions. The experiment should not, ideally, destroy the experimenter – or at least someone must be left to learn from it. Nor should the experiment cause irreversible changes in the environment. The experimenter should be able to start again, having been humbled and enlightened by a "failure." And, finally, the experimenter must be *willing* to start again.

There is now increasing difficulty in meeting these minimum conditions. Our trials are capable of producing errors larger and more costly than society can afford. While the individual parts of a nuclear plant, for example, can be tested to the point of failure, the full integrated system cannot. Moreover, when this integrated system is viewed as not just an engineering system, but one that links ecological and social aspects as well, then the variety of unexpected events – from coolant failure to sabotage – and the scale of the consequences make trial-and-error truly a way to live dangerously.

Moreover, even when errors are not, in principle, irreversible, the size of the original investment of capital and of prestige often makes them effectively so. This behavior has its roots in a very human characteristic of industrial man: we do not like to admit and pay for our past mistakes; we prefer to correct them. And the consequences of correcting an inflexible plan is often increasing investment, increasing costs for maintaining and controlling the system, and progressive foreclosure of future decision options. Retreat from error is difficult for three reasons: because of the scale and consequence of possible "irreversible" physical changes; because changes in expectations for future returns make traditional goals politically or economically unacceptable; because reserves of capital and faith are lost, and the governed rise up against the governors, forcing them to invest in order to satisfy basic constraints newly perceived.

But the search for a solution should not replace trial-and-error with some attempt to eliminate the uncertain and the unknown. That could only result in tighter monitoring, regulation, and control based upon an illusory assumption of sufficient knowledge. Rather, the proper direction lies in the design of policies and economic developments that can allow trial-and-error to work again. Efforts to reduce uncertainty are admirable. Much of this book concerns just that. But if not accompanied by an equal effort to design for uncertainty and to obtain benefits from the unexpected, the best of predictive methods will only lead to larger problems arising more quickly and more often. This view is the heart of adaptive environmental management – an interactive process using techniques that not only reduce uncertainty but also benefit from it. The goal is to develop more resilient policies.

STABILITY AND RESILIENCE OF SYSTEMS

Our concept of resilience emerges from a very specific understanding of the structure and behavior of ecological systems (Chapter 2). It seems to have a counterpart in the behavior of institutional and other systems. The way a system responds to a planned or unexpected disturbance depends on its stability properties. One view, implicit in many of man's past efforts to manage, assumes that there is global stability. That is, no matter how large the disturbance, the system will recover to its original stable condition, once the disturbance is removed. This is a view of a Benign Nature that can comfortably accommodate trial-and-error on any scale. In this view, "big," which is necessary for economies of scale to be achieved, is always allowable.

A contrasting view infers a high degree of instability of ecological systems. They are fragile and caught in a natural rhythm of small-scale extinctions. They persist because of diversity in structure and over space. Outside sources provide the source of recovery. This view of Ephemeral Nature naturally leads to "small-is-beautiful" and to concentration on the need for spatial variety, diversity of opportunity, and fine-scaled, local autonomy.

But the burden of examples and of analysis leads to a combination of these extremes. Natural systems often have more than one stable mode of behavior. As long as variables like population density, amount of nutrients or even level of unemployment stay within a certain range, small disturbances can be absorbed. Quantities may change, but qualitative behavior does not. Small disturbances can be introduced incrementally, particularly if no apparent danger signal appears in the system. Then one additional increment can "flip" the system across the boundary into a totally different mode of behavior. A river can become an open sewer, or the economy of a nation can suddenly begin to prosper. In this world, the prudent manager would be wise to view nature less as benignly forgiving than as a Practical Joker.

The "small-is-beautiful" theme can still operate much as before with a more focused sense of optimal spatial scale and a recognition of the need for a balanced dependency on outside forces. But "big-is-necessary" can also be accommodated; one need only be more cautious. Thus if boundaries exist separating "desirable" from "undesirable," then the task is to control the variables carefully to keep them well away from the dangerous boundary. In addition, the boundary itself may be made less permeable; the strength of the guardrail can sometimes be more critical than the characteristics of the highway. To achieve less permeability effectively, big might well be necessary as the only way to gain sufficient knowledge of the boundary, to monitor the distance to it, and to institute control procedures to maximize that distance.

Maximizing the distance from an undesirable region is within the highly responsible tradition of safety engineering, of nuclear safeguards, of environmental and health standards. It works effectively if the system is simple and known – say, the design of a bolt for an aircraft. Then the stress limits can be clearly defined, and the bolt can be crafted so that normal or even abnormal stresses can be absorbed. The goal is to minimize the probability of failure. For bolts, this approach has succeeded. The probability of failure of bolts in aircraft, for example, is extremely small. But in parallel with that achievement is a high cost of failure – the very issue that makes trial-and-error as now practiced so dangerous.

One additional view of stability is needed. The three views – of Nature Benign, of Natural Ephemeral, and of Nature the Practical Joker – have been described thus far in three steps of increasing reality and comprehensiveness. In each case, however, it was implicitly assumed that the rules of the game were fixed. But ecological – and for that matter, economic, institutional, and social – systems are not static or completely determined. Variability and change are the rule and provide the next step toward reality.

Chance events dominate some ecosystems. Fire, rather than being a disaster, is the source of maintenance of some grassland ecosystems. Shifting patterns of drought determine the structure of some savannah systems in Africa. In addition, the variables themselves can move, through internal forces, from one region of stability to another. That is one of the lessons derived in the case study of forest pest management discussed in Chapter 11. There, we see that periodic insect outbreaks can be triggered by chance patterns of weather, by dispersal of moths from other areas, or by the natural growth of the forest. Populations increase explosively from low stable numbers to high. While the high numbers are stable for the insect, the forest cannot absorb the level of defoliation. The forest dies back, regeneration occurs, and the clock is started again. Such large swings and movements between stability regions contribute directly to forest renewal and to the maintenance of diversity.

Hence the variables of natural ecosystems do not reside in one stability region far from boundaries. Locally, species may even become extinct, to be reinstated through contributions from other localities. The variables are moving continually and the stability boundaries are being tested periodically. There is an internal monitoring of boundaries.

And now the central issue: not only do the variables shift and move, but so do the boundaries between stability regions. In ecosystems, this "stability landscape" owes its features to natural selection, which responds to the variability that occurs naturally. The reason boundaries exist where they do is that they are tested periodically.

This dynamic pattern of the variables and of the basic structure lies at the heart of coping with the unknown. However much we may be sure of the stability landscape of a physical system, we will rarely know the societal or ecological stability landscape in any detail. Policies often attempt to reduce variability within these partially known systems, either as a goal in itself or as an effort to meet standards of safety, health, or environmental quality. That constricted variability in turn may itself shift the balance of natural, cultural, or psychological selection so that stability regions will contract. Paradoxically, success in maximizing the distance from a dangerous stability boundary may cause collapse, because the boundary may implode to meet the variables. If surprise, change, and the unexpected are reduced, systems of organisms, of people, and of institutions can "forget" the existence of limits until it is too late.

This final view is of Resilient Nature, where resilience is a property that allows a system to absorb and *utilize* (or even benefit from) change.

But, of course, a different perspective on the generic issue, even with a concept to give it form, is not enough. Flowing from it must be some effort to design and test specific procedures and techniques that allow at least one step to be taken in harmony with this perception.

PROCEDURES AND TECHNIQUES

Our recommendations for a specific procedure and a range of techniques come from our particular experience with a number of studies of renewable resource problems in different national settings: renewable resource management and disease control in Venezuela and Argentina; range and wildlife management in the United States; developmental and oceanographic problems in Europe; ecological process studies in the Soviet Union; renewable resource and pest management systems in Canada.

We provide five specific case studies (Part II) so that examples of the results of applying these methods can be exposed. The first is a detailed example of the lessons learned in developing and evaluating policies for a problem of forest pest management. This one has gone farthest in coping with existing management questions, validating alternative modeling techniques, and generating management alternatives and evaluating their consequences. It has resulted in the adoption by agencies of two Canadian provinces of the approach for setting research priorities and developing and evaluating management options. The second case study is an example of an analysis of new procedures to enhance and manage fish stocks in North America, in which adaptive management approaches are proposed that provide, as an integral part of the policy design, a way of reducing uncertainty. It has gone farthest in affecting and modifying a proposed new development to enhance fisheries populations. The third is an example of the results of one of the intensive 5-day workshops (whose details will be described shortly) that resulted in a preliminary but broad assessment of the consequences of development in a high alpine region of Europe. The fourth is a modeling and policy analysis of a major regional development in a sparsely populated region of Venezuela involving hydroelectric, forestry, and agricultural development. The fifth and final example deals with the impacts on wildlife populations of oil-shale development in the western United States.

In each case, the purpose was to develop a set of alternative policies or plans and assess their environmental, economic, and, in some cases, social consequences. At first thought, therefore, the process we recommend would seem more appropriate for environmental management than for assessment. Before addressing that question in the next section, however, we shall compare our recommendations with two procedures that are in common use.

At one extreme is the approach of having a small core planning staff contract out parts of the study – the hydrological analysis, vegetational or wildlife survey, and so on. Integration occurs on receipt of the contracted reports. But two difficulties emerge. First, the contracted pieces typically drift farther and farther from the question posed, and, since the parts are not linked with each other throughout, useful integration of the pieces becomes very difficult. Second, it is unlikely that a small core planning team will have sufficient breadth and depth of knowledge to identify those key elements or processes that deserve analysis. To protect themselves, there is a natural tendency for them to wish to measure everything they can think of. Typically, these are static quantities, both environmental and economic, or the more obvious physical processes. But the problems are not static; they are not simply physical; their behavior comes from the integration of the parts and not just from the parts themselves. As a result, much of the information gathered is unnecessary, and key items are ignored entirely. The cost is unnecessarily large, and the product incomplete.

At the other extreme is the large interdisciplinary team that attempts to develop the integration missed in the above approach by mobilizing most of the expertise within one organization. In order to avoid bureaucratic growth, a task force is sometimes established only for the duration of the study, with staff provided from a number of existing institutions. Such large teams, however, have a high financial, organizational, and emotional overhead attached to them. We suppose this could be overcome by appropriate organizational techniques, but the common experience is that it is not. Anarchy and fragmentation often develop. Separation of the team from the policymaker is common, and internal goals evolve that have more to do with survival of the team than with the original purposes.

In contrast, the process we have evolved depends on a small core group of two or three analysts and a support staff of one or two. The core group should have experience in two or three of the disciplines involved – for example, forestry, fisheries, economics, or ecology. At the same time, their prime experience should be in integrating information and coordinating people. In our case the integration comes from application of systems techniques – e.g., computer modeling of dynamic systems, mathematical analysis, optimization, utility analysis, and communication. The coordination comes from the development of a series of steps, each of which is initiated by a workshop that brings together key cooperators for short periods of intense interaction. The time between the workshops is spent in consolidation: the core group refines the model(s), develops initial alternative policies, analyzes data; the collaborators collect and integrate data and information both on behavior of the system and on goals of the project. The workshops that define the sequence of steps are the heart of the approach (Chapters 3 and 4). They provide a series of sequential targets, maintain integration while minimizing organizational and emotional overhead, and allow involvement of a wider spectrum of key actors than is normally possible. The policymaker, busy as he is, is involved at key points for short periods.

Each workshop draws upon up to twenty specialists, the choice depending on the particular stage of the process. The first workshop is critical, for it is then that the problem is defined and focused. It is essential to have all prime "actors" present at that time – scientists, managers, and policy people. The policy people and the managers provide a balance to the scientist's penchant for exquisite detail and excessive resolution. The scientists provide the rigor and understanding of fundamental physical, ecological, and economic forces. During such a workshop, impact categories are classified, key information needs defined, alternative actions described, and the framework and crude working version of a computer model developed. Even if, through lack of expertise, facilities, or time, a model is not developed, the techniques of organizing elements in preparation for a formal modeling effort are themselves of fundamental value. The point is that, at the very beginning of the study, all elements – variables, management acts, objectives, indicators, time horizon, and spatial extent – are jointly considered and integrated. Even the crude model that is developed at this stage can be a powerful device to explore the significance of unknown relationships. By testing alternative extremes, priorities can be established for data and for scientific and policy analysis.

That first workshop is followed by a period of consolidation. The model is further refined and tested by the core group. Some of the attending specialists assume responsibility for collecting detailed information on both scientific and policy questions. Subsequent workshops further define management objectives, construct alternative policies, and explore uncertainties. Some workshops involve only scientists when the goal is critical scrutiny of underlying assumptions. Some involve largely managers, when the issue concerns operational feasibility. Some involve only decision makers, when the purpose is to ensure relevance and understanding. In every instance, a period of consolidation follows the workshop.

One key technique makes it possible to set this process in motion. That is the ability to abstract the essential properties of at least some ecological and environmental systems and to represent them in a model that mimics behavior over time for a variety of conditions. By essential, we mean those properties that generate the minimal natural behaviors that must be retained in order for the model to be responsive to the management questions. The models, therefore, are not designed for general scientific purposes but for very specific management ones. Hence, they attempt to be both parsimonious (and hence tractable) and realistic (and hence useful).

Our professional experience is ecological and environmental. But it is obvious that at least regional economic systems can be treated in the same way and integrated with the ecological and environmental systems. Because this integration occurs in the very first step in the analysis, it is possible to achieve designs that work with rather than against natural forces. In so doing, more opportunity is provided for less costly and intrusive economic developments and even for the enhancement of natural systems rather than simply for their protection. We provide examples of this integration, as well as examples in which simple social phenomena, such as demographic and market processes, are included. More complex social behaviors are well beyond the state of the art and are better dealt with as they are ideally treated now – through experience, sensitive perception, and public dialogue.

The models conceived in the workshop process focus on one or more of the ecological, environmental, economic, or simple social forces underlying many developmental problems. They provide a credible "laboratory world," which makes it possible to mobilize a set of techniques for prescription and evaluation – techniques to allow the following:

- Generation of a range of alternative objectives
- Design of effective policies to achieve alternative objectives
- Generation of indicators (social, economic, resource, and environmental) of relevance for decision
- Evaluation of each policy in terms of the behavior of the indicators over space and time
- Partial compression of indicator information to facilitate screening of the most appropriate policies
- Communication and interaction between and among those who design, choose, and endure policies (staff, decision maker, and citizen)

The particular techniques chosen to represent or model the dynamics of a system need not be numerical simulation models. Beyond the constraints set by expertise, the characteristics of the problem in part suggest the technique chosen. There are three key characteristics; (a) the number of variables, management actions, and spatial elements; (b) the level and breadth of understanding of underlying physical, ecological, and economic processes; and (c) the number and quality of data. No matter what combination of these any specific problem has, there is a technique available.

Our exploration of techniques covered a range from nonquantitative cross-impact matrices, to "qualitative" modeling techniques that generate dynamic changes over time without data on magnitude, to simple simulation methods, and finally to fully detailed, large simulation modeling techniques.

If the level of understanding of processes is low, and data are scarce, all of these techniques seem to perform equally well or poorly. But even when data are scarce, there is usually more understanding of processes available than is generally recognized. And there are techniques available that organize and focus understanding of processes even in the face of scattered data. If these techniques are used, then we have found simple or complex simulation models to be clearly superior in predictive capacity, responsiveness to questions, and relevance of results (Chapter 5).

Even if we have a satisfactory dynamic model, however, one further step is helpful. Such models are complex. They are so difficult to understand that many are tempted to play computer games with them in a blind, undirected exploration. But there are ways to simplify these models so that we can understand the essential behavior. The structure of such a model can be analyzed in order to reduce the number of variables and interrelations to those that are key determinants of the qualitative behavior. Often a simplified set of equations can then be devised that is used to provide a depth of understanding that is enormously useful as a guide to intuition and judgment. Alternatively, topological or graphical representations can sometimes be designed to achieve the same purpose in a form more readily understood by nonmathematicians (Chapter 6). All these techniques provide a clear direction to this search for policies and impacts, and allow us to convey our understanding to the decision maker more effectively.

Before a model can be used as a laboratory world to test the consequences of alternative policies, its degree of credibility must be explored. Note that no model – mental or mathematical – is "true." But degrees of credibility and usefulness can be defined, not, as is often done, by attempting to tune parameters to fit a given set of historical data; rather, the effort should be directed to *invalidate*, and not to validate, the model (Chapter 7). That is in harmony with the scientific method, where only disproof, not proof, is possible. Invalidation requires information from extremes of behavior that can then be compared with model predictions for similar extremes. The data on extremes come from natural experiments that have been historically recorded – for example, the extreme weather that occurs in some particular geographical region or that has occurred at some past time. Further information on extremes comes from the behavior of the target system or similar systems that have been subjected to management by man. The more robust the model at these extremes, the more confidence can be placed in its behavior under newly designed policies.

That leads to the final set of methods, which use this laboratory world to develop, explore, and evaluate alternative policies (Chapter 8). These methods include the formulation of objectives, the definition of indicators, and the touchy job of evaluation.

There may be many ways of attempting to achieve a given objective. For example, maximum sustained yields from a fishery can be reached by controlling fishing effort through manipulation of open fishing days or by setting catch quotas. The role of the model at this point is to generate those indicators that best match the objective. Because costs and benefits arise in many forms, the manager usually needs a large number of indicators. One necessary step then becomes the compression of this mass information into a comprehensible form. There are several ways this can be done. Because of the breadth of their comprehensibility, we prefer indicator compressions that are graphical. The relative merits of alternative management actions can be evaluated using the indicator output from the model. Both formal and informal evaluation techniques are useful here, but in either case, they are used only to point out policies that should be more thoroughly explored. The object is not to derive some mythical "optimal" policy, but rather to compare and then combine alternative policies in order to illuminate the range and nature of available choices.

Methodologies are only parts of the process, however. Communication holds these parts together. The thick volumes that characterize the products of many impact assessment programs are an inefficient and ineffective way to communicate results. There are other ways to present the information, in which the level of detail and attention required are determined by the particular user (Chapter 9). The resulting reports, graphical summaries, and audiovisual materials become, with the workshops, an integral part of the procedure, allowing interaction and adaptive modification throughout.

That, then, completes our summary of the issues, concepts, procedures, and techniques. In closing this chapter, we discuss not their merit or lack of it, but whether it is at all practical to implement them in the face of present institutional realities.

THE PROBLEM OF IMPLEMENTATION

DEVELOPED COUNTRIES

To those conditioned by North American approaches to environmental assessment, where assessment is viewed as a passive reaction to an independently developed proposal, the process described above would seem too inclusive. Proposals are generated according to guidelines and are then reviewed by an informal panel. Certainly, the modeling techniques, at least, would be useful in forming a judgment. But, we would argue, the other techniques and the procedures themselves would make a qualitative improvement in even this reaction mode of assessment.

In order to assess something properly, there has to be a yardstick against which performance is measured. And that yardstick is some alternative policy or development. One is clearly the "no-policy" world. If that is the only alternative, then confrontation between no development and development is encouraged. But other explicit policies would provide a richer menu of alternatives that would sharpen and focus response to a proposal and suggest specific modifications. Once there is a requirement for such alternatives, if only for internal comparison by the assessment panel, then assessment is in the game of policy design. At that point all the procedures and techniques described above can apply.

Despite the breadth and depth of such an adaptive assessment approach, the cost is small. An experienced core group of two or three analysts and a support staff of two could comfortably undertake one major assessment a year, together with perhaps four to six preliminary "rough cut" assessments. Each, of course, would draw heavily on available expertise within the agencies concerned with the problem. Hence the benefit is not only the assessment itself but a growing body of experience within agencies. In nearly every instance, there are enough *existing* data, however, scarce, to begin, since we argue that the design of a program to collect data for establishing baselines or for monitoring must follow and be integrated with the approaches described here, rather than precede them. A modest budget is necessary to mobilize and organize existing data, but this can typically be managed within the cooperating agency. At most, it is a one-man-year effort. Similarly, computing budgets can be as small or large as facilities and expertise warrant. The resource in scarce supply is rarely money; it is expertise and experience in the techniques and procedures described here. If this expertise and experience are available or can be developed, the costs are an order of magnitude less than those typical in North American impact assessment efforts.

DEVELOPING COUNTRIES

When a new approach, such as the one put forward in this book, appears, it is useful to examine it from different viewpoints. Here an attempt is made to focus on some aspects that seem particularly relevant from the point of view of developing countries. Moreover, by adopting that perspective the lessons for industrialized countries might, paradoxically, emerge more vividly.

Problems are perceived very differently in developing countries, and, in addition, there is often a high within-country cultural diversity. Because of these differences, developing countries can sometimes more easily explore new ways of looking at problems and new solutions. An example is the perception of eutrophication in Southeast Asia. There, high nutrient loads, abundance of algae, and aquatic weeds like water hyacinth are considered desirable in rice fields, fishponds, and even in some natural water bodies. They are viewed as a resource and as enhancing the production process, rather than as a nuisance. Also, it was not coincidental that a totally different way of measuring socioeconomic growth in global models was originated in developing countries. In the Latin American World Model this was life expectancy at birth. Differences in the perceptions of problems made it necessary to look for alternative solutions.

In this book, a nontraditional perception of the behavior of ecological systems is presented. We link this with the potential richness of perceptions emerging from the present cultural diversity on our planet. This variety is prized because it is not yet possible to decide whether one, some, or many perceptual frameworks, or paradigms, are necessary in order to cope with different problems in different regions of the world. It is likely that new and evolving paradigms will be needed. And it is also likely that some of these will originate in developing countries, and will modify and enrich the views presented here.

Too often in the past, socioeconomic development and environmental quality have been perceived, or construed, as if they were quite opposite, antagonistic concepts. The conceptual framework proposed here is not only absolutely compatible with the dynamic concepts of development and the rational use of natural resources, but it also tends to promote the generation of self-reliant and endogenous approaches to the environmental problems – approaches appropriate to local conditions, needs, and socioeconomic structures.

For any one management or developmental objective, there are usually many alternative ways of implementation. We emphasize that it is essential to generate and consider a wide range of alternatives, especially in developing countries. Inadequate search for alternatives can make plans and projects fail utterly because they are not adapted to the local realities. This is evident in tropical agriculture, where there are many examples of attempts to introduce temperate-zone, capital-intensive technologies. And more important than alternatives for implementation, the generation of alternative objectives, or goals, is viewed as a fundamental process.

The emphasis throughout the book upon a permanent and inherent state of change in ecological systems suggests a richness of qualitatively different behavior modes that might be an appealing concept for the developing countries. It is often shown that attempts to force classical stability or constancy may lead to a shift of behavior into undesirable modes. But changes need not be catastrophic. By the same token, an explicit search could be made to discover desirable stability regions. Strategies might then be devised to move the environmental or socioeconomic system from an undesirable condition to more desirable ones.

Developing countries, perhaps more than others, are in a permanent state of change. Although it is an open question whether the perceived goal is always the desirable one, in most cases in the developing countries it is good to move away from the present state. Thus, developing countries, having no vested interest in constancy, might find the concepts of resilience, of managing with uncertainty or even managing uncertainty itself, appropriate and suggestive. The concepts might also have an influence upon the socioeconomic theories, approaches, and strategies of national, regional, and global development. For instance, the concepts emphasized in the book might help one to understand how some decisions and strategies reduce the stability region of a system, showing how some policies lead to a narrowing of the set of future options. So, even though the set of case studies utilized as examples in the book pertain to a small class, the implications of the approach impinge upon a much wider set of problems.

It seems clear that any approach that attempts to deal explicitly with uncertainty would be of particular relevance for the developing countries. Considering the needs for rapid socioeconomic development, the existence of unexploited natural resources, and the availability of technology for wide-scale projects, the uncertainties involved are not only great but are often of a qualitatively different nature than in developed countries. This, coupled with the great vulnerability of major segments of the population, suggests that the explicit consideration of uncertainties is a fundamental concern of developing countries.

While it might be argued that some of the techniques presented here are not universally adaptable, the main emphasis throughout is on an overall approach to the problems. This is why a range of techniques, from the simple and naive to the more sophisticated, has been explored. The choice and usefulness of a particular technique depend very much upon the particular situations and available resources. As an example, for a group of experts engaged in a regional planning project, even the simplest approach to the first steps in the workshop procedure has proved to be very valuable in reidentifying the relevant issues, promoting integration among disciplines, and producing a more global and coherent view of the problem and its solutions. This happened with a 2-day workshop in the Bermejo River basin in Argentina. Thus, the relevant question is not whether the approach presented here is the best possible one, but whether it is better than the traditional ones.

The adaptive approach is particularly useful in helping to make fast decisions where data are incomplete and uncertainty is great. All of the techniques discussed are accessible at a moderate cost, and some are very cheap. For a fixed budget, whatever its size, the approach can allow a substantial saving in terms of data collection, in the sense that the emphasis is put upon collecting only the relevant data, without following the traditional massive data collection procedure.

Finally, it is important to emphasize the value of the workshop procedure (one of the cores of the approach) in terms of its efficiency for mobilizing and organizing scarce critical resources (expertise, funds, time). It also has a high demonstration potential, thus encouraging institutional flexibility and the dissemination of integrated views about the relevant issues.

CONCLUSIONS

We have attempted, in this overview, to present the issue of uncertainty that underlies the major resource and environmental problems facing mankind. The concept of resilience, in which the different distinct modes of behavior are maintained because of, rather than despite, variability, is suggested as an overall criterion for policy design. The more that variability in partially known systems is retained, the more likely it is that both the natural and management parts of the system will be responsive to the unexpected. The very process and techniques we recommend, while aimed in part at reducing uncertainty, are designed as a changing adaptive process of policy design. It is the combination of the issue, the concept, and the process and techniques that makes for adaptive environmental assessment and management.

Although we see assessment as an integral part of management, in some countries these are viewed as separate activities. Because of this, we will separate our detailed conclusions into those most relevant for management and those most appropriate for assessment. First, the recommendations for adaptive management:

1. Environmental dimensions should be introduced at the very beginning of the development, or policy design process, and should be integrated as equal partners with economic and social considerations, so that the design can benefit from, and even enhance, natural forces.
2. Thereafter, during the design phase, there should be periods of intense focused innovation involving significant outside constituencies, followed by periods of stable consolidation.
3. Part of the design should incorporate benefits derived from increasing information on unknown or partially known social, economic, and environmental effects. Information can be given a value just as jobs, income, and profit can.
4. Some of the experiments designed to produce information can be part of an integrated research plan, but part should be designed into the actual management activities. Managers as well as scientists learn from change.
5. An equally integral part of the design is the monitoring and remedial mechanisms. They should not simply be *post hoc* additions after implementation.
6. In the design of those mechanisms there should be a careful analysis of the economic trade-offs between structures and policies that presume that the unexpected can be designed out, and less capital-expensive mechanisms that monitor and ameliorate the unexpected.

There are also specific conclusions relevant to the techniques of environmental assessment, some of which are summarized here:

1. Structural features (size distribution, age, who connects with whom) are more important to measure than values of individual variables.
2. Events at one place can re-emerge as impacts at distant places.
3. Monitoring of the wrong variable can seem to indicate no change even when drastic change is imminent.
4. Impacts are not necessarily immediate and gradual; they can appear abruptly some time after the event.
5. Variability of ecological systems, including occasional major disruptions, provides a kind of self-monitoring system that maintains resilience. Policies that reduce variability in space or time, even in an effort to improve environmental "quality," should always be questioned.

6. Many of the existing assessment methods (e.g., cost–benefit analysis, input–output, cross–impact matrices, linear models, discounting) assume none of the above occurs, or at least, that none is important. All such methods should be used with caution.

Part One

The Approach

2 The Nature and Behavior of Ecological Systems

Our perceptions determine the methods we use and the solutions we see. That is why puzzles fascinate and challenge, for their solution requires a shift of perception. Without that shift, the method for solution eludes us. Puzzles of ecological evaluation are the same. If present methods seem to be inadequate or even to magnify problems, perhaps the perceptions of the way ecological systems behave or are structured are partly at fault. Certainly, the different methods and approaches described in the following sections emerge directly from a very specific view of how such systems behave. It is important to make that view clear. At the least, by making our biases visible we make them testable.

Long before man appeared on the scene, natural systems were subjected to traumas and shocks imposed by drought, by flood, by geological changes. The systems that emerged are the ones that were able to absorb and adapt to these traumas and to their continual occurrence. Such systems hence are not fragile but are the creation of change. They are not, however, infinitely resilient. A forest can be turned into a desert, or a river into an open sewer. But to do so, man must often try very hard.

The evaluation of ecological policies is an attempt to assess how an ecological system will be affected by disturbances, both man-made and natural. Those disturbances may threaten survival, but they can, with care in design, enhance benefits. Examples of how ecological systems respond to shock and disturbance provide the core of our understanding of their structure and behavior.

Four properties determine how ecological systems respond to change and, as a consequence, how policies should be designed and how impacts should be assessed:

- The parts of an ecological system are connected to each other in a selective way that has implications for what should be measured.

- Events are not uniform over space, which has implications for how intense impacts will be and where they will occur.
- Sharp shifts in behavior are natural for many ecosystems. Traditional methods of monitoring or assessment can misinterpret these and make them seem unexpected or perverse.
- Variability, not constancy, is a feature of ecological systems that contributes to their persistence and to their self-monitoring and self-correcting capacities.

These will be discussed by example in the following sections.

THE ORGANIZATION OF ECOLOGICAL SYSTEMS

Everything is not strongly connected to everything else.

Smith and van den Bosch (1967) have prepared a particularly well-documented example of the response of a cotton ecosystem to disturbance. There is a series of valleys on the coast of Peru formed by streams running from the high Andes to the Pacific Ocean. Many of these valleys are under intensive agriculture and, because of the low rainfall, are irrigated. As a result, each valley is essentially a self-contained ecosystem isolated from the others by barren ridges. In one of these valleys, the Cañete, the crop was shifted from sugar cane to cotton during the 1920s. Over the years a group of seven native insects became significant cotton pests. The pest problem was essentially modest and the farmers of the region lived with the resulting economic damage. In 1949 chlorinated hydrocarbons like DDT, benzene hexachloride, and toxaphene became widely available, and the opportunity arose to dramatically decrease pest damage and increase crop yields.

The initial response to the insecticide treatment was a pronounced decline in pests and a 50 percent increase in cotton production. After two or three years, however, six new species of insects became as serious a problem as the original seven had been. The reason for the appearance of these new pests was the elimination of parasites and predators that were killed by the insecticides. Within six years the original seven insect pests began to develop resistance to the insecticide, and crop damage increased. In order to control this resurgence, the concentration of the insecticide had to be increased and the spraying interval reduced from two weeks to three days. As these control measures began to fail, the chlorinated hydrocarbons were replaced by organophosphates. But even with this change, the cotton yield plummeted to well below those realized before synthetic insecticides.

The average yield in 1956 was the lowest in more than a decade, and the costs of control were the highest: the agricultural economy was close to bankruptcy. This forced the development of a very sophisticated ecological control program that combined changed agricultural practices with the introduction and fostering of beneficial insects. Chemical control was minimized. These new practices allowed the re-establishment of the complexity of the food web, with the result that the number of species of pests was again reduced to a manageable level. Yields reached the highest level in the history of cotton production in the valley.

This example emphasizes the point already mentioned: many ecosystems are remarkably forgiving. The surprise is that such frequent application of a blanket of insecticide over an entire isolated valley did not have a more dramatic and destructive effect. But the effect that was triggered suggests the importance of the linkages within ecosystems. The complex of the original seven pests, the six induced pests, the cotton and other food sources, and the natural enemies represents a subassembly of the larger ecosystem of the valley. The insects are linked by various intensities of competition for different species of their food resource, part of which is shared, part specific. The parasites and predators establish further links and connections – some connecting a single parasite with a single host, some connecting with several hosts. This ecosystem provides an example of a food web, through which energy flows and material is cycled.

But note that the connections are organized in a special way. Each species has a limited number of connections with others that give a distinct organization to the ecological system. This organization results in a unique capacity to absorb or funnel impacts.

Before we explore these capacities, however, we shall cite one additional example from our own experience that emphasizes the importance of simply knowing who is connected to whom. The large open-sea fishes of the North Sea, like herring and mackerel, have been nearly eliminated by fishing pressure. At the same time there has been an increase in the number of bottom fishes. At first thought the spatial separation of these two groups – one living in the upper waters, one living in the lower waters – would make such a response unexpected. But removal of herring and mackerel relaxed the competition with smaller open-sea fishes such as sand eels, Norway pout, and the young stages of the bottom-feeding fishes. Since these species, unlike herring, migrate between upper and lower regions, they provide a conduit that carries energy and material to fishes living near or on the bottom. With their herring competitors and predators removed, this conduit could carry more resources downward so that bottom-dwelling populations increased. Thus, it is the number and kinds of these links that can induce unexpected consequences.

But note that the simple thought (often expressed in species lists or the popular rhetoric of ecology) that everything is intimately connected to everything else is simply not true. One might have expected the removal of large pelagic fishes to have had effects on many other groups, especially their ecological neighbors, the pelagic invertebrates. To the contrary, the available energy appears to have been diverted through one specific channel to a relatively distant part of the food web.

The persistence of a species would be precarious indeed if its fate depended on every other species in the system. Analyses of studies such as those reported above suggest that ecosystems exhibit patterns of connections resulting in subassemblies that are tightly connected within themselves, but loosely connected to others.

Simon (1962) has shown that such structures have remarkable survival properties. First, removal of one subassembly does not necessarily destroy the whole. Because of the minimal connection between subassemblies, the others can persist, often long enough for self-recovery. Second, for the same reason, these structures rapidly adapt to change. As long as the same connections are maintained to other subassemblies, major changes and substitutions can take place within the subassembly. Species can substitute for other species as long as the same function or role is performed.

The conclusion for environmental assessment is that even qualitative measurements of structure are more important than measurements of numbers of every organism possible. The structure depends on who is connected to whom and how.

SPATIAL BEHAVIOR

Impacts are not gradually diluted over space.

Both the cotton and North Sea fisheries examples also demonstrate an important spatial property of ecological systems. One of the reasons the cotton mangement system eroded so rapidly was the application of insecticide over the whole of a self-contained, isolated ecosystem. Hence, no recovery from outside the system was possible to either slow or reverse the disruptions. The North Sea example emphasizes that events can be very different in different parts of space. The fishes and associated organisms in the upper waters are different from those in the lower. And yet they are uniquely coupled to each other. Moreover, if we were to look in greater detail, we would see a mosaic of spatial elements – of patches – that differ in their biological and physical characteristics. The parts of this mosaic are not totally isolated from each other but are linked by movement of material, energy, and some of the organisms; movement dictated by winds, by currents, or by active dispersal of organisms.

The consequence of this spatial mosaic and the linkages within it have been well demonstrated in a study by Huffaker (1958) in which he examined the interaction between populations of a plant-eating mite and a mite-eating predator. When there was unimpeded movement throughout the experimental universe (a homogeneous world, therefore), the system was unstable and the populations became extinct. When barriers were introduced to impede dispersal between parts of the universe, small-scale heterogeneity was introduced and the populations persisted. Thus, populations that began to collapse in one small area could be reinforced by invasion from other populations that happened to be at the peak of their numbers.

This view of spatial behavior is different from that implied in many ecological evaluations. The more usual assumptions concerning spatial effects are shown in Figure 2.1*a*: the greatest impacts are expected to be nearby, with decreasing effects as we move away from the location of the change. We call this assumption the "dilution of impacts" paradigm. Harmful physical effects (pollutants) are assumed

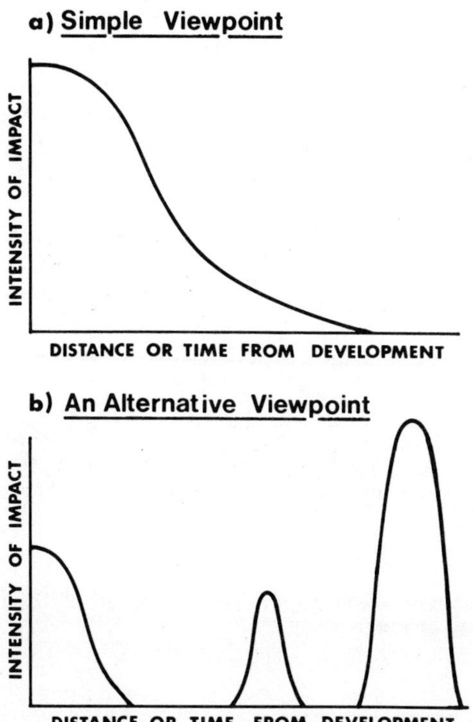

FIGURE 2.1 Alternative paradigms for the distribution of development impacts.

to diffuse in space, damages are assumed to repair themselves over distance, economic perturbations are assumed to be damped in a complex network of economic transactions, and so forth.

An alternative view is shown in Figure 2.1*b*. In this view impacts and problems are not related in any simple way to the location of the development. We would obviously not take this view seriously in dealing with many physical problems (though some pollutants can be concentrated to dangerous levels far from their source by biological and physical mechanisms). But it is not clear that the physical analogy holds in dealing with other subsystems. In particular, we argue that, within broad geographical and temporal limits, impacts mediated by social and economic processes need bear no obvious relation to the initial investment. For example, the local environmental impacts of a pipeline project in a developing region can usually be identified and ameliorated. But the induced effect of the invasion of capital and of construction workers on settlements remote from the pipeline can have dramatic social consequences that cause more significant environmental impacts than the pipeline itself.

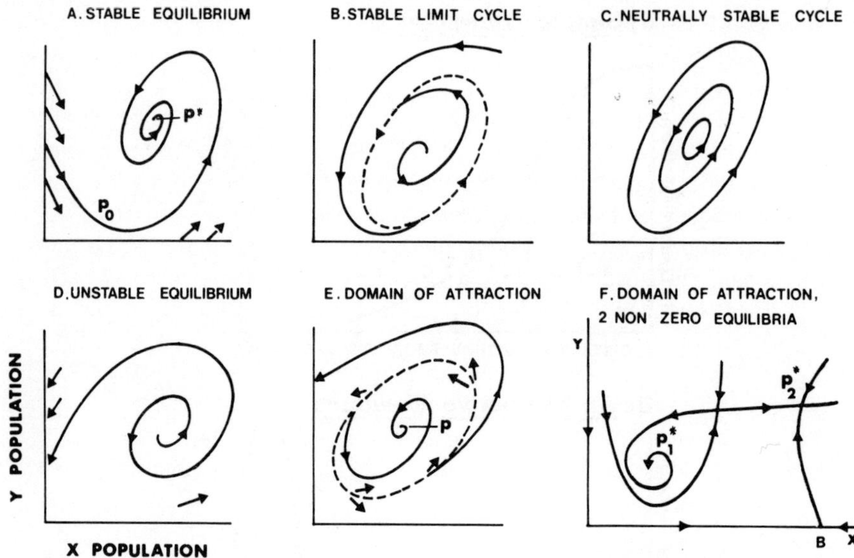

FIGURE 2.2 Ecosystem stability portraits. *A* to *E* are stylized and *F* is a specific example from Bazykin (1974).

STABILITY AND RESILIENCE

The unexpected can be expected.

Much of traditional ecological evaluation, policy design, and even ecological science itself implicitly or explicitly presumes that if a disturbance is removed, the system will ultimately return to its original condition. That is a view of an infinitely forgiving Mother Nature. But responses to disturbance can in fact take a number of different forms that can conveniently be represented by stylized portraits of stability (Figure 2.2). These representations are technically called phase portraits. The trajectories simply represent the moment-by-moment change in the value of two variables, given one starting point. The variables may be predator and prey, two competitors, or a herbivore and its food.

Consider the consequences in Figure 2.2*A*, Stable Equilibrium, for which the initial condition is at some point P_0 on the spiral. Given no intervention by man and no stochastic effects, the tendency of the system is to move inward along the spiral-like trajectory, taking steps of varying size in each successive time interval and in the limit approaching the equilibrium position (P^*). Stochastic influences derail the process, the size and direction of the random component usually being a function of location in the phase plane. But apart from these details, it is clear that systems characterized by case *A* will always migrate toward equilibrium. While long recovery times may be associated with larger displacements from an interior or quasi-equilibrium position in the phase plane, the fact of recovery itself is a certainty.

Case *B*, Stable Limit Cycle, demonstrates similar convergence. Any point in the plane converges to a closed loop that shows dynamic rather than static equilibrium. Any disturbance of the stable limit cycle produces ecological pressures that ultimately drive the system back to the cycle. If *X* and *Y* alone are plotted against time, the time series would show patterns characteristic of sustained oscillation; this is a typical consequence of simple predator–prey behavior.

The special property of case *C*, Neutrally Stable Cycle, is that any displacement results in a new, sustained oscillatory time series. This phenomenon has not yet been identified in real biological systems; indeed, there may not exist any such systems, but the case is included for completeness.

In Case *D*, Instability, every point leads to ultimate extinction. Recovery is possible only through reinvasions from other areas. This viewpoint reinforces the notion of the need for spatial heterogeneity as the only way to maintain persistence.

Cases *E* and *F* are of great interest for environmental management; case *E* is a general stylization and case *F* a specific example that will be discussed later. In case *E*, there is a closed region from which inward displacements converge on an equilibrium position or from which outward displacements diverge to some new domain of stability or to extinction of one (or more) species. Of course, small displacements will not necessarily result in these terminal positions, because movements in the phase plane contain random components that might push the trajectories across the boundary in either direction. It is useful to think of a domain of stability as a mesa. A particle moving on the mesa has a nonzero probability of falling off in one step, and the probability varies according to the location of that particle on the plane and according to the size of the step at any time. Once fallen, a particle can climb back onto the mesa and re-enter the domain of stability; the likelihood of such re-entry is smaller than that of falling off.

Another possibility is that the particle, having fallen, comes to reside on a new mesa. In biological terms, the system flips from one domain of stability to another.

If cases *A* and *B* can be viewed as Beneficent Nature, then case *D* is Ephemeral Nature and cases *E* and *F* are Mischievous Nature. In the last, the system will seem to be absorbing incremental disturbances but will then suddenly jump to another, unexpected mode of behavior. Such portraits are not simply mathematical curiosities. They find their counterparts in the behavior of the real world.

One of the more dramatic and extensively documented examples is the fisheries of the Great Lakes in North America. Data on catches exist from as far back as 1880, and a remarkably similar pattern has occurred in each of the seven most important commercial species in each of the five Great Lakes (Beeton, 1969; Christie, 1974). There was first an extensive period of sustained and modestly fluctuating catch. In a number of examples the catch suddenly increased briefly, but whether that happened or not, there was then a precipitous decline in catch over 2 to 3 years. In some instances the populations became extinct. In others the populations were driven to very low numbers. The populations were not held there by continued fishing pressure or the additional mortality from an introduced predator. Even when both fishing pressure and predators were reduced, populations did not return to their original levels; they persisted in this new configuration, this new equilibrium.

This is an example of a system that, in all likelihood, has at least two equilibria – one high and one low. If populations are displaced a small amount from either one of the equilibria, they will tend to return to it. But there is a limit to how great the displacement can be before the populations unexpectedly flip into the other equilibrium region. There are distinct stability regions and separations between them.

Even this picture of two separated regions of stability is oversimplified. The borders between equilibria of high and low densities are not simple "straight lines" determined only by the particular nature of the species in question. The unique relationships of a food web may allow a population to reach its high equilibrium by first being pushed to densities *below* its low equilibrium (Bazykin, 1974). For example, the phase portrait produced by one version of Bazykin's general predator–prey model is shown in Figure 2.2*F*. If Y is a predatory fish of commercial value and the system is at the equilibrium $P_1{}^*$, it might be desirable to shift the system to $P_2{}^*$, where there is a higher equilibrium. But note that addition of this fish would still keep the system in the stability region associated with the lower equilibrium. A modest reduction, however, can cause the variables to cross the stability boundary, and the system would naturally evolve to the higher equilibrium $P_2{}^*$.

The Great Lakes case is not an isolated example. Similar behaviors have been shown for a variety of fish populations in North America and Europe (summarized in Holling, 1973); grazing systems in North America, Africa, and Australia (Glendening, 1952; Noy-Meir, 1975); and insect pest populations in Asia, North America, and Europe (Sasaba and Kiritani, 1975; Jones, 1975; Southwood and Comins, 1976; Isaev and Khlebopros, 1977).

Larger assemblages of organisms demonstrate similar multi-equilibrium behavior. A history of herbicide spraying in a forested region in the United States (Niering and Goodwin, 1974) has succeeded in suppressing tree regeneration and growth to the point where shrubs so dominate the system that even after cessation of spraying the system remains a persistent and distinctive shrub community. Clearing large areas of tropical forests can similarly lead to an irreversible treeless condition because of exhaustion of the soil and leaching of nutrients coupled with the very low dispersal properties of tropical tree seeds (Gomez-Pompa *et al.*, 1972).

As a final example, Hutchinson (1970) has reconstructed the series of events occurring in a small crater lake in Italy from the last glacial period in the Alps (2000 to 1800 BC) to the present. Between the beginning of the record and Roman times the lake had established an equilibrium with a low level of productivity that persisted in spite of dramatic changes in surroundings from *Artemisia* steppe, through grassland, to fir and mixed oak forest. Then suddenly the whole aquatic system changed. This change towards eutrophication, or high productivity, seems to have been initiated by the construction of the Via Cassia about 171 BC, which caused a subtle change in the hydrographic regime.

We have dealt with this multiequilibrium behavior in so much detail because it lies at the heart of the uncertainty of ecological evaluation and design. A system can seem to be behaving according to one set of rules, until it suddenly flips into a radically different state. Incremental nutrient input to a lake may for a long time cause no noticeable change in water quality. But at some point, one additional increment may trigger the sudden appearance of eutrophic conditions. A fisheries system in the Great Lakes can seem to be yielding a constant and stable catch and yet be on the verge of precipitous collapse. A productive flood plain in the Orinoco delta can turn into an acid desert rather than intended agricultural land after draining exposes sulfur compounds in the soil to oxidation.

Just as there has traditionally been a "dilution of impacts" paradigm for impacts over space, so has there been a similar presumption for impacts over time. Impacts have often been presumed to be immediate and to be gradual. That implies that even if unpredicted, these changes can be monitored and detected in sufficient time to be remedied. It assumes that incremental approaches to planning and design, or marginal assumptions in cost–benefit analyses, or smooth discounting functions are all appropriate techniques of ecological policy design and evaluation. None of those assumptions holds in a world that has more than one equilibrium or stability region, where sharp rather than gradual changes can occur.

If we think of one variable affecting another only as an entry in an input–output table or a cross-impact matrix, we are implying a straight-line relationship, or at most, a smooth one. But many relationships have a form in which thresholds separate regions of no-effect from regions of effect, or where effects increase in one region and decrease in another. These nonlinear relationships contribute to the existence of multiple stability regions. They can turn the traditional tools of policy design and evaluation into the source of the problem, not the source of the solution.

DYNAMIC VARIABILITY

Environmental quality is not achieved by eliminating change.

One additional property remains. Ecological systems are not static but are in continual change – change in numbers, change in equilibrium conditions, change in species composition – and this dynamic change determines part of the structure, diversity, and viability of ecological systems. From a long-term perspective, the frequent droughts in the plains of East Africa are probably an integral feature that establishes the remarkable diversity of animals and plants. An argument can be made that the periodic destruction of trees by fire or elephants involves two dynamic forces that maintain a savannah rather than a forest. Certainly, a combination of fire and grazing can maintain grassland systems in temperate regions of the world. Similarly, many forest insect outbreaks, like those of the North American budworm (Chapter 11), are part of the natural cycle of renewal that maintains the resilience and diversity of forest systems.

Some of the changes are induced by internal mechanisms that actually force change independent of outside intrusions. For a time one group of species might gain ascendancy through competitive advantages, and their very abundance can release or trigger counteracting forces which reverse that process. Again, the budworm–forest ecosystem provides an example. Hence, for impact assessment as a review process, the impact of insecticides should be assessed not only in terms of direct ecosystem contamination. In addition, the reduction of the pest itself might significantly alter the renewal mechanisms of the forest, unless they are replaced by harvesting and silvicultural practices. And, for policy design, a forest mangement policy can be designed so that the pest itself becomes the forest manager at places and times where it is not economically feasible for man to do so. Ecological policy design can, by working with natural forces, turn them to economic benefit.

Other dynamic changes are caused by outside events – the erratic or periodic occurrences of flood, drought, cold, heat, fire, and storm. Natural systems are hence continually being "tested," and their adaptation to that experience affects their response to new intrusions. Some paleoecologists (e.g., Bretsky and Lorenz, 1969) have suggested that the species complex within intertidal communities has changed less than that in deeper water communities. The former are exposed to continual extremes through tidal movement; the latter experience a much less variable world because of stabilizing properties of water. Hence, when the inevitable unexpected occurs, the intertidal species can adapt while the deepwater species cannot. Watt (1968*a*) provides more rigorous support for this contention in his detailed statistical analysis of indices of abundance of 988 forest insect species throughout Canada from 1945 to 1965. Populations from regions with less variable maritime temperatures were affected more by a unit change in temperature than those from regions with highly variable conditions. And it is obvious that the impact of a rare frost on tropical vegetation or crops is a consequence of their evolution within a stable temperature region.

In a sense, therefore, the continual "testing" of these systems gives them the resilience they have. Their self-correcting responses to the unexpected exist because they are used occasionally. Hence, for impact assessment as a review process, the intensity of a disturbance by man cannot be assessed simply by its absolute magnitude. It must, at the least, be measured in terms of the degree of variability that has been historically experienced. And the corollary to that for policy design is that reduction of variability could lead to the gradual loss of resilience through relaxation of selective pressures. Placing a system in a straitjacket of constancy can cause fragility to evolve.

The traditional paradigm of ecological evaluation often is that the world is or should be designed to be static or constant. The developed countries in particular have recently experienced a growing emphasis on ecological and environmental concerns, in part as a reaction against past emphasis on growth and social and economic issues. But when that leads to a goal of ecological or environmental "purity" and constancy, it can no longer be labeled ecologically sound. Ecological systems are dirty, changing, growing, and declining. That is the source of their resilience and diversity. And, paradoxically, the developing world might be more capable of responding to the need for constructive variability because they themselves have been so subject to change and rapid adaptation.

These four properties – organized connection between parts, spatial heterogeneity, resilience, and dynamic variability – underlie all our attempts to develop and test the techniques described in the following sections. Several broad lessons emerge from these four properties:

1. Since everything is not intimately connected to everything else, there is no need to measure everything. There is a need, however, to determine the significant connections.
2. Structural features (size distribution, age, who connects to whom) are more important to measure than numbers.
3. Changes in one variable (e.g., a population) can have unexpected impacts on variables at the same place but several connections away.
4. Events at one place can re-emerge as impacts at distant places.
5. Monitoring of the wrong variable can seem to indicate no change even when drastic change is imminent.
6. Impacts are not necessarily immediate and gradual; they can appear abruptly some time after the event.
7. Variability of ecological systems, including occasional major disruptions, provides a kind of self-monitoring system that maintains resilience. Policies that reduce variability in space or time, even in an effort to improve environmental "quality," should always be questioned.
8. Many existing impact assessment methods (e.g., cost–benefit analysis, input–output, cross-impact matrices, linear models, discounting) assume none of the above occurs or, at least, that none is important.

The above lessons relate to the methods and data required for assessment and policy design. But there are, as well, lessons for the way environmental issues are incorporated within an institutional process.

THE BEHAVIOR OF INSTITUTIONS

The behavior of ecological systems is only one side of the equation. The other is the social and institutional environment. We have been careful, thus far, to concentrate only on the behavior of the ecological and environmental component. That is where our professional experience lies. But our recommendations are so contingent on the way people, as well as biological and physical systems, behave that our perceptions of the behavior of man and his institutions need to be at least briefly highlighted.

The key point is that our experience suggests that human systems have the same four properties that ecological systems have. These four properties lead to the same conclusion. First, agencies are strongly connected to a limited set of other constituencies (however bewildering the variety of signals). Second, some are near at hand, but some are distant (the centralization-versus-decentralization issue). Third, individuals, institutions, and societies have multiple stability regions (so that sudden shifts of behavior can become crises). Finally, dynamic variability is a benefit in maintaining an adaptive response to the expected (unless reminded by occasional change, people and institutions develop rigidity).

The last two properties are the ones that particularly color our recommendations for incorporating environmental analysis within the policy process at the very beginning and our recommendations for an adaptive process.

Earlier in this chapter we illustrated the alternative modes of stability by using stylized phase portraits (Figure 2.2). These can be generated by fairly simple coupled differential equations, which in no sense represent reality but rather are highly simplified caricatures of the essence of behavior. Bazykin (1974 and Figure 2.2) has done just that for ecological systems. The same approach has also been applied to institutional systems (Holling *et al.*, 1976) and societal ones (Häfele and Bürk, 1976). Just as in the ecological equations, the assumptions built into these simple caricatures generate separate regions of stability, regions, moreover, that can shift and change if parameters evolve through the action of cultural selective forces. In an early version of the Häfele and Bürk societal equations, for example, one stability region leads to high energy consumption per capita and low population, and the other to the reverse. A flip across the line of separation would seem for a time to be little different from the past, but the ultimate consequences would be radically different. Such equations should never be used as reasonable laboratory worlds for the development of explicit policies, but they are useful as perspectives, or metaphors of reality whose relevance depends on whether they match common sense and practical experience.

Certainly our experience with a number of institutions – management agencies, research laboratories, "think tanks," businesses, and universities – reinforces these metaphors (Holling and Goldberg, 1971; Walters, 1975*a*; Holling, 1976). Our conclusions are supported by more formal analyses as well (Cyêrt and March, 1963; Crozier, 1964; Etzioni, 1968). Those institutions that have developed policies that induced a rhythm of change, with periods of innovation followed by consolidation and back again, maintain a flexible and adaptive response. Expected problems and opportunities are detected and can be turned to benefits. Those institutions that have evolved toward stability, toward minimizing disturbance, toward being risk-averse, tend to react to problems and opportunities as crises. The adaptive response withers, and instead there is, paradoxically, an attempt to further reduce these uncomfortable intrusions. Options are rapidly foreclosed.

This matching of the metaphors and behavior of ecological systems with those of institutional systems leads us to specific recommendations for using environmental assessment as well for doing it. With this perspective, even the word assessment, implying passive reaction, is inappropriate. Adaptive environmental management is a more relevant term. Several broad recommendations emerge that will be reinforced in later chapters:

1. Environmental dimensions should be introduced at the very beginning of the development or policy design process and should be integrated as equal partners with the economic and social dimensions.

2. Thereafter, in the design phase, there should be periods of intense, focused innovation involving significant outside constituencies, followed by periods of stable consolidation.

3. Part of the design should include benefits attached to increasing information on unknown or partially known social, economic, and environmental effects. Information can be given a value just as jobs, income, and profit can.

4. Some of the experiments designed to produce information can be part of an integrated research plan, but others should be designed into the actual management activities. Managers as well as scientists learn from change.

5. An equally integral part of the design are the monitoring and remedial mechanisms. They should not simply be *post hoc* additions after implementation.

6. In the design of those mechanisms there should be a careful analysis of the economic trade-offs between structures and policies that presume that the unexpected can be designed into insignificance and less capital intensive mechanisms that monitor and ameliorate the unexpected (Holling and Clark, 1975). (That issue is explicitly addressed for the design of pollution control standards in Fiering and Holling, 1974).

7. The above points imply changes in institutions and legislation. We find, unexpectedly, that such changes seem more feasible in "less efficient" developing and developed countries. Whether intended or not, the unexpected has been part of their history, and adaptive change can be perceived as a modest shift from past experience.

3 Steps in the Process

As a relief from the philosophical, conceptual, and abstract discourse of the first two chapters, we turn now to a more concrete and pragmatic discussion of the steps that are involved in the process of adaptive assessment and management. Although we would ideally like to integrate assessment into management, we realize that this is not yet institutionally possible in many cases. Therefore, we treat them separately, first describing the major events and aims that are critical ingredients in environmental assessment. Even here we see two types, each with its own tactics: a long-term (1-year) assessment project and a quick (2-month) project. Many of the steps described also apply to an environmental management program. In addition, there are also steps needed for effective communication to, and implementation in, the responsible management agencies.

We must emphasize that this chapter is *not* intended to provide a "cookbook"; such a prescriptive device is the antithesis of the proposed adaptive management process. Rather, we hope this chapter provides readers with enough of a sense of the order of events that they can begin such an adaptive process on their own. Each situation will be different, however, and the steps described here should be molded to meet specific requirements in each case.

ENVIRONMENTAL ASSESSMENT

A 1-YEAR ASSESSMENT PROJECT

This section is written for the person charged with preparing an assessment of the environmental consequences of some proposed action. He is responsible for gathering together and coordinating a team to examine the problem, analyze the possible consequences, and prepare a report that will be used as an aid for decision. While we suggest a hypothetical timetable (Figure 3.1) for the tasks and events that

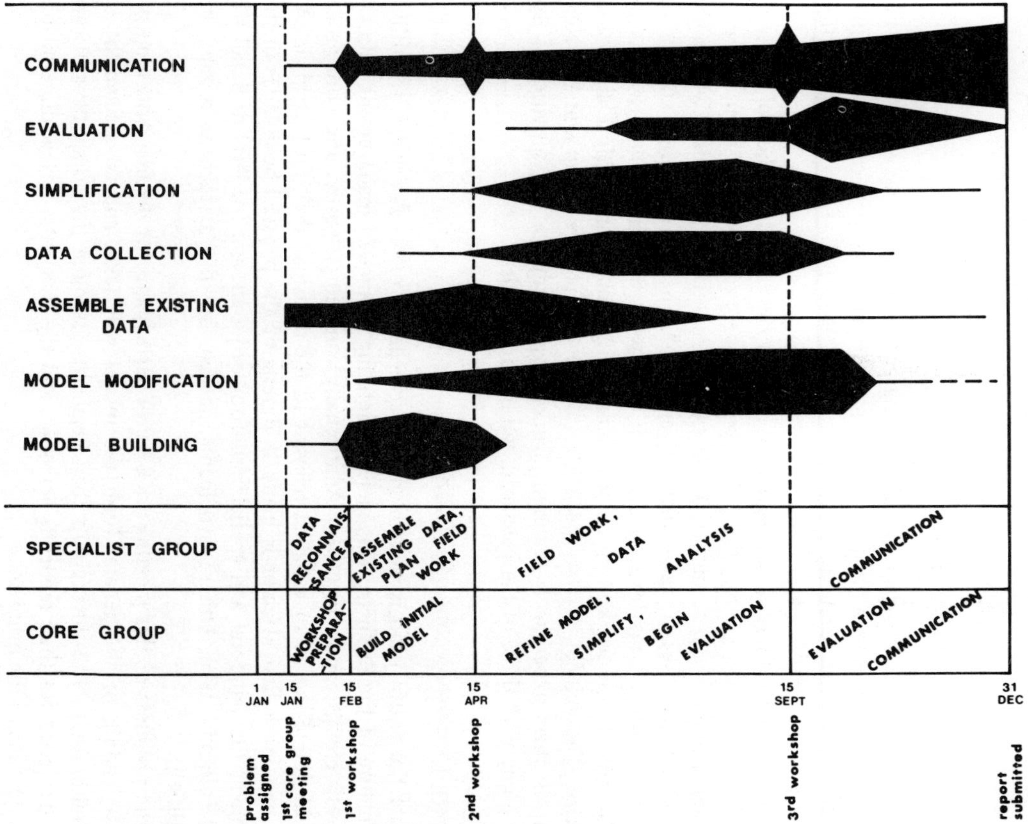

FIGURE 3.1 Activities and timetable for a 1-year assessment.

constitute the assessment, no two assessment problems are the same and they cannot be successfully treated with a fixed agenda. Therefore we have synthesized our experience into a "typical" scenario – flexibility and adaptability remain paramount. We have tested these procedures and are confident that they work. Specific procedures for operating the scheduled workshops are detailed in the next chapter.

January 1: The Assessment Begins

On January 1 the program manager is charged with preparing a report on the likely consequences of a major development. The report is to be completed within 1 year, and he may draw upon scientists and advisors both from his organization and from collaborating ones.

The program manager's first task is to identify the central members of his team. These fall into two groups, those who possess analytic skills (e.g., computer programming, data analysis, statistics) and the subject matter specialists, who might be biologists, geologists, economists, or engineers. The analytic group and one or two of the subject matter specialists will form what we call the *core group*. This group will run the workshops, do the computer modeling, and analyze alternative policies. The subject matter specialists outside of the core group will be called upon as their expertise is required. Workshops coordinate the activities of the core group with those of the specialists and methodologists.

January 15: First Meeting of Core Group

Before the entire team is assembled, the core group meets *in camera*, to outline the nature of the problem. This includes defining a range of management options, interest groups, and objectives. Additionally, and importantly, the core group should define the set of variables relevant to the decisions that must be made. At this meeting a first attempt is made to determine the physical boundaries of the problem, the temporal and spatial resolution required, and the level of detail the model should take. Other participants needed for the assessment groups are identified.

The products of this meeting are a list of participants for the first workshop, an understanding of the general form the model will take, and an assignment of responsibilities. The core group then begins to assemble the computer software and hardware for their modeling activities, and the specialists review the available data relevant to the problem.

The stage is now set for the first workshop. Although the core group has a preliminary definition of the problem, it is tactically important that these preliminary decisions remain invisible during the first workshop and that they be readily abandoned if it seems appropriate. In the workshop related decisions will be made again by all the workshop participants and will be modified as a consequence of the broader experience of the participants. It is important for these decisions to be made extemporaneously – and more important that they appear to be made so. The commitment of participants to the project in future workshops depends on their self-identification as creators of the model. However, it is also important that the first workshop establish momentum and that it does not become stalled over technical indecision. It is for this reason that the core group must have a set of "shadow decisions" in their back pocket to draw upon if the workshop falters.

February 15: First Workshop (2–3 Days)

This workshop is attended by the core group and all the specialists. In addition, it is critically important that the higher level decision makers and managers be involved as much as possible. Frequently, they will be able to attend only the first day, or even only the first hour, but it is of the utmost importance that they be there even for that hour, and at least two or three should attend the whole workshop. If the person who requested the report participates in the opening of the first workshop, he knows what is happening and feels a part of it. The ultimate decision makers can so guide the initial discussions as to ensure that the exercise remains relevant to their needs. A group of biologists left alone might produce a very interesting model of a game population, but one irrelevant to the management of that species. The presence of decision makers thus provides needed guidance in the early stages of the program.

This workshop follows the general rules described in the orchestration chapter (Chapter 4). The first days are concerned primarily with defining and bounding the problem, selecting the variables, and designing the framework of the model. Unless the core group is especially experienced, it is unlikely that they can have a rough model operating by the end of this workshop. The important point is that they have all the information and materials they will need to write the computer program before the participants leave. The core group must have the model structure defined for programming and must also have the estimates, however rough, of the parameter values for this model. The subject matter specialists must leave the meeting with a firm understanding of the data that are needed for further modification and refinement of a model that can be responsive to the management questions.

Three critical steps must be completed by the end of the workshop. First, the problem must be clearly defined – management actions, key variables, spatial extent and resolution, and time horizon and resolution. This definition should have led to at least a crude outline of a model. The core group will then use this information to develop, modify, and refine the model. Second, the key data needs must be defined, and preliminary research plans outlined by the specialists for the coming field season. Finally, the person requesting the assessment must have been so involved that he and the group are assured that the relevant information will be obtained. The more he is involved interactively in this critical 2 to 3 days, the more likely that this condition will be satisfied.

April 15: Second Workshop (2–3 Days)

By this time, two months later, the core group has a version of the model running on the computer. They have developed, as well, some alternative policies to the one proposed so that comparisons can be made. The specialists have obtained as much information as possible from the literature and have formulated their final research plans for the collection of the remaining data that are needed.

On the first day of this second workshop, the core group incorporates the specialists' data in the model and makes any necessary changes in the programming. Much of the technical work is done before the workshop, the actual meeting time being used to focus the activity and provide opportunity for communication. Once the changes are made and the data are incorporated, the model is ready to run. The workshop uses this running model to explore and test the suggested alternative policies and scenarios. Again, it is most useful to have the policymaker or manager present when policy options are being considered.

The last task of this workshop is to review each specialist's plans for data collection, thoroughly analyzing them to assure that the data are truly needed. Emerging from this meeting is a set of research plans for the specialists and a set of management options to be considered and tested rigorously by the core group.

The core group then begins the tasks of simplification, invalidation, and evaluation (see Chapters 6, 7 and 8). The model as it now stands is incomplete, since some major changes can be expected as a result of the specialists' field research, but the core group should start the analysis now. New data can be added when available, and in the meantime the analysis will help shape a better study.

September 15: Third Workshop (5 Days)

The first 2 days of this workshop are devoted to incorporating the revisions in data and model structure from the past 5 months of research. Again, this need not all be done within this workshop, as the core group will have begun this effort as data became available from the specialists. The final 3 days of the workshop are set aside for gaming with the model and evaluating alternative policies. A top policy person should be involved during these sessions. He can see the types of results generated and the direction that the final report will take.

The job of everyone involved for the remaining months of the year is communication. The core group must complete evaluation runs, produce informaton packages and graphs, and describe the likely outcome of options. Numerous demonstrations of the model should be made for the higher level administrators, as the final report constitutes only a part of the assessment output. The purpose of the entire program is to affect decision making, and all of the creativity of the team should be employed to that end.

December 31: Final Report Handed In

With the report finished, the 1-year task is now complete. The above schedule is fairly ambitious. As described, it involves 4 core group members and perhaps 15 specialists for 1 year. Frequently, these people would not work full time on this one project: the core group might have 3 or 4 similar simultaneous projects, and the specialists might devote half of their time or less to this project. Full-time commitments might, however, be appropriate for the analysis of a very large power generating station or transmission corridor, for example. For such projects the specialists might have several assistants who do much of the field work.

Lessons from the Guri Study

Of the five case studies reported in Part II, that of the Guri hydroelectric development (Chapter 14) comes closest to the intensive assessment scenario described above. The purpose of the study was to compare alternative forestry and agriculture practices in a $3 billion hydroelectric development, proposed for an undeveloped region of Venezuela. It was not, however, meant to be a comprehensive environmental study. The entire process of model building, evaluation, nomogram construction, and report writing required one coordinator for a year and twelve other participants for three months, full-time. This is considerably less than the 10- to 20-man-year program described above. No data collection was done in the field; all data were available from government maps, the scientific literature, and other commonly accessible forms of information. All computations were performed on a Hewlett-Packard 2000 (32,000 words); computers of this capability are commonly available in most cities around the world.

A SHORT-DURATION ASSESSMENT PROJECT

How can this workshop procedure be used if there are only 2 months instead of 12 to prepare the report? The first two workshops will have to be very close together, and there will be no chance for serious data collection or extensive evaluation. We have frequently been called upon to do a full assessment in 5 days, including model construction, alternatives definition, and policy evaluation.

The Obergurgl study (Chapter 13) serves as a prototype for such a short-term study. Its purpose was to examine the likely consequences of several options available for this high alpine region of Austria: zoning changes, building subsidy or taxation, ski-lift construction. In a 5-day workshop a model was built, and the alternative futures under the different options were examined. The results of this exercise became a topic of major consideration in the region, and we believe they made a significant impact on decision making. After a 1-day planning meeting, a core group of 5 methodologists and 15 participants met for a 1-week workshop. Some of these participants were specialists from the University of Innsbruck, some were regional government planners, and some were residents of the village itself. After the workshop, one person spent 2 weeks writing a report on the results. A PDP-11 computer (28,000-word memory) was used – again a computer of a size commonly available throughout the world. The investment in time and money was small, and the payoffs were great. This type of workshop could probably be used in many short-term evaluation programs; some parallel examples are outlined in Walters (1974).

Several important problems were defined and clarified by the Obergurgl model. The initial concerns about environmental quality receded to minor significance. Of more concern was the obvious inability of the village to maintain its current style of life, which is associated with continued growth of the hotel industry. The land will run out; subsidization, taxation, and zoning changes can only alter the date. When the Obergurglers returned to their village after the workshop, they initiated a series of public discussions about the future of the village. This period of discussion reached a peak during a 1-day presentation in the village of the results of the model by the modeling group. The need for a change in life style and expectations became obvious to many of the villagers; the search for a solution began. The model could not provide a solution, but the people can. They are now actively exploring means of expanding the economic base to provide nonhotel employment, and more important, the children who are now growing up are doing so with a better understanding of their future.

ENVIRONMENTAL MANAGEMENT

It is more difficult to prescribe a generalized sequence of steps for the process of designing policies for management. In many assessment situations the institutional authority, however narrow, is at least clear and undivided, and a useful sequence can therefore be generalized. Most environmental management situations, however, are much more complex. There is often a division of responsibilities for research from those for policy design and management. In such instances, as a consequence, the research often drifts from a focus on management and policy questions to a focus on general scientific questions. And those developing policies find themselves isolated from appropriate research information either because it was never obtained or because it is hidden behind institutional barriers. Moreover, in many problems of development or resource policy design a bewildering number of agencies seem to have, or desire, some voice. Finally, policy design, more than environmental assessment, must face the conflicting objectives of different governmental, industrial, and public interest groups.

Because these problems and the cast of actors concerned will be different in different situations, the best we can do now is attempt to identify the lessons we have learned from our various case studies. All our studies have contributed insights, but the budworm (Chapter 11) and salmon (Chapter 12) work, having gone farther toward introducing concrete change within agencies, have been the major learning experience. Both these case studies give the flavor of the institutional complexity that faced us.

In the broadest sense, the steps described above for the assessment process still apply. There is, however, greater explicit emphasis on designing a range of alternative policies and on involving a larger variety of institutions, role players, and constituencies in the actual design and evaluation. As a result it takes more time, more flexibility, and more adaptive response to opportunities as they emerge.

The major conclusions drawn from our efforts to implement the process and techniques within operating agencies follow:

1. Transfer of analysis, of the process, and of techniques means more than mailing the computer codes and writing a report. It also requires a program of workshops and intense "user" involvement so that the local scientists and managers end up as the real and acknowledged experts. A measure of success is the extent to which the original analysis group becomes less and less visible and the local groups more and more visible as the program moves into implementation. The initiators' very strong and markedly parental inclinations to keep control too long must be resisted, or transfer will fail.

2. Vigorous institutional support and protection is necessary but not sufficient; the policy design approach can be transferred only to people, not to departments. Respected local leadership of the program is essential.

3. The analysis must be made fully transparent and interactive. Hence extensive use of graphic presentations (Chapter 9) and an interactive computer environment are important to allow easy examination and modification of model assumptions. Cooperating scientists and managers can therefore explore their own experience and assumptions in the context of the models and so develop a critical understanding of the strengths, weaknesses, and limitations of the analysis.

4. Communication of the results must go beyond the traditional written forms. Modular slide–tape presentations describing the approach, the problem, and the model can communicate the essential features vividly and rapidly without compromising content (Chapter 9). In the budworm study, for example, a 4-minute motion picture of space–time dynamics under various management regimes better revealed that behavior than any amount of static discussion and analysis.

5. A sequence of participatory workshops beginning with scientists, proceeding to managers, and finally involving policymakers builds a foundation of confidence and understanding. A "top-down" sequence would, by contrast, force the technical analysis group into a premature position of prominence, alienating local experts and promoting little but suspicion.

6. The final – and perhaps the most restrictive – requirement of effective transfer is time. The budworm policy analysis *per se* took less than 6 months; the full program to implementation more than 3 years. Some of this time was spent in the workshops described above and in Chapter 4, but much was an incubation

period. A prerequisite for effective implementation seems to be time for the analysis group to appreciate the real options and constraints, time for the local managers and scientists to become truly conversant with new concepts, and time for the policy people to credit the analysis group with relevant intent. In retrospect, we doubt that the process could be rushed without fatally prejudicing the results in one way or another. Successful implementation requires patience.

Responsible policy choices by the decision maker are based on understanding and control of, not necessarily belief in, the technical analysis. If such understanding is not clearly communicated, if such control is not effectively transferred, then mere technique surreptitiously replaces political judgment as a basis for public policy decisions, with no accountability for the results. That would simply be the promulgation of another undesirable myth – the one Lewis Mumford has called the Myth of the Machine – in systems analytic disguise.

4 Orchestrating the Assessment

In Chapter 2 we discussed many characteristics of ecological systems that make them particularly difficult to understand and manage. In addition, it has become obvious in recent years that environmental management problems encompass biological, economic, and sociological factors, and that these must all be considered when evaluating development plans or when assessing alternative resource management options. The complex nature of environmental problems raises three questions of special concern to the resource manager or impact assessment team:

- How can the problem be bounded or delimited so that it is tractable and manageable?
- How can information and expertise that is scarce or widely dispersed best be applied to the problem?
- Finally, once the analysis is done, how can the complex results or recommendations be most effectively transferred to the decision makers and to the public?

CURRENT PRACTICE

Two major responses to the complex characteristics of environmental problems have emerged recently: the formalization of environmental impact assessment procedures and the creation of large interdisciplinary teams to tackle resource management problems. There is little argument about the need in assessment studies to call upon expertise from a number of disciplines. In most cases it has been deemed sufficient to establish a series of study tasks, or consulting contracts, with only minor provision for coordination in administrative matters, data gathering, and preparation of the final report. Statements are elicited from different specialists about the probable impact of a given development or management decision on their particular area of concern. Thus, a wildlife biologist might be consulted about the effects of a dam on big game animals, an economist about effects on recreation, a hydrologist about water flows, and a fisheries biologist about effects on fish. However, this approach often omits consideration of cross-disciplinary interactions, such as the effect of changing recreational demand on big game and fish populations (Walters, 1974).

In contrast, the interdisciplinary team approach exemplified by many recent research programs has attempted to promote communication among disciplines, which was lacking in the first alternative. Computer models are usually the focus of these team efforts, and because these teams involved many disciplines, the models are usually large and complex. However, it is now believed that the original goals of many of these team efforts were not met (Holcomb Research Institute, 1976; Mar, 1974; Mitchel *et al.*, 1976; Watt, 1977). The research was not significantly more integrated than in nonteam programs (Mitchell *et al.*, 1976), and models originally developed for research purposes were not necessarily appropriate for decision making (Holcomb Research Institute, 1976; Peterman, 1977a). In addition, the large number of people, large budgets ($1–2 million/year) and long time frame for project completion (~ 5 years) created an environment where studies within disciplines became bogged down in details irrelevant to the management questions, where cross-disciplinary interactions were ignored, and where group activities drifted off in different directions (Ford Foundation, 1974; Holcomb Research Institute, 1976; and Mar, 1974). Moreover, the highly complex models that resulted from these large team efforts often defied understanding by either the modelers or the client decision makers (Lee, 1973; Holcomb Research Institute, 1976).

Both the interdisciplinary team approach and the formalization of the environmental assessment process were nobly motivated efforts, often expensive and experimental because they were so new. It is the history of that experience, of successes and of failures, that has led to a thread of tested concepts and techniques that deserve broader application. The failures were both expected and necessary; that is how we learn. Since the approaches have been admirably reviewed elsewhere (Ackerman *et al.*, 1974; Council on Environmental Quality, 1976; Dasmann *et al.*, 1973; Ford Foundation, 1974; Holcomb Research Institute, 1976; Lee, 1973; Mar, 1974; Mitchell *et al.*, 1976; O'Neill, 1975; Peterson, 1976; Schindler, 1976; Watt, 1977), we will only comment that these failures appear to have been consequences of inexperience in bridging the gaps between disciplines, data, techniques, knowledge, institutions, and people.

WORKSHOPS, THE CORE OF ADAPTIVE ASSESSMENT

In contrast to the individual-discipline or large-team approaches to environmental impact assessment and resource management, we have used an approach to bridging some of the above gaps that depends upon a small group of people that interacts with a wider set of experts during a series of short-term, intensive workshops. Most of our workshops have used the construction of a quantitative model as a focus for discussion, but as we will demonstrate later, many benefits will arise from workshops even if other predictive methods are substituted. Both the process and the product of these workshops are directly applicable to assessment and management problems.

Involvement of small teams and short time spans in these workshops circumvents the scientist's natural tendency to break problems down into components, and those components down into subcomponents, and so on. This tendency is a natural response to complexity and is deliberately encouraged in disciplinary training, especially in biology. But it is often not suitable for dealing with management concerns that are at a different level from those of the scientist (Mar, 1974) and that are likely to lie between usual areas of disciplinary interest and training. Instead, a small group of people working with a specific goal (model) in a well-structured atmosphere over a short period of time has advantages. Participants are forced to recognize that not all the components of biological or economic systems are of equal importance and that judgments will have to be made about the relative importance of the various pieces of the problem. Some details of workshops, such as size of group and budget, have already been discussed in Chapter 3.

From experience in more than two dozen cases (e.g., Himamowa, 1975; Clark *et al.*, 1977; Walters, 1974; Walters and Peterman, 1974; Walters *et al.*, 1974; Part II of this volume), we have found that small teams interacting through modeling workshops over a relatively short time can successfully carry out an assessment while addressing the three issues raised at the beginning of this section. Watt (1977) and Mitchell *et al.* (1976) have also concluded that small teams are most productive. However, success can be achieved only if appropriate people are involved at the various stages of analysis. The main participants are disciplinary specialists; methodologists who are familiar with techniques of analysis such as modeling; and decision makers who will ultimately use the information that results from the analysis.

There are obviously many environmental problems that cannot be solved without long-term studies by large research teams. But it is pointless and wasteful to initiate such studies without a clear and reliable strategy for insuring continued coordination and cooperation, particularly on issues that the individual specialists will tend to avoid. We suggest that modeling workshops can help to provide a brain for the body of the research team – they provide periodic reassessment and redirection.

We have used workshops in three ways during our studies of environmental problems. First, workshops are an effective way to begin a problem analysis, that is, to bring people together, to define the problem clearly, to examine existing data, to formulate some initial predictive scheme, and to identify future steps in the analysis. Second, workshops can form the backbone of a longer term, in-depth analysis in which alternative models or predictions are made and alternative management or development schemes are evaluated. Finally, workshops are a useful mode for transferring and implementing the results of the problem analysis to individual clients or agencies that did not participate in the assessment. While we will discuss the characteristics of all three types of workshops, we will concentrate on the most critical of these, the workshop that begins the problem analysis.

THE INITIAL WORKSHOP

THE WORKSHOP MODEL

We have found that it is critical to have the development of some sort of model predictions as an enunciated workshop objective. At this stage the model is not viewed as an end in itself; indeed, its predictions are usually not very precise. Rather, the model provides a focus for communication and a point of departure, allowing objective discussions of the importance of various components. The model is a device to promote objectivity and honesty. In interdisciplinary discussions that do not have such a focus, much time is wasted in general discussions of what is "important." When factors are brought into the open and quantified as part of a larger model, their importance can be judged by all the workshop participants. It should not come as a great surprise that many specialists find modeling workshops exceedingly painful: many of the "important" factors always turn out to be irrelevant for prediction.

Before describing the steps involved in a workshop, we must emphasize an important idea about simulation models: they should never be more detailed than is necessary to capture the essential behavior of the system being studied (see, for example, the spruce budworm case study described in Chapter 11). There are two reasons for this, one pragmatic and one technical. First, we wish the model to be as understandable as possible; a complex model may end up being as unfathomable as the real world and therefore unlikely to be understood by decision makers (Ackerman *et al.*, 1974; Holcomb Research Institute, 1976). Second, more detailed models do not necessarily result in greater predictive power. In fact, more complex models *may be* less reliable than simple ones (Lee, 1973; O'Neill, 1973): as one includes more detail (variables) in a model, the number of explicit assumptions made about interaction between those variables rises exponentially (imagine the implied interaction matrix). Therefore, the probability of making a *wrong and critical* assumption increases rapidly, and it has been found that the predictive power of a model usually declines after some level of detail has been exceeded. Unfortunately, there are no specific rules for how detailed a model should be; this judgment usually is a result of experience and intuition. Finally, we have found that breadth rather than depth is usually more appropriate for answering complex management questions of the sort that concern us here. Rather than concentrating on a few disciplines in great detail, models should include many disciplines (see also Watt, 1977).

From our experiences with models at many levels of detail, it is easy to look back at the field of ecological modeling as it was in the early 1970s and point out the difficulties inherent in the approach of building very large, detailed models of complex ecosystems. But at the time this approach seemed the obvious path to follow; computers were getting much bigger, faster, cheaper, and more accessible, and more data were becoming available. We have now gone through that unfortunate yet necessary phase in the development of ecological modeling that exactly parallels the trials with large models in atmospheric, water and urban modeling (Holcomb Research Institute, 1976; Lee, 1973). The approach we are proposing in this book incorporates many of the lessons learned from that experience.

PROBLEM ANALYSIS

Let us review the general steps of problem analysis to illustrate what is done and what the benefits are. First, an environmental problem arises, such as a proposed dam in a valley rich in wildlife or the extension of territorial claims on the ocean to 200 miles. One of the first steps in problem analysis is to recognize the institutional situation that governs the way decisions are made in the problem area at hand. It is best to choose that level of analysis that most closely fits the needs of an easily identifiable client (Mar, 1974). For example, it may make more sense to work on problems on an entire watershed than on those of subsections within the watershed if the planning commission or other decision-making body acts at the watershed level. Generally, it is possible to identify several levels of decision making within the client's responsibility, from broad and long term (investment strategies, facilities siting, and so on) to narrow and short term (construction tactics, remedial regulations, and the like), corresponding to levels in the organizational hierarchy. The problem analysis should state clearly which levels are to be addressed, and which are to be taken as given constraints or minor issues to be resolved as they arise in the field. However, as noted in the discussion of the myths of environmental management and assessment in Chapter 1, one should be very careful to look for impacts that may occur beyond jurisdictional boundaries.

Soon after the client and the problem have been defined, problem analysis should start by involving a small group of people in an early workshop to build an initial model. These people should include the required disciplinary specialists and a few of the decision makers and methodologists. It is best to involve decision makers at this point to ensure that management objectives are made clear and that appropriate management variables are considered. Early involvement of a few decision makers or administrators will also smooth the path for the specialists and methodologists. An assessment program is doomed to failure if administrators are not willing to invest sufficient people, facilities, money, and time in the project. To increase the chances that such an investment and commitment will be made, the decision makers should be given and should accept a role in shaping the course of the analysis through participation in one or several early workshops. Moreover, higher level administrators, along with other participants, should be provided with a series of payoffs during the course of evaluation (Holling and Chambers, 1973). The problem analysis can often result in substantial reordering of research priorities and identification of new data requirements, a benefit to researcher and administrator alike.

The first workshop for the specialists, administrators, and methodologists can take the form of one or two 3–5-day sessions whose goal is to produce a working first-approximation model that can be used for testing alternative management or development schemes. A common reaction to an early attempt to build a model is the feeling that not enough data are available. However, we have found that if useful data are ever going to be collected in a research program, some conceptual models must exist to guide the collection. In an attempt to quantify those conceptual models, the assumptions underlying them are brought out into the open and appropriate test data are more clearly defined. Thus, with a modest amount of basic survey information and knowledge of similar systems, the first workshop can begin.

The key element of this first workshop, as well as of subsequent ones, is the small core team, in our cases made up largely by people with some background in both the methodology (simulation modeling) and some resource discipline. This group integrates the information provided by specialists and managers. If and when subsequent workshops are conducted to deepen and broaden the analysis, this core group provides the continuity of experience needed to carry on the problem analysis. For those readers that have little experience with workshops of this type, we must emphasize that most of the art of conducting them is in dealing with people, not in facility with techniques. Holling and Chambers (1973) and Walters (1974) discuss some of the "people" lessons revealed through our own experiences, but the best and quickest way to learn modes of successful operation of workshops is to build a body of experience by conducting some. A full description of the steps we have taken in first workshops, those devoted to initial problem analysis, follows.

THE WORKSHOP PROCESS

First, some management goals need to be defined; even for a development scheme there must be some overall objective. Even if the decision makers present agree on an objective, a wide range of alternative objectives should still be considered so that the model can be responsive to possible future changes in objectives (Holling and Clark, 1975). By a *range of objectives*, we mean goals as extreme and as simple as maximizing economic return from a renewable resource versus preserving the natural state of that resource. While no one of these goals would be realistic, together they would cover a wide enough range that any real objective would fall somewhere within it (Clark *et al.*, 1977). The importance of an early statement of questions to be answered by the exercise cannot be overemphasized. As Brewer (1975) points out, too many models have been built with unclear program goals, resulting in too many inappropriate models.

Next, it is necessary to identify the variables, or indicators, that the client decision makers can use to judge how well alternative management actions meet given objectives. These indicators are really performance measures, such as level of employment, number of animals harvested, or kilowatts of electricity produced. As a consequence of the identification of objectives and indicators, the problem to be analyzed begins to be bounded. Further decisions have to be made concerning the range of management actions to consider, the temporal horizon and resolution, the spatial extent and resolution, and the ecosystem variables to be included. For example, should a salmon fisheries model consider a set of management actions ranging from building of enhancement (artificial propagation) facilities down to specific controls on insurance against bad times? Should the model consider only one small fishing area and the boat movements within it, or should it consider the whole coast and movement of boats between areas? Should the model explicitly consider all species of fish that potentially interact with salmon, or should only the major salmon species be accounted for? These questions are of the type that define the problem, and their answers are, in large part, determined by the management needs established earlier. A detailed example of problem definition in the spruce-budworm/forest-management case study can be found in Chapter 11. This first step of defining or bounding the problem through indicator identification is very critical; the rest of the analysis will in large part reflect decisions made at this early stage. Too narrow a conceptualization of the problem can eliminate from consideration a perfectly viable set of management options, or lead to predictions that overlook some key management concern.

One of the main purposes of the workshop is to promote interdisciplinary communication and to focus the scientist's expertise on the real management questions that the assessment is to address. To initiate communication, we have found it effective to use a process we call "looking outward." In the usual kind of impact assessment or management design program, each specialist is asked to predict how his own subsystem, such as the fish population or the vegetation, will behave. His natural tendency is to devise a detailed conceptual or numerical model consisting of many variables and relationships that reflect current scientific knowledge within his discipline. However, this conceptual model is usually more complex than is necessary to predict the behavior of a subsystem at the level of management indicators. Worse, each narrow conceptual model usually does not consider important links with other subsystems. In the "looking outward" approach we simply reverse the standard question asked of the specialist. Instead of asking "what is important to describe your subsystem *X*?" we ask "what do you need to know about all the other subsystems in order to predict how your subsystem *X* will behave?" Thus, the specialist is asked to look outward at the kinds of inputs that affect his subsystem.

After each subsystem has been subjected to this questioning process, each specialist possesses a list of "output" variables whose dynamics he has to describe so that these variables can serve as inputs to other disciplines. These cross-transfer variables that link the subsystems are essential in describing a picture of the overall system dynamics, and the modeling of each subsystem can be greatly simplified when the desired outputs from the subsystems are known precisely. For example, it may not be necessary to calculate changes in ten different classes of vegetation if the animals that utilize the habitat only distinguish between two classes of vegetation. Only after cross-transfer variables and variables needed to calculate management indicators are established should the specialist be permitted to add other variables that are of interest only to him.

The "looking outward" process, which is a modification of interaction matrix methods such as the Leopold matrix, is normally done by setting up an interaction table in which the system variables (deer population size, vegetation type and abundance, water level, and so on) are listed both down one side of the table and across the top. Then one asks for each element in the table, "Does the variable on the left in this row affect the variable in this column? If so, how?" In this way, cross-disciplinary information flows are identified. Systematic use of such an interaction table reduces the probability of leaving out some important interaction. During the "looking outward" process, there may be some disagreement about what variables or interactions should be omitted. Often, a bit of simple calculation can determine whether some detail is important to the final management indicators. If a decision cannot be made, then the disputed variable or relation can be held for later testing in the model as an alternative hypothesis to see if it makes any difference to predicted impacts (see Chapter 7).

Finally, some quantitative description needs to be made for each possible interaction identified in the "looking outward" table. Small subgroups of specialists can do this in a relatively short time by drawing upon existing information. Compared to the initial bounding and conceptualization steps, this step is generally surprisingly easy.

Finally, at the end of the first workshop, as submodels are quantified and interfaced, some validation and evaluation of management alternatives can be begun. This evaluation is the workshop product that is of most relevance to assessment (see Chapter 7 and 8).

BENEFITS

A number of benefits usually are realized from the first few steps of the workshop. Gaps in existing information are exposed, so future data collection programs, which are a major part of any assessment, can be more efficiently designed. The specialists get a better feeling for how their subsystem fits into the total system, and they gain an appreciation of the management questions. Similarly, managers learn of the importance of the various subsystems within the total management system. The need to clarify management goals and performance criteria is also established. Note that these benefits emerge even before a working model is produced and persist even if no credible model is built. Thus, this initial workshop can be valuable almost regardless of which predictive method is being used, and even if the time constraints on problem analysis are such that the first workshop is the only workshop. In such a case, which unfortunately occurs too often, the resulting model is probably the best synthesis of data and knowledge that can be produced over a short period. We therefore see a role for this first, intensive workshop both as a mechanism for making first-cut predictions that will then point the way for future study and as a means of making "best guess" predictions under severe time constraints. In addition, because of its nature and form, the workshop is an effective way to use scarce resources efficiently, be they data or people.

Because the process of putting together almost any kind of model, but particularly a quantitative one, results in recognition of new data needs, an assessment program or problem analysis can benefit significantly from a data-gathering program that is intimately tied to the modeling program. Often masses of data gathered before the synthesis begins turn out to be superfluous or irrelevant. It is for this reason that we suggest that modeling is more useful when it is done early in a program instead of as a final synthesis.

STEPS IN THE FIRST WORKSHOP

After holding several of these workshops, we have been able to compress all of the above steps into an intensive 5-day session. In this section we describe the sequence of steps by assuming that they will occur over 5 days, but we fully expect that initial workshop attempts by readers may stretch over two weeks or more. Nevertheless, the order and relative length of the steps should still be the same.

The first day is devoted to clarification of the problem, conceptualization, and definition of indicators and state variables. During the second day, interactions between variables are generally listed, and responsibilities of subgroups (those dealing with particular sections of the overall system) are laid out. Then four or five subgroups begin to define the interactions that need to be considered and data (which participants have brought with them) are applied in these submodels. On the third day, subgroup meetings continue, and subgroup coordinators begin to program and test submodels. Late on the fourth day the submodels, with luck, can be integrated. Serious debugging, validation, and policy evaluation can begin on the last day. Clearly, a special kind of leader is needed for such workshops. He must be someone with broad perspective on the problem, who is willing to make bold assumptions and move onward when proceedings bog down and who can channel trivial arguments into useful directions. Except for this individual, requirements for expertise and facilities for such an undertaking are not great, as was discussed in Chapter 3.

Two logistical details help to make workshops successful. First, they should be held at a neutral location where everyone is removed from his normal responsibilities and other distractions. Second, it is important that participants have the opportunity to run through some of the analyses themselves. For example, computer terminals that permit individuals to ask "what happens if . . ." questions of the model can be extremely beneficial in making model assumptions and limitations clear, in suggesting further refinements, and in revising performance criteria. Only modest investment in computer software and hardware is needed to create this important "hands-on" gaming capability (see Chapter 3 again).

SECOND-PHASE WORKSHOPS

The kind of workshop just described serves to start a problem analysis. The resulting model is clearly incomplete, and further efforts may be required to clarify data needs. The next phase of analysis can involve additional workshops, the number depending on the problem being studied. These workshops aim to revise the model and define new information needs, particularly as new data become available. In some cases a credible process of evaluation can be completed with only two workshops, held several months apart; other cases may require a series of workshops that are held over a year or two. The same mix of people, though not necessarily the same individuals, should participate in these later workshops: methodologists, specialists, and decision makers. The time between workshops is spent in data collection, model testing, and evaluation of management policies (Chapters 7 and 8), the last two activities largely being carried out by the small core team.

Again, the second phase of workshops can be equally valuable, whether participants are operating in an active, integrated policy design mode or making a relatively independent assessment of proposed policies. The value derives from the more careful focusing on critical issues, data needs, and questions. Some of these second-phase workshops were illustrated in Chapter 3.

TRANSFER WORKSHOPS

Finally, as the analysis or assessment nears completion, the phase of transfer to the contracting agency or other clients who were not involved during problem analysis begins. Here again workshops have proved valuable (Gross *et al.*, 1973; Clark *et al.*, 1977; Peterman, 1977a) in both an impact assessment setting and a resource management program. When the model is used as a focus for discussion, the assumptions underlying the analysis are clarified and the "client" decision makers can ask various questions of the model through interactive gaming. This so-called "implementation" phase is quite critical; without a smooth transition, even the best analyses are incomplete. Thus, attention must be given to the best ways of communicating the information. Chapter 9, on communication, illustrates some of the most effective ways we have found to transfer information.

5 Choosing a Technique

There are a great many analytic techniques and modeling styles, and the environmental assessment team must choose among them. The choice is important: the factors considered, the scope of the evaluation, and the eventual credibility and usefulness of the effort are tied closely to the techniques chosen. However, the choice is not immutable. Adaptive modeling contributes to adaptive assessment and management, and therefore we expect that the number and nature of techniques employed and of models constructed will grow, evolve, and shift as the analysis progresses and as understanding emerges.

Many of the chapters in this book call for the comparison of alternatives: alternative objectives, alternative developments, alternative models. Equally, alternative analytical and predictive techniques should be mobilized – each chosen for its usefulness and appropriateness for some particular aspect of the study. In this chapter we shall offer our views of the strengths and weaknesses of several of the techniques that we have utilized in our own environmental assessment and resource management problems.

The choice of technique follows from the nature of the problem at hand. The scope of that problem demands a complementary capacity in the tools used to address it. At the same time, however, the limitations of available data and information constrain and modify the selection of techniques and the means by which the assessment proceeds. All too often, it is the technique that grabs the lead, and the problem is then bent and redefined to suit. Every analyst or consultant has his favorite methods for solving problems, and it is only natural for him to advocate their use. The authors of this book lean heavily toward simulation modeling, but we feel it very important to maintain as much breadth and flexibility in our methods as possible in order to be responsive to a wide range of environmental and management problems.

To emphasize the importance of putting the nature of the problem ahead of technique, we first compare and classify nine of the major case study problems with which one or more of us has been involved. Some of these are described in detail as the supporting case studies of this book (Part II). Other problems are introduced here to enlarge the present discussion.

These nine problems cover three broad types of environmental concern. The first type of problem concentrates on the social and economic system and focuses on the dynamics of human behavior and associated economic causes and effects. For the most part ecological phenomena are not treated explicitly but are handled by transforming the socioeconomic variables into indicators of environmental effects. The problems of this type that we consider here are

Obergurgl. A study of land use development in a high-alpine Austrian village. The conflict between resort development and farming in the face of an expanding population is a central issue (see Chapter 13).

GIRLS (Gulf Islands Recreational Land Simulator). A study of land use and development in the Gulf Islands of western Canada. A strong emphasis is placed on the effects of speculation and perceived quality on the real estate market (Chambers, 1971; Holling, 1969).

Georgia Strait. A study of the interaction and conflicts between recreational sport fishing and the commercial harvest of salmon in British Columbia's Strait of Georgia.

The second type of problem concerns large-scale resource development projects. These problems call for an exploration of the dynamics of the environmental changes that will result from extensive interventions. Typically, many biological species and habitats are considered, but the socioeconomic system is not treated in depth. Problems of this type include

James Bay. A study of a large (440,000 km^2) hydroelectric development in the Canadian subarctic. Wildlife preservation and native Indian welfare are two major facets considered (Walters, 1974; Munn, 1975).

Guri. A study of an extensive regional development program in connection with a hydroelectric project in the Orinoco River basin in Venezuela (see Chapter 14).

Oil Shale. A study of the impact of oil-shale mining and exploitation on wildlife communities in the western United States (see Chapter 15).

The third type of environmental management problem concerns the population dynamics of a few species. Typically, only the dominant species of interest and its immediate prey and predators are considered. This is true whether the central population is a harvestable resource, a pest, or an endangered species. The dynamics of the socioeconomic system in which the biology is embedded are not treated explicitly: rather, the ecological variables are translated into the appropriate social and economic indicators for management decisions. We consider in this chapter the following three studies as problems of this third type:

Budworm. A study of forest management in the face of a major insect pest, the spruce budworm. This study focuses on the design of ecological policies for the Canadian province of New Brunswick (see Chapter 11).

Caribou. A study of the population dynamics of caribou herds in northern Canada (Walters *et al.*, 1975).

Capybara. A study of the capybara, a large and commercially important rodent, in Venezuela.

These nine sample problems of resource management and environmental assessment are also useful because they represent a broad range of variation in many characteristics besides the three problem types under which they were presented. In the next section we develop a classification scheme to organize our perceptions of the important aspects of any problem. We propose three broad measures that, for all our case studies, characterize the challenges to, and opportunities for, creative and adaptive management. If we think of these as three axes of a graph, it is possible to locate the nine case studies, and others, on the graph (see Figure 5.1). The three axes of this problem classification scheme are

- The common, though usually subjective, measure of problem *complexity*. This complexity comes from several sources, which we describe in the next section.
- The amount and quality of *data* available. Of course, the amount of relevant and usable data may be a small fraction of the total.
- The degree of conceptual *understanding* we have of the inner workings of the system in question. This understanding reflects our ability to identify and analyze the causal relationships of the principal ecological and social processes involved.

When we organize our perceptions of a problem's characteristics along the three axes of this classification scheme, we are in fact characterizing the model that will be used to analyze the problem. The way that the model is conceived and constructed depends on whether the problem is complex or simple, has many or few data, or involves processes of which there is considerable or little background understanding. How the model, or other analytic technique, relates to the problem will be clearer after we locate the nine sample case studies according to the classification criteria and then consider what modeling technique was used in each of these cases.

In the third section of this chapter we move from a general classification of the whole problem along the three axes – complexity, data, and understanding – and begin to consider how the problem analysis can be addressed with the analytic techniques available. Operationally, of course, headway can best be made by dealing with submodels of individual ecological or social processes, rather than by treating the entire problem in one lump. Each of these constituent processes will have its own location along the complexity, data, and understanding axes and thus will have its own requirements for analytic technique.

The various mathematical assessment and analysis techniques can be thought of as sitting on a continuum that stretches from highly qualitative to highly quantitative. On the qualitative end would be such non-numeric procedures as species checklists and cross-impact matrices, while on the quantitative end we place detailed simulation models and other more analytic procedures, such as formal optimization methods.

When we examined the mathematical techniques we have used, we found we had no modeling techniques that could address incompletely specified problems – systems that had few available data and that were poorly understood. One candidate technique for filling this gap we call "qualitative simulation." In the fourth section of this chapter we describe a modest effort to explore the effectiveness of such qualitative simulations when applied to problems with various amounts of data. This exploration served primarily as self-education, and we present as its principal product a list of the major lessons learned.

COMPLEXITY, DATA, AND UNDERSTANDING

The classification presented in this section highlights some of the sources of complexity in a problem analysis and points to ways to minimize and organize that complexity. Additionally, much attention is given to the distinction between quantities of data and extent of understanding. These two are often confused and interchanged. However, the type of analysis employed is very much affected by the mix of these aspects. Specifically, we show that one can proceed farther than is normally thought possible in the face of meager data by mobilizing available insight into the system's constituent processes. As an illustration we shall take one of the case studies and examine some of its processes and how they are analyzed from the viewpoint of this classification.

COMPLEXITY

Complexity is a relative concept at best, and in the world of modeling it has been used to mean so many different things that it no longer conveys much information. We can explicitly list some of the attributes contributing to complexity, but whether the whole model is called simple or complex remains a matter of opinion.

A quantitative measure of complexity has several parts. Perhaps the most obvious is the number of variables required to describe adequately the dynamic conditions of our system at any moment. Typical variables used in our models include the number of spawning salmon, the flow rate of a river, or the fraction of available capital that Obergurglers hold in their savings accounts. In the budworm case study one variable is the number of insects, two other variables keep track of the amount and condition of the foliage, another represents the weather, and seventy-five variables account for the number of trees in seventy-five single-year age classes. We view a model with 79 variables as modestly large, but, in this case, the fact that 75 of these variables have nearly equivalent functions somewhat reduces the effective complexity.

Most environmental and ecological problems are not contained in a single location, and it is often necessary to disaggregate a model into several spatial areas. In hydroelectric developments, large areas are involved, and separate impoundments must often be treated as explicit units; the Obergurgl village/farm/ski-resort region is subdivided into ten spatial units. In the budworm study the tremendous dispersal capabilities of the moth and the operational needs of the forest managers require modeling 265 separate land areas. When the 79 variables from one area are replicated 265 times, we suddenly have 20,935 state variables! Spatial disaggregation results in an explosive increase in the state variable count.

A third component of model complexity is the number of different management acts being considered. These acts represent the interface between man's intended activities and the subsequent alterations in the environment. Again in a hydroelectric development, the construction of a dam of a certain size at a certain place in the watershed is an act. Complexity arises when the variety of ways to design a network of dams and the variety of possible construction sequences are considered. In the budworm study the available acts are "cut trees, plant trees, or kill insects." Even here, however, one must ask: Cut trees of what age? Kill budworm at what life stage and at what time in their outbreak cycle?

Acts are man's inputs to the system, and various social, economic, and environmental indicators are the outputs. These output indicators are a fourth component contributing to model complexity. The natural system may operate according to state variables, but the people who are concerned with, or who manage, resource and environmental problems respond to other measures of performance. Winter tourists in Obergurgl may respond to crowded ski slopes, while those who come in summer may object to roads, clearings, and pylons obscuring the alpine vistas. A small sample of the indicators generated for the budworm study is given in Table 8.1 of Chapter 8. These include the costs and profits to the logging industry, the volume of wood "in reserve" as young trees, and the number of high-quality recreational areas.

A final component of complexity concerns the way time is handled in the model. Often a simple, uniform time step is adequate. During one time period (a year, say) all current variable values interact to create new values for the next time period. In the budworm study we had the happy congruence of a once-a-year insect generation and a yearly management operating period. In other cases processes operate on different time scales, time lags between events occur, or the dynamics of some variable depend conditionally on variable values from previous time periods. Such mixed-time-period dynamics contribute to a model's complexity.

TABLE 5.1. Components of Complexity for Nine Sample Environmental Case Studies

Case Study	Number of State Variables	Number of Spatial Units	Number of Manage-ment Acts	Extent of Socioeconomic Impacts Considered	Time Resolution
Obergurgl	Many	Few	Moderate	High	Simple
GIRLS	Many	Few	Many	Moderate	Simple
Georgia Strait	Moderate	Very few	Few	Moderate	Simple
James Bay	Many	Moderate	Many	High	Simple
Guri	Few	Moderate	Few	High	Complex
Oil shale	Very many	Very many	Many	Moderate	Simple
Budworm	Many	Many	Few	Moderate	Simple
Caribou	Few	Very few	Few	Low	Simple
Capybara	Few	Very few	Few	Low	Moderate

These five components start to describe complexity, even if they do not define it. The important point to remember is that the total complexity is not the sum of these components, but rather the product. The benefits of parsimony at any stage are multiplied in the final product. Even so, the final working management model may still be too complex to allow useful interpretation. If the model appears to be nearly as complex as the real world, it will be difficult to achieve creative assessment and management. In the next chapter we describe some steps to cut through the remaining complexity of the working model and to reach a level of simplification for improved understanding and interpretation.

To make this discussion of complexity more concrete, in Table 5.1 we subjectively score our nine sample problems for each of the five components. These nine particular case problems were selected to illustrate a wide range of variation among these components of complexity. The Obergurgl, Guri, oil shale, and budworm studies are documented in Part II; the others can be visualized in relation to these. The numbers of state variables and spatial units are not given precisely because the model may exist in several adaptive versions of different size, the number of state variables may differ between spatial units, or the spatial disaggregation can be changed by the model user. From this table we see that Capybara and Georgia Strait are the least complex while Oil Shale, Budworm, and James Bay are the most complex.

DATA

The second axis of our problem classification scheme represents the amount of data that can be brought to bear on the problem. Some data are required for the calculation of the parameters in the descriptive functions of the model. Assignment of numbers to these parameters is what actually makes a model quantitative. Some data are needed for invalidation – the process of establishing a "degree of belief" in a model. This is done through an active search for comparisons of model and real-world behavior that show where the model is wrong, not where it is right (Chapter 7). Ordinarily, the time behavior of only a few of the state variables is known. Because the duration of a dynamic system depends on its starting conditions – different starting conditions lead to different outcomes – we need data that give a complete description of all variables at some specific moment. Without this, any direct comparison between real and simulated history is hampered by an extra burden of ambiguity.

The data need not all have been procured as part of the resource development program. Many usable data, for example, may have been gathered incidentally or may concern similar situations.

Sheer volume of data is not necessarily helpful in and of itself. Too many of the data normally collected prove to be utterly useless for constructing a management model, even when the data are scientifically sound. What science and scientists emphasize often bears little relation to what is needed for establishing environmental policy. And even research that is undertaken for management will surely end up with information missing if the research is not organized with at least a hypothetical management model in mind. It is for this reason that we advocate model-building workshops at the very early stages of a project. The benefits in organizing the research and identifying problems that would have been overlooked make the effort worthwhile.

The models associated with the nine case examples in Table 5.1 were built from a wide range of data bases. One reason that the budworm was selected as a case study for the development of ecological policy design techniques was its rich research foundation – both intensive and extensive. Few ecological systems have been studied as much. Detailed life history studies of budworm had been made; significant information was available about such biological processes as parasitism, reproduction, the effects of foliage condition on survival of trees and budworm, and the effects of insecticides on the target species. Additionally, population estimates had been made for over 25 years at many locations in a 50,000 km^2 area.

For the oil shale problem, a broad range of data was available, most of which were not as statistically sound as those available for the budworm study. There was some information on many species but very little information on the relationship between species and between other ecological factors. In Obergurgl a surprisingly large amount of data could be extracted from the village records: birth and death records were used to build a very reliable demographic model; other records established patterns between economic profiles of groups and investments in savings accounts and hotel construction. For Guri, on the other hand, there were virtually no data other than those pertaining to the strict engineering specifications and basic hydrology.

UNDERSTANDING

On the final axis of our classification scheme is the extent of basic understanding we have of the processes that underlie the behavior of the systems. This information can be derived from a growing literature of laboratory and field experimental research: with it, we can know in advance the necessary and sufficient attributes that characterize a particular process. Without this prior knowledge of form, we would require a great many observations, over a range of variation, to establish a functional representation. However, as soon as we know that a particular mathematical function will describe a process, the information requirements are suddenly reduced greatly. Now we need only estimate values for the few parameters of that function. In some cases parameters will have a strict physical or biological interpretation that makes their evaluation direct.

When faced with the problem of sending a spacecraft from the earth to the moon, the "managers" know and use the equation describing gravitation and other well-developed laws of physics. Parameters must still be set, such as the mass and location of the moon and the configuration of the craft, but these are specific parameters for known functional relationships. Here, the known and understood processes of gravitation and thrust reaction are the core of the controlling "management model."

Many ecological problems can be treated in an analogous fashion. Rather than using arbitrary relationships between variables – such as those provided by statistical regressions – we can mobilize a substantial body of theoretical and experimental work and place the representations of relationships on a firmer foundation. Predation is one ecological process that is particularly well documented. It is now possible to take a predation equation "off the shelf" and use it in a model. An example of this is discussed later in this chapter and in Chapter 11, on the budworm case study.

Of the nine case examples, Budworm and Caribou had the most supporting knowledge of the constituent processes. Human social phenomena as found in the Obergurgl and GIRLS studies were not so well understood, and in the oil shale problem there was insufficient knowledge, even of which variables were connected to which, so that the potential of using process understanding could not be realized.

CLASSIFYING OUR EXAMPLES

We can make a loose, subjective placement of our nine examples within the dimensions of complexity, data, and understanding (Figure 5.1). The variation among these nine studies is evident in the figure. The models and other analytic procedures applied to each of these studies can in some measure be determined by the location of the study in this figure. The nature of the problem – whether it is a socioeconomic question, a resource development project, or a population dynamics problem – does not influence the style of analysis nearly as much as does its location in this classification.

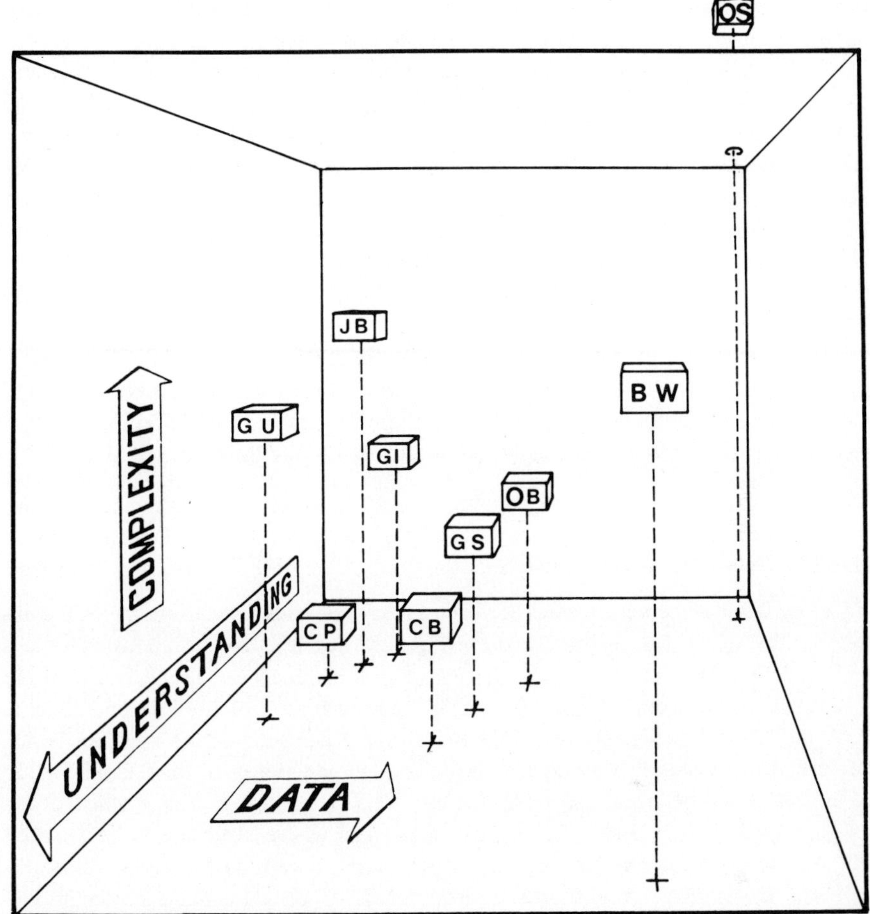

FIGURE 5.1 The location of nine sample case studies of environmental assessment and management in a problem classification scheme measuring degree of complexity, amount of available data, and degree of background conceptual understanding. The case studies are OB: Obergurgl; GI: GIRLS; GS: Georgia Strait; JB: James Bay; GU: Guri; OS: Oil Shale; BW: Budworm; CB: Caribou; CP: Capybara.

For example, the oil shale problem is isolated in the high-complexity/high-data/low-understanding corner of Figure 5.1. This problem was also treated very differently from the others (as can be seen in Chapter 15). The budworm study is also at the periphery of this constellation, being rated high for each of the three measures; this accounts to some extent for the relatively advanced development of the budworm case study. It also accounts for the ubiquitous appearance of the budworm to illustrate points in this book. A larger number of lessons have been learned through the challenges and opportunities afforded by the available data, the prior understanding, and the inherent complexity of this system.

Clearly, any management problem has some parts for which there are sufficient data and others for which there are not; some parts whose processes we know from other sources and some not; and some parts that can adequately be described by a simple function and others that require more elaborate mathematics. It is precisely this that had led us to utilize simulation modeling as a technique for assessment and analysis. With simulation models we have the flexibility to program a wide variety of functions and relationships and thus make full use of the knowledge we do have. Simulation model construction also helps us identify those areas where information is scarce and needed.

Placing an entire model on a chart such as Figure 5.1 requires subjective aggregation of all the parts – the strong with the weak. In the following section we shall look in more detail at the parts of one of these studies – the budworm study – to see how their location in this classification affects the way they were treated.

MODELING THE PROCESSES

An effective management model requires an explicit causal structure in its formulation. The quest for realism, however, should not lead to the inclusion of excessive detail. The challenge is to restrict what is included to the minimum, while still retaining an accurate and "workable" representation of the key phenomena.

A model that accurately describes the ultimate behavior of the variables is not enough. Almost any arbitrary model, given enough parameters to tune, can be made to match a set of historical observations. This is, of course, the essence of regression-type models and other forms of analysis whose structure is determined not by the problem but by extrinsic motivations – such as the desire for mathematical tractability. Any useful environmental or resource management model must be able to respond to unique changes and unprecedented perturbations that alter the system's conditions. New management acts will cause the system to move into new regimes of behavior; the model, to be useful, should be responsive to these same shifts. If the model has an appropriate causal structure, it will respond to these new conditions more faithfully.

There will always be some uncertainty about a model's flexibility in responding to novel conditions. Whole new mechanisms may enter the picture, or elements that were excluded from the original model may become important in unexpected ways. But this will always be the case, no matter what form the analysis takes. If the model has a logical causal structure, new items can be easily incorporated as they are discovered. This is an important aspect that makes the modeling procedure part of the entire adaptive process.

The most direct way we have found for ensuring a causal model structure is to focus on the level of the constituent processes. These are the operating subdivisions that link the variables of a system. Looking at processes also has the advantage of capitalizing on generality – because processes extend across many situations, we can draw upon the knowledge and understanding gained from other cases and other research.

The examples of processes in this chapter are primarily ecological and are illustrated by the budworm. However, the other cases are formulated in a similar manner. In Obergurgl there is a market process relating tourist demand to hotel and ski-lift construction, as well as an inverse process relating existing facilities to demand. Hydrological developments such as James Bay and Guri involve such processes as stream scouring and erosion. The Georgia Strait study must consider how the commercial catch affects fleet investment, as well as the effect of angling success on sport fishing activity.

Ecological processes include such things as growth, reproduction, competition, predation, and natural selection. Such "natural" processes exist across a very wide variety of situations. The ecological processes are very like those that a meteorologist would list: advection, convection, evaporation, and the like. The analogy is worth pursuing, for the meteorologist seeking to explain or predict a given pattern of weather does not start each study *de novo.* Rather, he makes extensive use of the discipline's existing stock of well-tested process theories, parameterizing and combining them in modular fashion as each specific situation demands. The individual modules provide an *a priori* structure for interpretation of the data, can often be individually tested, and inevitably highlight the weak or missing aspects of the analysis.

THE BUDWORM PROCESSES

The major processes in the biological phase of the budworm study are shown in Figure 5.2. These processes represent the important phenomena that affect budworm population growth, forest development, and the interaction of the two. Details of these processes can be found in Chapter 11 and in Yorque *et al.,* 1978).

In Figure 5.2, we locate the individual processes of this study upon the axes of data availability and conceptual understanding. We do this to emphasize the range of variation that is inherent in any environmental study. To develop a management model, all the parts necessary for a holistic picture must be included. The scattering of the parts on the data/understanding plane to a variety of challenges and approaches for any study. The axes of Figure 5.2 are in many ways complementary – a low value on one can be compensated for by a high value on the other. Too often, however, amount of data is assumed to equal amount of understanding. In traditional environmental assessment work and in some large ecological modeling projects, data acquisition becomes an end in itself, and there is too little creative exploitation of the existing background understanding.

The budworm processes Figure 5.2 span four distinct areas of the plane (I–IV in the figure); and each area requires its own type of analysis. To address the corner

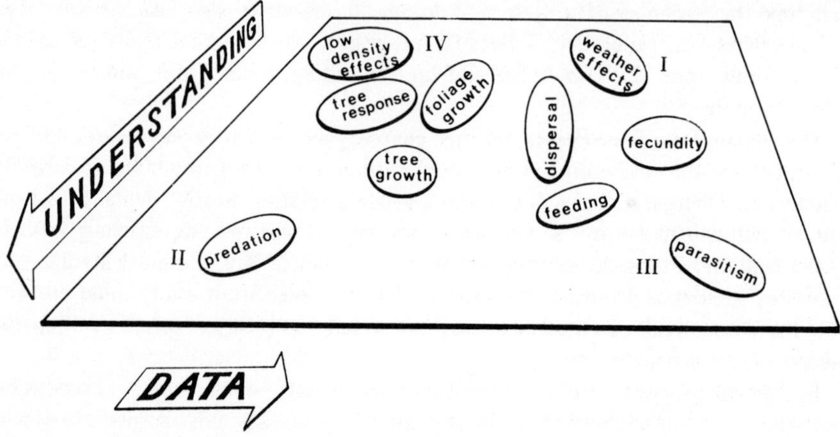

FIGURE 5.2 The location of individual ecological processes from the budworm study on the axes of amount of available data and degree of background conceptual understanding.

with much data but little supporting understanding (I) we have available a whole battery of techniques from statistical analysis. Though statistically fitted curves do not "explain" (despite the misuse of that word in the context of statistical tests), they can describe a relationship in a mathematical form that will at least allow the analysis to continue. The more data and the broader the range of observations, the more comprehensive will be the resulting submodel. But without a foundation based on theoretical understanding, any extrapolation of this submodel to new situations will be dangerous.

Masses of data have been collected on the relationship between a variety of weather parameters and budworm survival rates. Missing from these data is information concerning weather-induced shifts in insect "quality," shifts that could lead to selection of different "types" of individuals that would alter future generations and the dynamics of the outbreak cycle. Also, without knowledge of the mechanisms that actually link weather with survival, we have little guidance for suggesting policies of forest management that could alter the microclimate of this pest species.

In the opposite corner of Figure 5.2 (II) we have few data but considerable conceptual understanding. We have come to the conviction as a result of our case study experience that much can be done when data are scarce but good backup knowledge of process exists. Predation in the budworm system provides an example. In this particular case we are fortunate because predation has been well analyzed at the level of process needed for the model. On the other hand, data are scarce because predation has it major impact when budworm are scarce; at low densities it is very difficult to obtain meaningful samples.

From our knowledge of predation we can specify in advance the mathematical characteristics of the governing functions. Once we know this and have picked a candidate function that meets the requirements, then even scattered data can be applied to establish parameter values. In the budworm case we were able first to classify the various bird predators into distinct parameter classes and then to establish for each class feasible maximum and minimum parameter values. The sensitivity of the simulation model to this range of parameter values can easily be tested through simulation runs, the emerging behavior being used as one criterion for judging the importance of predation.

Along the diagonal region of Figure 5.2 (III and IV) specific data and understanding are more in balance. When both components are large, modeling and analysis are straightforward. The difficulty comes when a process is modeled with glorious sophistication simply because the information is available. In the budworm example, enough was known to construct an elegant and detailed submodel of parasitism. However, such an effort would have been out of keeping with the rest of the model and in violation of our rule of parsimony. The result, in this case, was to use only a single, simple equation that expressed rate of parasitism as a function of budworm density.

Where there are fewer data and where the functional form is not known, it is best to set up alternative testable hypotheses. In the case of dispersal, for example, two extreme alternatives were taken. The first was that dispersal was a random "diffusion" process dictated by weather. At the other extreme was the hypothesis that insect movement was highly clumped and directed. Again, sensitivity tests were made with the model using the recorded spatial dynamics for comparison. In this case the choice between alternatives depended on field data on the overall system behavior. If such field data are not available, then we have identified a research priority. (But note that in highly periodic systems there are often qualitative data available on such things as frequency and amplitude under various conditions.)

When there are few data and little understanding, the requirement for alternative hypotheses becomes even more critical. Sensitivity tests must always be made to check for important shifts in management effectiveness. Technically, there are no "tricks" for modeling such processes other than ensuring logical soundness and checking to be sure that the functions adopted have not introduced unwanted mathematical artifacts into the computations.

CONCLUSIONS

From the predation, dispersal, and other examples we have concluded that one can indeed go farther than usually thought with qualitative analyses of processes. When we are able to use such analyses to complete a causally structured process model, the results are superior to those obtained with any prepackaged modeling "language" or externally imposed mathematical framework.

A SPECTRUM OF TECHNIQUES

Our emphasis on causal relationships based on processes comes from our experience with numerical simulation models. This same process orientation is also appropriate for other "problem-solving" methodologies, such as dynamic programming and other techniques of optimization. Unfortunately, the mathematical structure of these techniques very often places severe constraints upon the way a model can be expressed. At least with a simulation model you are free to "say it the way you want to." However, simulation is such an open forum that it is easy to say too much – this is why we put such strong emphasis on parsimony. One successful technique for reducing the problem to the bare-bones essentials is "looking outward," as practiced in the workshop setting (Chapter 4). These efforts help to keep the resulting management model itself manageable. The next chapter discusses additional steps that can be taken to further simplify and gain understanding.

Simulation modeling, however, covers only a part of the spectrum of mathematical techniques available for environmental assessment and management. As suggested earlier, we think of this spectrum as spanning a range from qualitative to quantitative.

Techniques on the qualitative end, such as interaction matrices, rely on intuition and deep understanding for useful projections of the environmental effects of man's proposed interventions. However, these techniques founder where there are too many variables and relationships linking them, too many nonlinear processes, or too many available actions and potential consequences. Basically, difficulties arise when the problem becomes too big and complex or when its internal interrelationships differ radically from the rather simple form implicit in matrices.

On the other hand, numerical techniques, such as simulation models and optimization procedures, rely on accurate identification of relevant variables and the form of their interrelations, on data for parameterizing those relationships, and on accurate descriptions of the available actions that can be taken. Unfortunately, these models can fail through the mind-numbing barrage of complexity that sometimes appears to exceed that of the real world. Additionally, simulation models built from a base of too few data and, more important, with too little understanding, can lead one quickly and easily to false conclusions.

Within these two extremes, how do we steer a course toward a model that will adequately address any particular management or assessment problem? Our bias toward simulation is stressed throughout this book. Many other workers performing environmental assessments have extensively used and described a variety of cross-impact techniques such as the Leopold matrix and its improved descendants. Our own preconception was that such matrices were probably the best techniques available when very little was known about a situation. Nevertheless, it seemed unlikely that there would be much gain in understanding for improved management – and that any gain might be deceptive because these methods were formalized procedures.

A question arose as we examined a growing range of environmental studies: were there techniques available that would be appropriate for only partially defined systems? We were thinking of situations where more was known than an impact matrix could utilize but perhaps not enough to embark on a normal simulation modeling effort. We thought that if such techniques did exist and were useful, they would have particular merit in developing countries, where the call for development and action is strong but the background of research is limited. We describe in the next section some explorations we and our colleagues have made in response to this question.

EXPLORATION OF QUALITATIVE TECHNIQUES

We were sure that there were ways to effectively analyze systems that possess insufficient information to allow construction of a normal simulation model. Often, all that is known is the major variables and how they interact qualitatively – when A is large, B will decline. We realized that most environmental studies do not rely on simulation models, but the techniques that are employed in these studies often fail to utilize the information that is available.

In response to this perceived need, and to satisfy our own curiosity, we set out to explore the possibilities offered by assessment techniques thay lay between static impact matrices and more complete dynamic simulation models. We call these intermediate methods "qualitative simulations" because they are formulated on a qualitative rather than numeric base, yet they dynamically project the implications of their interactions into the future. We focused our explorations on the performance of qualitative modeling across a range of data quality and quantity in order to determine if there was a useful matching of these methods to a certain level of information.

These explorations took the form of a gaming exercise. We enlisted ourselves and several of our colleagues in a series of mock environmental assessments. Preliminary sets of data from a few of our well-developed case studies were given to "assessment teams" who attacked them with one or more analytic methods. Others who were very familiar with the case studies were the "judges," comparing the mock assessments with their own hindsight. The real evaluations, however, came from the users' own experiences of the advantages and disadvantages of each technique. An ideal experimental design would use a number of test projects and have several teams of experts analyze each one using a different assessment methodology. We would then wait 10 to 50 years and see how well each methodology predicted the impacts and why some techniques performed better than others. In lieu of this ideal, we approached these explorations as a learning experience for ourselves; consequently, the major product was a set of lessons and observations. These are reported below.

One auxiliary feature of this exercise was its cross-cultural character. In all, about 50 people participated in this series of assessments over a 2 year period. They came from groups in Venezuela, Argentina, and Canada, and they had varying amounts of background skills, though most had been schooled in ecology. We were surprised to find that there were no apparent differences in the groups' ability to utilize various assessment techniques; there was also an unexpected uniformity in their judgment of the relative strengths and weaknesses of the methods.

Because this exploration was a mock exercise, and therefore somewhat artificial, we decided to "anchor" it to our previous experience and to the experience of others who have undertaken environmental assessment. To accomplish this, we subjected the data packages from the sample problems to assessment by simulation modeling and by the Leopold matrix (Leopold *et al.,* 1971) as well as by "qualitative simulations." Although the Leopold matrix is no longer widely used in its original form, it is the precursor of many currently advocated techniques and so was taken for the present purpose as representative of that class of methods.

The product of these explorations was a scorecard like that shown in Figure 5.3. A rating was placed in each box indicating how well each technique did at each level of data quantity. The success of a technique consists of how well it does at, among other things, accurately predicting impacts, adding to our understanding of and insight into the problem, and providing a means for guiding policy. In keeping with our noncookbook style, we will not fill in Figure 5.3, but will let the reader draw his own conclusions from the participants' comments given below and from his own experience.

We next briefly describe the techniques that were used in this exploration, expand on the description of the assessment protocol, and present the lessons and conclusions that we drew from this activity.

THE TECHNIQUES USED

The techniques used were qualitative modeling, the Leopold matrix, and simulation modeling. Since this gaming exercise was primarily a reconnaissance into qualitative modeling, we examined two different qualitative modeling techniques – GSIM and KSIM. We describe both of these, plus the Leopold matrix, below; simulation modeling has already been discussed thoroughly throughout the text. More detailed descriptions of all four techniques can be found in Appendix A.

GSIM

GSIM is a qualitative modeling approach requiring the least information of the four techniques evaluated in this exercise. The user need only specify the relevant system variables and then decide whether the relationship between each pair of variables is positive (an increase in A leads to an increase in B), negative (an increase in A leads to a decrease in B), or zero (an increase in A does not directly

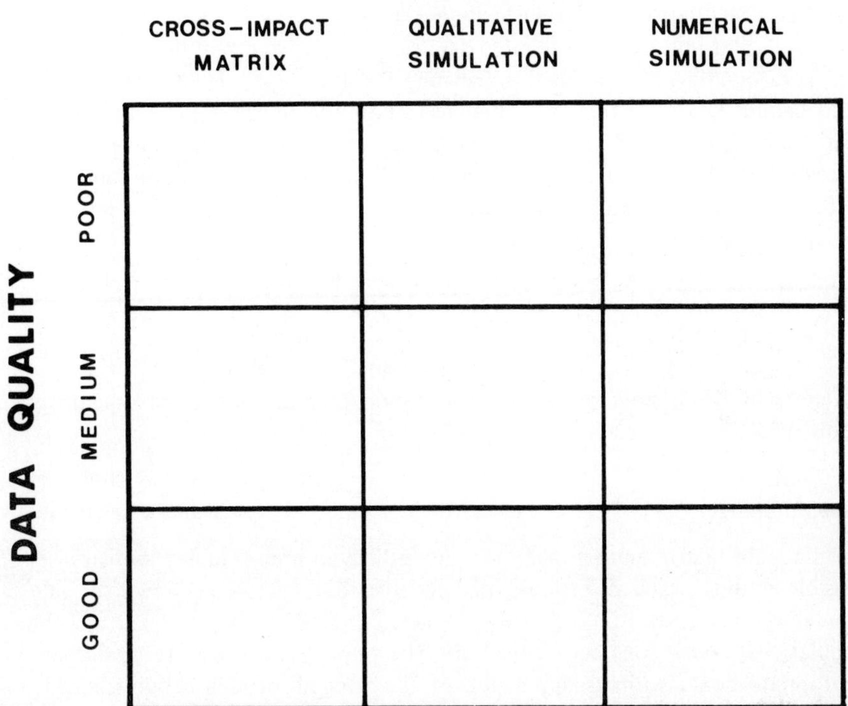

FIGURE 5.3 A hypothetical scorecard for ranking three types of techniques given three levels of available data. This matrix of combinations guided the exploration of techniques described in the text.

affect *B*). The GSIM technique, readily implemented on a computer, evaluates the dynamic implications of these specified relationships. If additional information is available on the relative "importance" of the variables, this is easily incorporated into the evaluation. The principal advantage of this approach is that it allows one to consider the dynamics of the systems and the interactions among variables at an information level too sparse to allow the construction of a standard simulation model. Other advantages are the speed with which the user can structure the model and the very low hardware requirements (a desk computer or even desk calculator is sufficient). This kind of model can provide only rough qualitative trends of the variables and cannot reliably handle situations sensitive to precise numerical balances of the variables.

KSIM

KSIM is a qualitative simulation technique that begins with the same information used by GSIM but also incorporates data on the relative magnitude of interaction effects (a doubling of A leads to a halving of B and so on). The two basic assumptions behind KSIM are that everything has a potential maximum and minimum and that if among factors of equal importance there are many that cause some variable to increase but few that cause it to decrease, it will increase. KSIM allows some factors to be more important than others and also allows factors to act, for example, more strongly when they are near their maxima than when they are near their minima. The technical details of KSIM are moderately complex, and readers desiring an in-depth understanding should consult the technical description in Appendix A. KSIM may be adapted to accommodate a great deal of quantitative detail, but it then becomes more of a direct simulation than a qualitative technique. For this reason, our tests of KSIM were restricted to a version that did not require quantitative information.

Leopold Matrix

The Leopold matrix and its many variants utilize an impact table that lists a set of possible actions (water diversions, road construction, and so on) down the side of the table, and a set of potentially impacted indicators (water quality, wildlife populations, and so on) across the top. The impact assessment team fills in the appropriate boxes with its impression of the strength of each action's impact on each indicator as well as the importance of the impact, using a subjective scale of 1–10. The result of the Leopold matrix is a very large table describing the effect of each action on each impact indicator. Matrices of this form are a common predictive technique used in environmental impact assessment in North America.

We use the original Leopold matrix here. Some of its defects have been eliminated through various modifications, but the general structure remains substantially the same.

WHAT WE DID

Our initial belief was that the properties and capabilities of a technique should be matched to the characteristics of a particular problem. In the present context, we felt that the extent and detail of the data associated with a problem were the most critical characteristics. We have stated above that background conceptual understanding of the processes can compensate for missing data. Although we knew how this compensation is made in a simulation model, it was not clear if either the Leopold matrix or the qualitative models would have this flexibility. Hence no effort was made to draw benefits from this conceptual understanding. It can be accommodated easily only in a quantitative simulation environment and would unfairly bias the results toward numerical simulation. Therefore in these explorations the only characteristic that was varied from trial to trial was the amount and quality of the data available to the analysis and assessment team.

A group very familiar with one of the case studies was the "expert" during this exploration of techniques. That group took all the material from the problem and assembled three packages of data in a form that might be available to an assessment team charged with analyzing such a problem and predicting the effects of alternative management options. The lowest level data package consisted of only a general description of the system and a minimum of quantitative information. The highest level package was very detailed and included most of the relevant data at the expert's disposal. The third package was intermediate.

The experts also drew up a set of specific questions about the nature and behavior of possible impacts of developments specific to their particular case. The experts, having been intimately involved with the study, knew the answers from hindsight, and in retrospect felt that an environmental assessment team should have been able to predict them.

These data packages and questions were given to other groups – the "assessment teams" – who knew little or nothing about the particular case study. Each team applied one or more of the four techniques, using one of the data packages, and attempted to answer the management questions. As participants we found the project exceptionally useful. As we explored the possibilities of these techniques in various situations, we were frustrated, we were excited, we were angry, but above all we learned a great deal. We attempt to convey the flavor of that experience in the next section.

WHAT WE LEARNED

One lesson of this experience confirmed our original bias: as we moved from poor to good data, only numerical simulation models were able to use the additional data effectively. The qualitative models did not have the capability in their intrinsic structure to utilize numerical data. Indeed, when a group using such a technique was given a set of good data, they often abandoned the qualitative techniques and started doing numerical calculations with pencil and paper.

This exercise also crystallized our feelings about the Leopold matrix. Despite its ubiquitous use, it is in no way a predictive technique. However, it was often a great help in guiding intuition and as a check for overlooked relationships.

In the course of these explorations we were surprised to find that simulation models often fared poorly, failing to answer some of the critical questions about impacts properly. This failure of the assessment teams' models was underscored by the fact that a simulation model built for the original case studies had performed so much better. We attribute this failure of the simulations to two factors.

First, there was a lack of time. This led to misinterpretation of data, logical mistakes, and computer programming errors. But this can happen in any real

TABLE 5.2. Advantages and Disadvantages of the Leopold Matrix

Disadvantages	Advantages
The 88 × 100 matrix is oriented toward construction projects so, categories of actions and characteristics incomplete and not general	Easy to use, no computer facilities needed
Categories too broad, cannot look at specific interactions for which information is available	Promotes communication between disciplines
Gives false sense that all possible interactions have been considered once the matrix has been filled in	Relatively little hard data required
Not really a predictive technique – predictions based only on the user's intuition and experience	Useful as a check against other methods to see if particular categories of actions or system characteristics have been omitted
Time and effort required large relative to the technique's value	
User not forced to articulate assumptions	
Cannot distinguish between rare and common interactions	
Hard to separate "importance" from "magnitude"	
Rankings of interactions from 1 to 10 highly subjective	
User not forced to define mechanisms of the interactions	
Cannot handle nonlinear impacts	
Relations or interactions assumed constant through time	
Results cannot be summarized in a form easily communicated to the decision maker	
No distinction between processes at different levels in the hierarchy of natural processes	
Uncertainties cannot be included	
Many actions and characteristics have different levels of resolution: some very specific and others very general	

environmental study where deadlines loom and bugets are tight. Errors of these types are always waiting in the wings. Practice, learning, and interactive model construction help reduce these problems, but they never eliminate them. The solution, to the extent that there is one, is to acknowledge the possibility of errors, establish a "degree of belief" through invalidation, and design policies that are robust to these technological difficulties.

TABLE 5.3 Advantages and Disadvantages of GSIM

Disadvantages	Advantages
Cannot handle numerical effects or behavior modes directly dependent on precise numerical balances	Handles very imprecise or qualitative data without introducing too many unwarranted assumptions
Time units arbitrary	Only small computer facilities required
Because of sequential discrete structure, only rough approximation to continous processes	Easy to conceptualize, program, and understand the causal determinants of the response
Care necessary about the order of the variables in a causal chain, taking into account whether the impact of some variables upon others should be in phase or out of phase	Handles a large number of causal chains
	Handles multiple relations, feedback relations, logical decisions ("IF" statements), time-lags, simple nonlinearities, threshold effects, discontinuities, etc.
Changes in variables assumed to be unitary, so GSIM does not differentiate among variables that change at numerically different rates	Forces the user to think about very basic forms of causal connections in terms of the user's own conceptual background, thereby reducing the probability of being caught in the details of the system
Results sensitive to assignment of possible ranges of values of the variables	Handles short-term, transient behavior as well as long-term outcomes

The second factor that led to poor model performance was the modelers' unfamiliarity with the underlying processes of the system being modeled. The modelers depended completely upon the data packages and did not have access to the breadth of knowledge needed to supplement the always incomplete supply of data. The mock assessments failed in this regard because we did not follow our own recommended procedures – the models were built by modelers and not by a workshop. A major reason for beginning with workshops is to bring together those people who do have the breadth of familiarity to address the problem adequately.

What was learned by the participants while exploring these techniques is much more important than any scoring and rating of them. We have collected their specific comments in Tables 5.2 through 5.5. Some comments could reasonably be applied to other techniques; some reported advantages and disadvantages are mildly contradictory. We make no attempt to resolve these contradictions but retain them as part of the record to illustrate the need for flexible and adaptive attitudes toward technique selection.

All these classes of technique have a role in environmental assessment and management. The Leopold matrix, or its descendants, are useful for screening but are not intended to be predictive tools. Qualitative simulation models like GSIM and KSIM provide an easy way to formulate a trial dynamic model and to experiment with alternative policies but are of little help for detailed predictions. Numerical simulation models provide the best prediction when the data are good and are still

TABLE 5.4 Advantages and Disadvantages of KSIM

Disadvantages	Advantages
Behavior essentially logistic	Relatively little knowledge about the mechanisms of interactions between variables needed
Built-in assumptions not necessarily made clear to the user	Good at promoting interdisciplinary communication and getting decision makers involved
Arbitrary time scaling possibly confusing	Helps to identify some variables and interactions that should be investigated or used later in a more detailed simulation
Relations between variables assumed constant through time	Helps to bound the problem, that is, limit the variables to be considered
Difficult to assign values to relations in the input interaction matrix, particularly if observations on the real system are of a "process" type instead of time series	Good for a "quick and dirty" simulation
All variables bounded between 0 and 1, making it difficult to compare the relative impact of each variable	Graphic output a good way of communicating impacts
Difficult to guess what initial conditions should be assigned to variables (e.g., are 60,000 trout equal to 0.2 or 0.8 of the maximum number possible?)	Alternative management schemes can be compared relatively easily by changing values in the input matrix and rerunning model
Detailed information on processes often cannot be used in the KSIM framework	Handles large numbers of different *kinds* of variables (physical, sociological, biological, etc.)
Graphic output can delude; gives false sense of security in precision of predictions	
Fails to allow measures of degree of belief in data or assumptions to be reflected in final results	
Users often adjust values in input interaction matrix in order to give "reasonable" output: i.e., data are adjusted to fit preconceived notions of what should happen – obviously not useful in the context of environmental impact assessment	
Users cannot distinguish between processes at different levels in the hierarchy of natural processes	
Computer facilities needed	
Cannot include uncertainties	

useful for guiding research when the data are poor. There is no reason why all these techniques could not be used if the assessment process is to be adaptive. The judgment of proper timing and mixing of techniques comes best from experience.

TABLE 5.5 Advantages and Disadvantages of Simulation Modeling

Disadvantages	Advantages
Requires computer facilities	Promotes communication between disciplines
Requires expertise and a fair amount of time	User forced to clarify assumptions and causal mechanisms
Results may be too easily believed by decision makers	Any form of relationships can be handled – linear or nonlinear
Results are usually complex (if there are many variables) and are therefore difficult to communicate to decision makers	Helps to identify key variables or relationships that need to be investigated or are sensitive
Fails to allow measures of degree of belief in data or in the assumptions to be reflected in final results	Can include uncertainties of various types
Relations between variables usually assumed constant through time	Can easily compare alternative management schemes
	Can use detailed information concerning processes in the natural system
	Graphics output a good way of communicating impacts
	Can utilize information about known processes that have not been investigated for the particular system of study but that have some generality (e.g., predation, population growth).

We mentioned above that the simulation models built during this exercise differed from those originally constructed for the case studies. Although extenuating circumstances rooted in the nature of these explorations contributed to these differences, it still remains true that models of the same situation built by different groups will not be the same. If they are not the same, then which is the right one? Our answer, which should be easily anticipated by now, is that there is no "right" one. A model is only one piece of evidence that contributes to creative design of environmental policy and assessment. An adaptive approach to technique selection relies on alternative models emerging from alternative forms of analysis. The broader the range of evidence, the better, it is to be hoped, will be the conclusions.

Many environmental decisions must be made now, and we hope they will be made well. The developing countries should not be asked to stop resource development simply because our predictive tools are not perfect and therefore we cannot foresee and avoid all the unwanted consequences. The shortage of food and material for the people of these countries is real, and doing nothing solves nothing. Actions will not, and cannot, wait in the developed world either, where the pressures to develop are also real. On the other hand, the pendulum can swing too far the other way. All development should not go blindly ahead simply because we lack the tools to confidently predict the bad effects.

We need to learn how to gain information as we proceed with management. We need to choose an adaptive analysis that utilizes a variety of techniques so that insight from one will help foster understanding of another. We need to learn how to avoid irreversible decisions at the beginning, when data are being acquired. Above all, we need creative methods for acknowledging uncertainty and progressing in the face of it.

6 Simplification for Understanding

Complexity and simplicity each have a place in the adaptive analysis of environmental problems. A model that adequately represents the real world will necessarily contain some of the world's complexity. Although we strongly advocate parsimony, there is always a limit to the number of complications that can be removed from a management model if reliability is to be maintained. Ecological behavior stems directly from nonlinear dynamic linkages, time lags, and spatially heterogeneous distributions – each of which promotes model complexity. A model that is too simple will lack credibility, and one that fails to address a level of detail coincident with management operations will not be usable.

Simplicity, on the other hand, permits comprehension – a prerequisite for developing understanding and gaining insight. Simplified versions of the "working" management model provide alternative perspectives and avenues of analysis that foster innovative policy design. These same simplified versions are also useful for making trial assessments of candidate environmental policies and for identifying and investigating the system components that are sensitive to perturbations. Additionally, effective communication between analysts, managers, and the public depends on concise, unencumbered, but accurate formats that are easily developed from a formal process of simplification.

An adaptive approach to environmental problems avoids choosing a single level of complexity. Rather, it deliberately seeks to meet the requirements of reliable representation and credibility by using an adequate degree of realistic complexity. The adaptive approach also addresses the requirements of understanding, critical evaluation, and communication by using creative simplification. Failure to address both sides of this dichotomy will jeopardize important elements of assessment and management.

We propose an active and deliberate blending of the simple with the complex. We accomplish this by creating a collection of simpler, but complementary, representations of the management model. The simplifications are caricatures that help describe the properties, behavior, and possibilities of the environmental situation that confronts us. Because these simplified versions are unified by the detailed management model from which they were derived, exchange of ideas between them is facilitated. Interpretations from one version provide a backdrop for others.

These various representations form a hierarchy of alternative models, each providing a different perspective or a different level of detail. In no case are these simpler versions substitutes for the complete, "official" model.

Although this is a "technical" chapter, simplification is not a technique, but rather an attitude based on curiosity and a desire to get the most out of an analysis. This attitude is made operational by iteratively transferring ideas developed at one level into another level for testing and evaluation. Thus we take a policy suggested by one of the graphical techniques described below and implement it in the complete management model, where a fuller range of constraints and interactions is brought into play. The performance of the model under this new policy is one piece of evidence used to corroborate or reject the potential of this proposed policy. Similarly, ideas generated by the management model are tested at a higher level of complexity – a carefully designed and monitored field trial. Eventually, the ideas and analyses that have performed successfully at all levels available are applied to the real world.

There are no fixed procedures to follow in these modeling extensions, but we shall indicate through some detailed examples the range of things that can be done and the benefits both to us as analysts and to the case study clients – the people in the various management positions to whom the case study materials will be ultimately transferred.

We shall discuss three types of simplification:

- Smaller models created by extracting submodels that are explored independently of other submodels.
- Sets of differential equations incorporating fewer variables and parameters than the complete simulation model.
- Pictorial diagrams that display the underlying structure of the model. These serve as powerful analytical tools for penetrating to the heart of the model, and they require no "mathematics" to use.

SUBMODEL ANALYSIS

As mentioned, the complexity of the budworm model reflects both the large number of state variables and its variety of behaviors. We can eliminate much of the numerical complexity by extracting the biological submodel from one forest area so that its behavior may be explored separately from the other 264 areas. While this circumscription reduces the direct forest management relevance, the simpler

79-variable biological model still contains much of the dynamic character of the complete spatial model. By treating this biological model (which we call a *site model*) as a stand-alone entity, we can cheaply, easily, and more thoroughly explore the causes, range, and significance of those dynamics.

Operationally, we found it very helpful to embed this site model in a computer software environment that allowed quick graphical interaction between the model and any user. This interactive program package (Hilborn, 1973) was the first computer software item that was installed during the process of transfer to management personnel in New Brunswick, Quebec, Maine, and elsewhere. With this simulation system it was possible for a person, upon his first exposure to the model, to ask questions, make changes, propose alternative hypotheses, and receive an immediate graphical response. When changes produced significant results worthy of further investigation, those changes were made in the complete spatial model and examined in detail. Thus the simplified site model served both as a convenient experimental tool for the analysts and as a convenient "doodling-pad" for the potential policy maker.

There are a great number of submodels and combinations of submodels that can be isolated in a similar way. When a part is examined separately, it is necessary to set the conditions explicitly for all the excluded variables. We are completely free to set them at realistic or at interesting values. Thus in the case of the isolated site model mentioned above, the effect of dispersal from other forest areas was partially mimicked by establishing a particular fixed background of immigrating insects. Behavior of the site model with and without management controls under various levels of constant immigration was a stepping-off point for examining the more complex space–time patterns that the complete spatial model exhibited. (The complex behavior of the spatial model is shown in Figures 11.8 and 11.9 in Chapter 11.) This leap from one site to many was bewildering enough that an intermediate model with only a few sites and simple geometry and meteorology was useful (Stedinger, 1977).

At the other extreme it is often necessary to add a more complex level to the hierarchy. Baskerville (1976) chose to expand the model from 265 to 450 spatial units and to record 120 tree ages explicitly rather than 75. This expansion was operationally necessary because of the questions and concerns of a particular set of administrators.

SIMPLE ANALYTIC MODELS

The second class of simplification steps back from the complete model and seeks a smaller, less complex alternative using only a subset of the variables and functions. This subset aims at retaining the major causes of the system's behavior but, being more amenable to analysis, helps to crystallize our understanding of the important interactions and the possible effects changes will have.

In the case of the budworm, this simplified model took the form not of a simulation but of a set of three coupled differential equations (Ludwig *et al.*, 1977). One variable was the budworm density, the second was the developmental stage of the forest, and the third was the physiological state of the trees. These equations were constructed from our assessment of the important components and adapted by continually comparing their mathematical behavior with the complete model.

To give some indication of the economy achieved in this way, all of the elaborate programming of budworm biology and survival reduced to the following equation:

$$\frac{dB}{dt} = rB\left(1 - \frac{B}{k}\right) - \beta\frac{B^2}{\alpha^2 + B^2},$$

where B is the budworm density and r, k, α, and β are parameters that depend to some extent on forest conditions. We will not go into detail here, as a complete description is available in the paper cited above. We wish only to highlight the possibility that simple alternative models can pinpoint important relationships and provide the raw material for rigorous penetrating mathematical analyses.

The interaction among a collapsed set of variables was also formulated as a set of differential equations in the study of recreational development in the high alpine valley of Obergurgl, Austria, described in Chapter 13. In this case a few differential equations were able to replace the complete simulation model without a significant loss of capacity to mimic the full behavior of the larger model. While the Obergurgl model was not complex by "modern" standards, it still contained sufficient detail to prohibit adequate analysis of its internal workings. The full model contained more than 100 variables, each with a value representing the condition of some piece of the system, such as the number of villagers in various age groups. The major variables were collapsed into a set of five coupled differential equations. Each equation was much simpler than its analogous submodel but faithful to the main interrelationships. These equations produced behavior qualitatively equivalent to the behavior of the full model. The payoff was an increased ability to explore the model's calculations, and to discern why the output changed when alternative starting conditions and hypotheses were used.

These differential equations alone are inadequate for the design of economic policies for Obergurgl. For one thing, the ten spatial areas were lumped into one. To the villagers, each of the subareas has special meaning in terms of things that affect their lives. Even so, by using only five variables, we obtain important clues about "how the system really works." The awareness that these five variables could account for a large fraction of Obergurgl's socioeconomic structure was a conceptual advance over what was believed before the first workshop. Actual policy and social decisions must, however, address the more complex features reflected in the complete model.

MANIFOLD ANALYSIS

The third and final class of simplification requires more detailed description – not because of any inherent difficulty, but because of its novelty. The product is a set of pictures or graphs that can be easily comprehended and require for their understanding no mathematical skills (although the graphs themselves are founded upon mathematical principles). These diagrams are not models in the sense of a simulation, but rather are alternative representations of the internal structure of the model. They are analogous to medical x-rays that reveal the structure of the skeleton without removing the surrounding flesh (this was done in the simplified models described above). And as with x-rays, our perception of structure improves with several complementary views taken from different orientations or perspectives.

These pictures are useful and usable because they make strong use of qualitative information rather than opting for the quantification espoused by most scientific disciplines. The qualitative property of interest in the budworm example is the classification of forest conditions into those that cause budworm numbers to increase and those that cause them to decrease. At first this may appear to be a minimal criterion, but in many management situations knowledge of gain or loss would be prized information, if available. (Imagine the profit to be made with the same information on the stock market.)

The powerful aspect of this qualitative division is its inclusion in a topological view of the system. The interface between regions of increase and decrease defines conditions for no change – that is, equilibria of the system. Our topological view links the basic dynamic behavior to the number and interrelation of equilibrium states and focuses as well on our central concern for ecological resilience and policy robustness. Just as the skeleton determines much of an organism's appearance, the structure of the equilibrium states determines the system's dynamic behavior.

Our first step is to use the complete simulation model to generate a population growth rate, or "recruitment rate," curve of the sort introduced by Ricker (1954) for the analysis of fish populations. The recruitment rate is

$$R = \frac{N_{t+1}}{N_t},$$

that is, the ratio of the population in the next generation $(t + 1)$ to the population in the present generation (t). This is the number of times bigger, or smaller, next year's population will be than this year's. In Figure 6.1 R is plotted against the present density of budworm for particular forest conditions. The recruitment rate curves condense all the reproduction and survival functions within the model, and a unique curve can be calculated for each state of the forest. Three selected curves are shown for three levels of forest development – immature, intermediate, and mature. In reality there is a continuum of curves, each representing a particular forest state. Each point is computed simply by starting the simulation model at

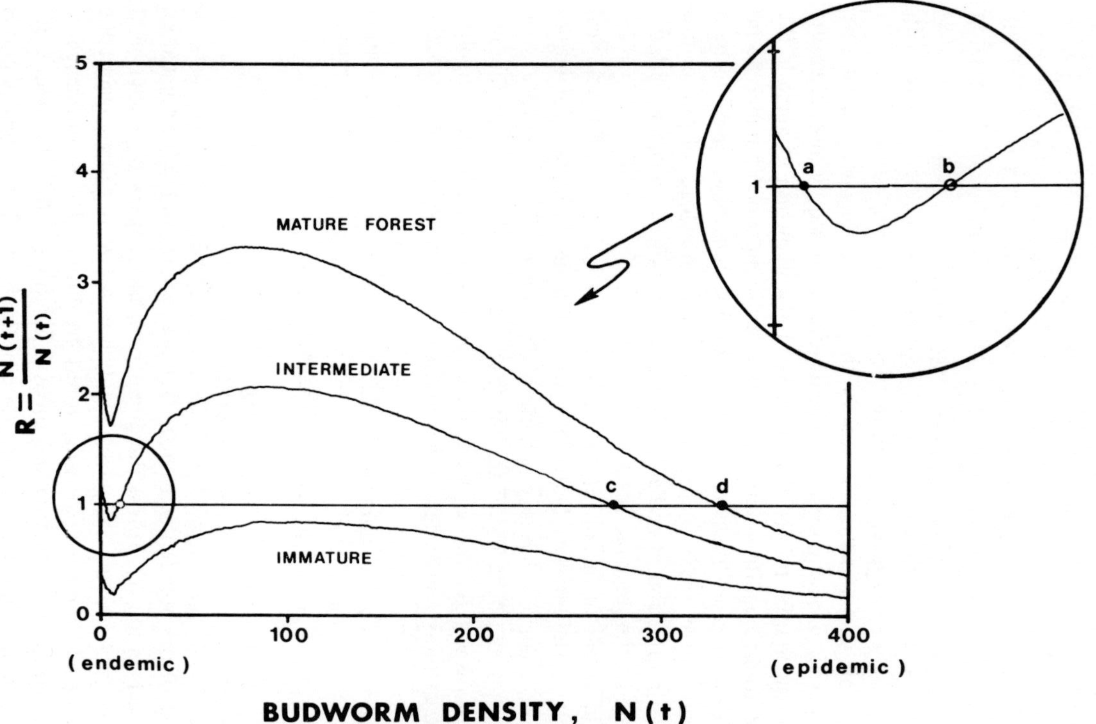

FIGURE 6.1 Recruitment rate curves for budworm. R is the rate of population growth from one generation to the next as a function of current population density. Each of the three curves represents a particular state of forest maturity; all other variables are assumed fixed at their nominal values. See text for a discussion of the significance of points a, b, c, and d. The insert expands the circled part of the intermediate forest curve.

the specified values [here, $N(t)$ and forest state], running it for one time interval, and noting the resulting R.

Interpretation of the curves is straightforward. We start by focusing on the location and properties of the equilibrium points – the points where the recruitment rate takes a value of 1.0. These equilibria may be stable or unstable, depending upon the slope of the curve as it passes through the $R = 1$ line. Briefly, if a slight increase in density from the equilibrium point results in further increases in the next generation (i.e., if $R > 1$), or if a slight decrease results in further decrease ($R < 1$), then the equilibrium is unstable (represented as an open circle in Figure 6.1). In contrast, where a slight increase in density from the equilibrium point is offset by a decrease in the next generation ($R < 1$), and a slight decrease is offset by a subsequent increase ($R > 1$), then the equilibrium is stable (shown as solid dots in Figure 6.1).

Subsequent discussions draw heavily on these recruitment curves, so it is useful to consider their structure in some detail. The high-density equilibrium points (c, d in Figure 6.1) are established largely through competition among budworm for the available foliage. Although these points are stable equilibria for budworm, they are unstable for trees. At such high budworm densities, defoliation is so heavy that older trees die and are replaced by seedlings and understory growth. This shifts the system onto the immature forest curve with a lower budworm growth rate. Since $R < 1$ for the immature forest at budworm density d, the insect population declines. In summary, when the forest is immature, R is less than 1 for all budworm densities and no outbreak is possible. With a very mature forest, however, budworm will increase from all densities less than d, rising until they reach this upper equilibrium. The ensuing defoliation and tree death bring the population back to low numbers.

There is almost no information available about the fate of budworm at very low densities (lower than can be shown on the arithmetic scale of Figure 6.1). Either the local populations become extinct in immature areas of the forest ($R < 1$ for all densities) and dispersers must re-establish populations at the site, or the local populations can be maintained at some very low level ($R > 1$ at densities less than this low level). In either case there is a lower equilibrium, which is zero or some low density. The remaining curves are appropriate for either situation.

The dip in the recruitment rate curves at low budworm densities reflects the activity of avian predators, augmented to a degree by parasitism. When the forest is of intermediate age, this dip introduces two low-density equilibria – one stable at a and one unstable at b (see insert, Figure 6.1). The population may persist at density a until improved forest conditions raise the bottom of the dip above the $R = 1$ line. When this happens, only the high equilibrium remains and an outbreak occurs. But an outbreak can occur even in an intermediate-aged forest if a sufficient number of budworm are imported by dispersal from outside areas. Thus, in Figure 6.1, a small number of budworm added to the population that is at equilibrium a will result in an increase in density above the unstable equilibrium density b. As R is greater than 1, an outbreak starts.

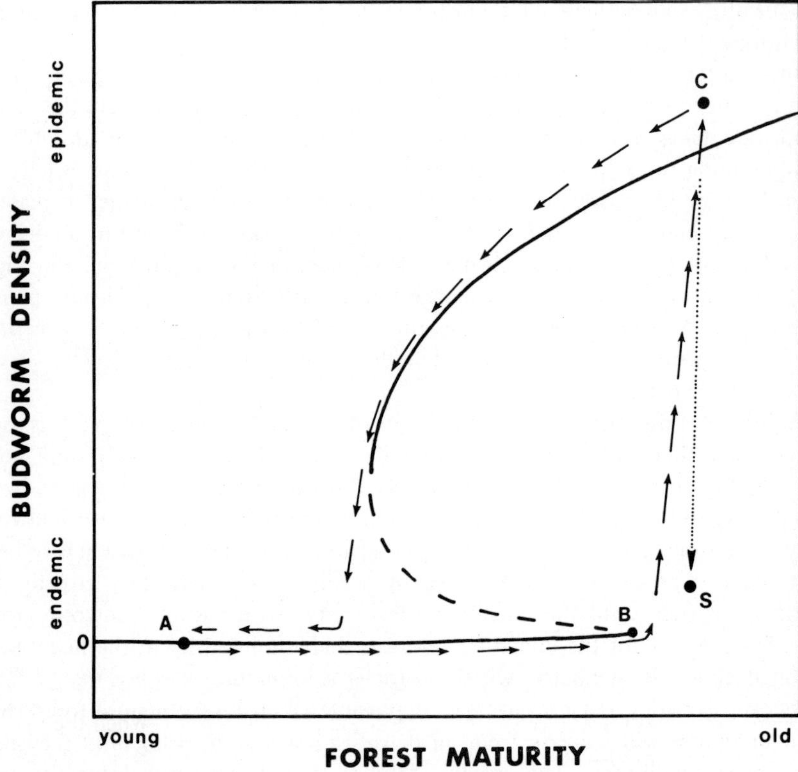

FIGURE 6.2 The equilibrium manifold of budworm densities for different forest conditions. The solid line represents the location of equilibria; the dashed line separates the high and low budworm densities. A normal cycle begins at *A* (young forest, few budworm) and progresses to *B*, where the low equilibria are lost and the system can no longer maintain a low budworm population. An outbreak is triggered. The budworm density is drawn toward the upper curve and arrives at point *C*. The feeding stress at this magnitude of budworm density causes tree mortality, and the forest is forced back to a younger condition, taking the budworm population down with it. The cycle returns to point *A* and begins anew. If 80% of the population at *C* were killed by insecticides, the system would move to point *S*, where there is little loss to the forest but high vulnerability to any suspension of spraying.

The recruitment curves as described do not yet include the stochastic elements of weather that affect both survival and dispersal. When these effects are included, there is a third trigger for outbreak – a sequence of warm, dry summers, which can raise normally low recruitment rates above the replacement line.

A more complete and succinct summary of these multiple equilibria can be obtained by plotting the location of only the equilibrium budworm densities (the dots from Figure 6.1) for all levels of forest maturity. The heavy curve in Figure 6.2 shows just such a relationship. The lower, solid segment corresponds to endemic densities such as a in Figure 6.1; the middle, broken segment corresponds to the unstable points such as b; and the upper, solid segment traces the epidemic densities such as c or d. Note that, just as in Figure 6.1, when the forest is immature there is only one low equilibrium, and when the forest is mature there is only an epidemic equilibrium, but when the forest is of intermediate maturity, there are two stable equilibria separated by an unstable equilibrium.

We call the collection of equilibrium points such as drawn in Figure 6.2 an *equilibrium manifold*. In the remainder of this section we shall examine some of the useful properties of this manifold and explore the ways that its shape changes under the influence of changing conditions. The shape of the manifold governs much of the dynamic richness of this system.

With these manifolds we can follow the shifts in the number and position of equilibria. The same is true with simple two- or three-variable models where the equilibria are easily determined analytically. As was indicated in Chapter 2, the organization of the equilibria of a system has a fundamental effect on its dynamic behavior. The equilibria are easy to find in a simplified model, and, having found them, we know where to look in the complex model. It is also important and useful to study the positions of the boundary lines separating different areas of stability. Some configurations of these boundaries can lead to unexpected outcomes. For instance, in some situations a decline in the population of a pest species can lead directly to an "explosion" to high densities (Bazykin, 1974; and Figure 2.2*F*, Chapter 2).

The focus and use of equilibrium manifolds are suggested by that part of the field of mathematical topology evocatively called "catastrophe theory" (Thom, 1975; Zeeman, 1976). An expanded exposition of this theory in terms of budworm outbreak dynamics is given in Jones (1975), and Jones and Walters (1976) and Peterman (1977b) have related it to fisheries management.

Returning to Figure 6.2, we show how the particular configuration of this manifold dictates the essential features of the classic outbreak cycle. A normal sequence begins with a young forest (at point A). Such forest conditions will support very few budworm, as reflected by the single low equilibrium. The ruling property of these manifolds is that the budworm densities will either increase or decrease as governed by the population growth curves illustrated in Figure 6.1 until they reach a point of equilibrium – a point on the solid branch of the manifold. If the budworm densities are on the manifold, then they will try to remain there even as the level of forest maturity changes.

Thus, as our typical forest grows older, the budworm densities follow smoothly and evenly along the lower branch from point A to point B, showing very little change in density. However, the moment the forest grows beyond point B, the lower equilibrium is lost, and the only one available to the system is the upper, epidemic level. An outbreak is triggered. As the budworm population begins its rapid increase, the forest continues its growth, and the system trajectory moves upward toward point C.

The manifold we are following portrays the movement of budworm numbers in response to forest conditions. There is also a manifold that portrays changes in forest conditions as the forest is affected by budworm densities. Rather than show this second manifold graphically, we shall rely upon a verbal description of how it comes into play and influences the trajectory that has reached point *C*. The manifold at *C* is an equilibrium for budworm only if forest conditions remain unchanged. However, the feeding stress imposed by this density of insects causes severe tree mortality, and the forest reverts from a mature one to one that is young. As the forest condition collapses, the budworm population falls along with it. The cycle returns to point *A* and begins anew.

We can immediately draw several very broad and important conclusions from Figure 6.2. First, it is clear that if the forest has the capacity to reach a condition beyond point *B*, then an outbreak is inevitable. Much of the mystery about the "cause" of outbreaks disappears when we view them as a simple playing out of the mechanism inherent in this manifold configuration. We also see that once an outbreak is triggered, it is destined to continue its course even if we could restore the forest to a pre-outbreak condition slightly below point *B*.

The second conclusion is that if we were to prevent the forest from ever reaching point *B* (by logging or thinning, say), we could happily maintain the budworm at an endemic level. However, it is clear that such a system is extremely vulnerable to invasions of budworm from outside areas. This is the same conclusion we drew earlier: even though an intermediate forest would not suffer outbreak spontaneously, outbreaks could be triggered by a pulse of immigrating insects. Through this mechanism a central mature stand can initiate an epidemic that spreads throughout surrounding less mature areas. We will return to this point later and develop a manifold that expresses these conditions directly.

A third obvious conclusion from Figure 6.2 has important policy relevance for budworm control. If during an outbreak (point *C*) insecticide spraying is initiated, the system would be displaced to a state such as point *S*. Because this point is far from an equilibrium, it is being held "unnaturally" in an unstable condition. The longer this policy is followed, the larger the area that requires spraying – both because more areas are maturing and because surrounding less mature areas are being invaded by insects leaving the sprayed areas. The maintenance of desired system behavior is therefore extremely sensitive to any intervening failure in implementing the policy, be it through evolved genetic resistance, errors in spray formulation and delivery, or legal restrictions on spray dosages, targets, and frequency. The entire system would collapse. This is the predicament in which eastern Canada now finds itself.

For the purposes of easy understanding of the nature of the manifolds, we have defined "forest condition" in a causal and intuitive manner. The measure of "maturity" of relevance to the budworm is the surface area of branches, which is the area available for habitat. As a forest stand ages, the total area of branches increases monotonically. However, there is an additional component of forest condition that affects a budworm's life. That is the foliage quantity – the amount of food available

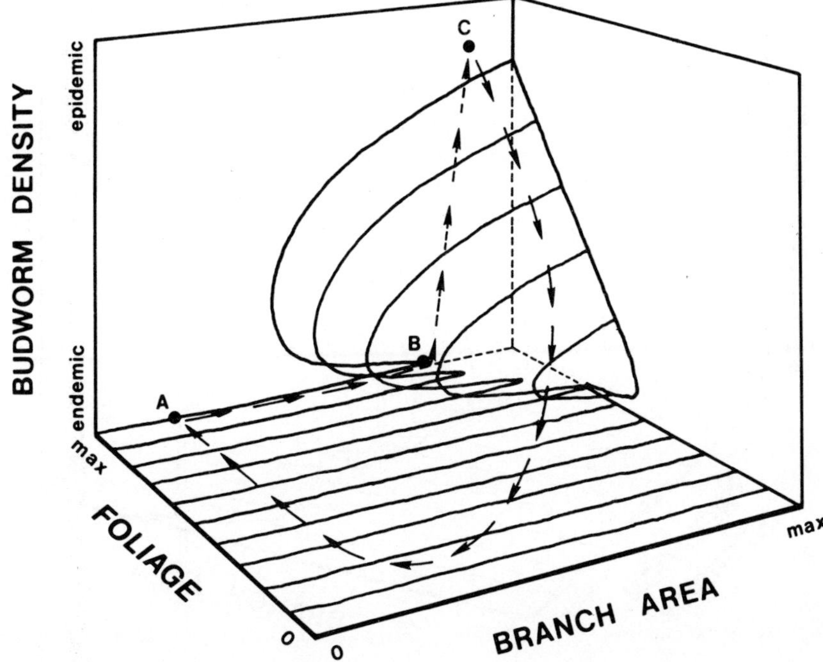

FIGURE 6.3 The equilibrium manifold of budworm densities as a function of the two measures of forest state: foliage condition and branch area. Branch area was called 'forest maturity' in Figure 6.2; the curve at the back of the box (foliage = max) is the same as the manifold in Figure 6.2. The typical budworm outbreak cycle is repeated here (points *A, B,* and *C* are the same) to show how foliage and branch area interact during an outbreak collapse.

per individual. When we include foliage as a second measure of forest condition, the budworm manifold becomes a surface in a 3-dimensional box, the axes now being foliage, branch area (what we earlier called "forest maturity"), and budworm density. The manifold surface for these variables is shown in Figure 6.3. Note that the curve at the back of the box (where foliage is maximum) is exactly the same as that of Figure 6.2. The same budworm cycle trajectory is repeated in Figure 6.3, with points *A, B,* and *C* as before. Now we see that, starting at point *C*, the foliage goes first, and its loss leads to the death of trees and a reduction in branch area.

The equilibrium manifold representations also prove to be a powerful device for exploring the consequences of changes in ecological processes or management approaches. In progressing from Figure 6.2 to Figure 6.3 we saw how the manifold changed shape as foliage quantity varied from its maximum down to zero. In any ecological model there will be a great many significant factors whose variation would also change the manifold. The number of predators, the number of parasites, the weather condition, the intensity of immigration, and the intensity of insecticide

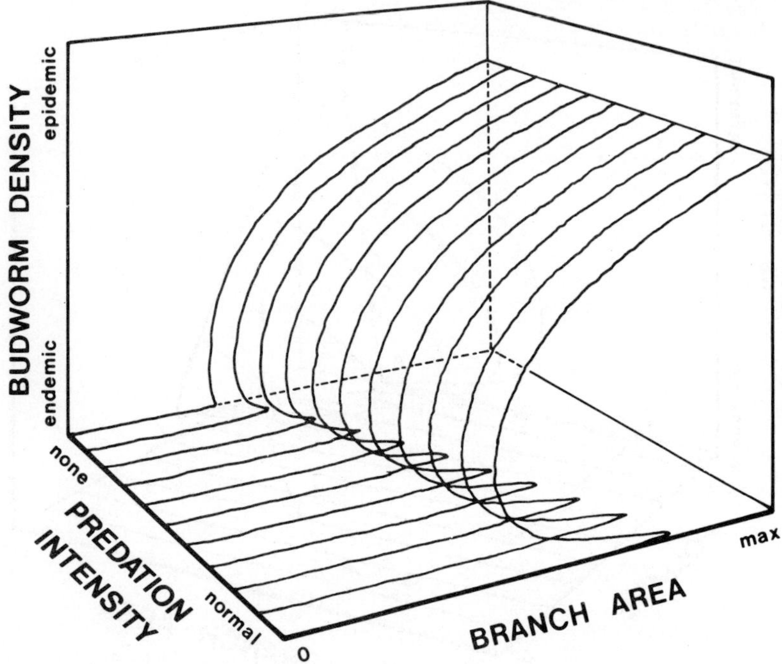

FIGURE 6.4 The predation manifold. This shows the changes in the budworm equilibrium manifold for different intensities of predation by insect-eating birds. The curve at the front with normal predation is the same as that shown in Figure 6.2.

spraying have all been mentioned as important components of the budworm/forest system. On any one three-dimensional figure, such as Figure 6.3, we can only look at the effects that two factors have on the budworm equilibra; all other factors are fixed at their nominal values. To look at a new factor graphically we must sacrifice explicit portrayal of one of the variables in Figure 6.3. In the present case, it is most useful to return to Figure 6.2 (with foliage fixed at its maximum value) and implicity retain our understanding of how the foliage dynamics produce the cyclic trajectory shown initially on Figure 6.2. We now can start with this simpler manifold as a base and investigate how it changes under the influence of other factors, one by one. We know that, in the background, the foliage will continue to operate according to the scheme shown in Figure 6.3.

As an example, Figure 6.4 shows an equilibrium manifold that looks at the effect of different intensities of predation. When predation is at the level occurring in nature ("normal" on the scale), the "pit" responsible for the lower equilibrium is pronounced (again the same curve as in Figure 6.2). But as predation is relaxed, the pit gradually disappears, along with the folded character of the manifold.

Under such conditions, the behavior of the system is radically and predictably

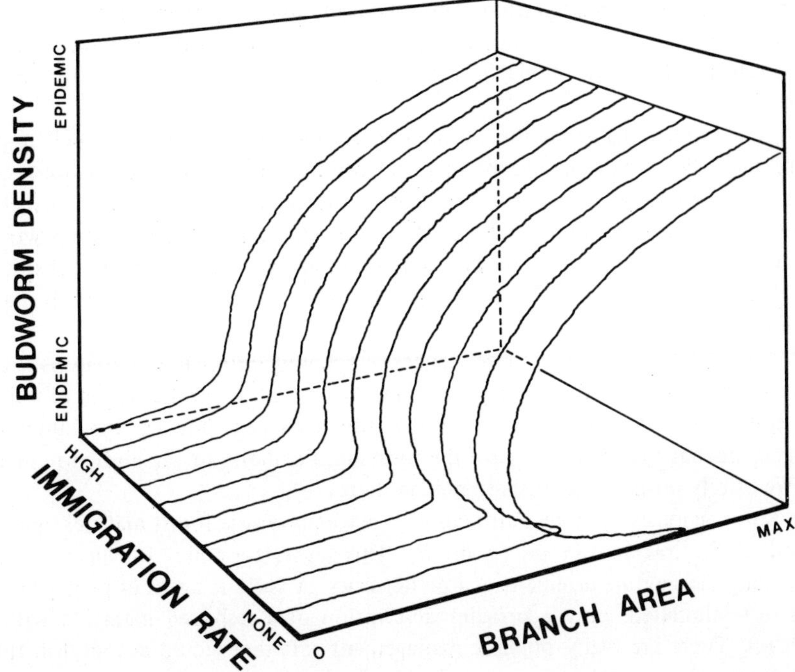

FIGURE 6.5 The dispersal manifold. This shows the changes in the budworm equilibrium manifold for different intensities of immigration by budworm from other forest areas. The curve at the front with no immigration is the same as that shown in Figure 6.2.

altered, since the natural "boom-and-bust" pattern is intimately associated with the reflexive form of the manifold. Simulation runs conducted to check this topological implication of reduced predation show a world with a perpetually immature forest, where moderate budworm densities oscillate with a 12–16-year period. This residual oscillation is a typical "predator–prey" cycle between budworm and foliage. Since insecticides have exhibited a potential for reducing vertebrate predation directly through mortality or indirectly by affecting food availability, the significance of this finding for management is obvious.

Another example is shown in Figure 6.5, where the manifold is used to explore the qualitative implications of dispersal. The immigration-rate axis reflects the intensity of budworm moths immigrating from outside areas. The similarity of this dispersal manifold to that for predation is striking and significant. An increased rate of immigration clearly has qualitative properties much like those of a decrease in predation. This is in keeping with the earlier analysis of recruitment rate curves (Figure 6.1) where the quantity of immigrants necessary to release a budworm population from its low density equilibrium was directly related to the size of the predator–induced pit. As would be expected from the comparison of manifolds, a systematic increase in immigration rate affects the dynamic behavior in very much the same way as a systematic decrease in predation, flipping the budworm–forest system into its alternative mode of a sustained outbreak with a 12–16-year insect–foliage cycle.

The greatest payoff from the topological simplifications comes in their implications for policy. In discussing the recruitment rate curves of Figure 6.1, we noted that a forest could be so immature that no outbreak was possible under any conditions ($R < 1$ for all budworm densities), or so overmature that an outbreak would ensue if any budworm were present ($R > 1$ for all subepidemic budworm densities). This phenomenon is reflected more clearly as the budworm–foliage–branch manifold in Figure 6.3.

We have shown the policy consequences of spraying outbreak populations – the system is perched precariously at point S in Figure 6.2. In our discussion of policy evaluation procedures (Chapter 8) we describe two new policies for budworm management that explicity recognize the form and flexibility of the budworm manifold. We briefly outline one of these policies here.

We saw previously that an outbreak occurs whenever the forest matures beyond the end of the low-density pit (point B). This suggests a policy of "pit enhancement," emphasizing management at *low* densities. A specific agent or management act is not stipulated, only a broader description of a reshaped manifold with a deeper pit. There are many possible management acts that would accomplish this; for instance, any mortality agent applied only at low insect densities. To have a significant effect, the added mortality need not be anywhere as high as the 80 per cent common to epidemic spraying. We could combine this new act with a supplementary insecticide capability to push outbreak populations back into the newly deepened pit whenever unexpected events occur. Because predation by birds is primarily responsible for the basic pit, we know we must also include efforts to maintain them as an important budworm control resource. When this policy was introduced into the complete simulation model, it proved very effective, with radically reduced spraying requirements.

In summary, a compressed and simplified version of a dynamic model can be captured in topological manifolds that focus upon its multiple equilibrium properties. These manifolds are then exploited to improve understanding of the system behavior and structure and to qualitatively diagnose regions of policy sensitivity and potential.

Clearly, if the descriptive part of the analysis stops at the development of a complex simulation model, the clarity of understanding needed for creative environmental management and assessment is seriously compromised. Creative simplification is necessary for understanding.

7 Model Invalidation and Belief

Once we have formulated a model and have subjected it to analysis through simplification, the natural question is whether the resulting products should be believed. Are they valid representations of reality?

The so-called validation process is really nothing but hypothesis testing because models are merely statements of hypotheses. We have little new to say on this subject, and our treatment here largely reviews some of the more fundamental guidelines and dangerous pitfalls involved.

The majority of environmental modeling efforts are silent on the model testing issue, apparently assuming high-quality predictions once all known relations between variables are included (Mar, 1974). Most studies that do address the validation problem seem intent upon proving models to be correct (see Ackerman *et al.*, 1974; Ross, 1972). They tend to emphasize "tuning" to historical data and elaborate statistical testing against replicate study areas or against independent data withheld from the model development exercise. None of these approaches is worth much for assessing the value of management model predictions, simply because management actions often move the system toward conditions that have not been historically encountered.

In fact, it is the central tenet of modern scientific method that hypotheses, including models, can never be proved right; they can only be proved wrong (Popper, 1959). This is why the frequent claims of – and demands for – "valid" models in ecological management, impact assessment, and policy design are so unsound. Provisional acceptance of any model implies not certainty, but rather a sufficient *degree of belief* to justify further action. In practice, the problem is one of model invalidation – of setting the model at risk so as to suggest the limits of its credibility. The model is subjected to a range of tests and comparisons designed to reveal where it fails.

There is no checklist approach to intelligent invalidation, just as there was none for model formulation. But our experiences have suggested three major considerations relevant to the critical assessment of model credibility:

Data, model structure, and invalidation
Evidence for invalidation
The analysis of alternative models

DATA, MODEL STRUCTURE, AND INVALIDATION

THE MODEL AS CARICATURE

Any model is a caricature of reality. A caricature achieves its effectiveness by leaving out all but the essential; the model achieves its utility by ignoring irrelevant detail. There is always some level of detail that an effective model will not seek to predict, just as there are aspects of realism that no forceful caricature would attempt to depict. Selective focus on the essentials is the key to good modeling, and invalidation tests must recognize this as a strength and not a weakness.

WHAT WE PREDICT

There is no sure way to decide what to predict and what level of detail to include in order to produce a believable model. This depends in large part on the bounding decisions made earlier and the sorts of predictions needed for the assessment. At a minimum, however, a believable model should accurately predict qualitative properties of the temporal and spatial patterns characteristic of the historical system.

An extreme example of the distinction between predicting exact numerical detail and predicting qualitative behavioral properties is provided by the budworm–forest analysis presented in Chapter 11. The model of this system predicted insect numbers and tree condition for each of 265 geographical cells, representing a continuous area of about 50,000 km^2. Historical data were available for the same variables at each location over a 25-year period.

No model, however detailed and accurate, could be expected to reproduce the historical detail exactly. The bounding decisions leading to parsimony described in Chapter 4 make this impossible. Random effects and unique but unrecorded events in the historical record also prevent an exact mimic. But independent of this fine detail, historical data showed general, stable patterns in space and time: they revealed a characteristic 30–45 years between insect outbreaks, a local outbreak duration of 3–6 years, and an outbreak spread rate of about 50 km per year. Model predictions corresponded very closely with each of these qualitative characteristics of the historical record, although there were quantitative discrepancies when predictions and history were compared at individual points in space and time. This qualitative comparison of time–space predictions and behavior served to substantially strengthen our belief in the model, though it did not, of course, "validate" it. Further invalidation tests, which we describe below, strengthened our belief in other ways – no one test was sufficient or even dominant.

The opposite effect, that of definitive invalidation, can be demonstrated with a study of an oceanographic model. Marine plankton data required for fisheries studies are usually highly variable, making most space–time models effectively untestable. However, by looking at the data in a different way, one finds that this variance from place to place consistently *increases* when larger and larger areas are compared. With a focus on this pattern, it becomes possible to use the variation as an aid to invalidation rather than treating it as a hindrance. It is often assumed that this pattern in the variance results from the interaction of growth rates of the organisms with the effects of horizontal mixing. A model incorporating simple prey–predator interactions and lateral diffusion was developed (Steele and Henderson, 1977). The output was expressed explicitly in terms of variance as a function of horizontal scale so that it could be compared with a set of data from the North Sea. In this case, predicted variance *decreased* with increasing scale, thereby invalidating this simple picture of reality and requiring the development of alternative models (Evans *et al.*, 1976). These models in turn will require further testing before they can be used in a fisheries management context.

While this example illustrates that a single critical test can invalidate a model, there is no predetermined number of tests that will establish a sufficient degree of belief in it. This depends on the use to which the model will be put.

SOME CAVEATS

Two caveats must be mentioned with respect to treatment of historical observations. The first is that comparison must be carried out with verified observations, not with second-hand interpretations or impressions. It is appalling how often in ecology we find that supposedly well-established past observations or case examples turn out to have been badly distorted by well-intentioned researchers wishing to support some hypothesis or to report something interesting. One example of this is the Kaibab Plateau deer irruption reported in most ecology texts. There is now good evidence that it never occurred at all (Caughley, 1970). Another example occurred in our own budworm work (Chapter 11), where the model predicted that forest volume would decline independently of insect damage, while it was "common knowledge" that volume was high and would remain so if insects were controlled. We spent 2 months checking the model for errors when we should have been spending 2 days looking at the available raw data on forest volume. When we belatedly took this obvious step, the model was vindicated and "common knowledge" was shown to be at variance with the data on which it should have been based. We suspect that this is not a rare occurrence.

The second caveat is the obvious one that correlation does not imply causation. Lack of reasonable model correspondence with the historical picture speaks strongly for invalidation. But the achievement of such correspondence, while gratifying, really only lets us move on to the next step in the process. It does not "validate" anything, and it tells the manager precious little about how much he should believe in his model as a predictor of future impacts. This is true because practically any complex model can be "tuned" to fit practically any given pattern of historical data. Since the causal structure of such a "tuned" model need have nothing in common with that of the real world, its predictions under the new conditions of development or management are highly unlikely to correspond to reality. This situation is similar to the well-recognized danger of extrapolating (or, for that matter, interpolating) from general polynomial regressions to situations outside the range of observations.

MODEL STRUCTURE

A few additional points regarding the relationship of model structure to the invalidation process should be mentioned here.

Our view of model building emphasizes the advantages of modeling in terms of causal or "functional" components. To the extent that such causal modeling is possible, one's ability to assess the resulting model's credibility will be greatly enhanced. Although belief must certainly relate to the total model's prediction, it is also a function of the logical consistency and clarity of the model's structure. Relationships involved in the prediction should agree at least qualitatively with experimental experience. Biological relationships should make sense when interpreted in terms of lower levels of organization (physiology, behavior); economic relationships involving market situations should be consistent with known behavioral characteristics of firms; and so forth. In short, it should be possible to see how the predictive model could arise by aggregation of more detailed components than those actually employed. If the model is not cast in the form of functional components, then the path to establishing credibility is obscured – we lose the benefits of analogy in understanding the model. We will show in the next two sections that when the model has been causally structured, its comparison with historical evidence and alternative models is also greatly facilitated.

Finally, we have one observation regarding model structure that is very much at odds with conventional wisdom. A great deal of present practice in environmental management and impact assessment modeling implies that the more detailed the model structure, the more boxes and arrows and variables considered, the better will be the model's predictions (e.g., Goodall, 1972). Our own experience and other explicit tests of this notion (Lee, 1973; O'Neill, 1973) suggest that it is often, perhaps systematically, false. Those scientists, managers, and administrators who call automatically for more detail often produce giant reports rather than useful predictions. As emphasized in Chapter 6, it is not detailed complexity but rather comprehensible simplification that gives rise to understanding. And it is on understanding alone that a critical assessment of model credibility must ultimately be based.

EVIDENCE FOR INVALIDATION

TRIAL-AND-ERROR EVIDENCE

Historical data reflect behavior of the system only within the narrow range of circumstances encountered in the past. New programs or developments will change those conditions, and our principal concern is in the believability of the model's predictions for the new situations. We are, after all, interested in a management model. In order to assess the model's credibility as a predictor of new management impacts and future uncertainties, we need to assess the range of possible behaviors over which the model is applicable.

The usual but often impractical approach to this problem is explicit trial-and-error. For example, our model might predict that if a proposed equipment restriction is implemented in a particular fishery, then fish harvest will decrease by 20 per cent. If we adopt the new equipment restriction policy in an actual fishery and the predicted harvest decrease occurs, then our belief in the model's predictive ability is appreciably enhanced.

The problem with trial-and-error evaluation of predictive limits is that it always takes time, is frequently expensive, is limited to the particular trial undertaken, and often risks disaster if the predictions prove wrong. Nonetheless, the potential benefits of combining operational activities with experimental goals may be great enough to justify or even demand trials. The rationale for considering such experiments as an integral part of the management program is discussed in Chapter 10 and is treated at length by Walters and Hilborn (1976) and Peterman (1977b). When opportunities for trial-and-error invalidation of the model are limited, however, we must look for natural trials as well.

NATURAL TRIALS AND EXTREMES OF SYSTEM BEHAVIOR

Useful natural trials exist wherever there are examples of ecological or environmental systems that are similar to the one we have modeled but that exhibit qualitatively distinct behaviors. In reference to three of the case studies in Part II, we might look for comparable situations where an alpine village still farms its potential hotel land; where a salmon stream provides unusually high yields; or where a previously mined area supports a particularly low diversity of wildlife. If minor, plausible changes in the parameter values or structure of the model replicate these extreme forms of actual behavior, then the range and degree of belief in the model as a predictive tool under future extremes of management and uncertainty are enhanced accordingly. We at least gain confidence that no significant component of the system has been left out.

The procedure for comparing the model with the results of natural experiments is best conveyed by example; we draw again upon the budworm–forest management study. As noted above, the original budworm model predictions corresponded well with the historical patterns of insect outbreak in the Canadian province of

New Brunswick. But an explicit search for atypical behaviors uncovered some patterns that did not match the New Brunswick norm (Holling *et al.*, 1975). In northwestern Ontario, for instance, outbreaks are more intense and tend to occur at intervals of 60 or more years rather than the 30–45-year period observed in New Brunswick and predicted by the model. The principal differences between the regions are a lower proportion of susceptible trees and better weather for budworm in northwestern Ontario. When these differences were introduced into the New Brunswick model, the Ontario behavioral pattern was reproduced.

A similar opportunity for invalidation was presented by consideration of outbreak histories in Newfoundland, an island more than 200 km off the New Brunswick coast. Historically, outbreaks there have been extremely rare and short-lived. This pattern changed only recently, coinciding with management activities in New Brunswick that produced an increased outbreak frequency there and consequently a source of emigrating budworm. In Newfoundland, the proportion of susceptible trees is greater than in New Brunswick, but the weather is worse for budworm. Again, these parameter changes were introduced into the New Brunswick budworm model, which then predicted the very rare, very brief outbreaks typical of Newfoundland. When pulses of immigrating budworm from New Brunswick to Newfoundland were also introduced into the model, the predicted outbreak frequency, though not the duration, increased, again matching actual behavior in the real world.

A final invalidation test consisted of adding to the basic New Brunswick budworm model a management submodel mimicking insecticide application and harvesting activities introduced there in 1950. This test, described in detail in Chapter 11, showed that the unprecedented outbreak pattern actually experienced in the 1950s and 1960s could in fact be reproduced by the basic biological model linked with the management rules.

The set of extreme behaviors tested during the invalidation studies directly increased our belief in the model's predictive abilities under a range of weather conditions, susceptible tree densities, and insecticide-induced mortalities. Indirectly, these tests supported a provisional belief that the model's credibility was not limited to the narrow range of circumstances defined by local history.

The sort of highly qualitative natural experiment or "extreme behavior" data necessary for invalidation studies almost always exists. The manager's challenge is to find the data and mobilize them in spite of the invariable insistence of the scientists and specialists that they do not know enough to say what the effects of extremes will be. The result is usually worth the battle.

THE ANALYSIS OF ALTERNATIVE MODELS

THE NEED FOR ALTERNATIVE MODELS

A model could make all the testable predictions referred to above and still be the wrong representation of reality. The chance always exists that other models will meet these historical tests equally well but give very different predictions of future impacts or management success. For example, budworm outbreaks could be largely caused by changes in the nutritional quality of the foliage or by changes in the genetic structure of the insect population instead of by the interaction among predators, parasites, and budworm as presently formulated in the model. We can never eliminate the possibility that these other models could adequately represent historical observations, but we can take further steps to refine our degree of belief in the impact predictions of the model(s) upon which decisions must finally be based. The basic approach is to design alternative models of the system under study.

The critical need to seek alternative interpretations (or models, or explanations) rather than try to seek validation of any single one is most obvious in the statistical concept of "the power of tests." We can establish belief or disbelief in any hypothesis only by reference to some alternative. The closer the alternative is to the original hypothesis, the more difficult it becomes to tell which one is more likely to be correct with a given set of data. When we make only a vague assertion like "this model must be wrong because it is too simple-minded" (or too complex, or whatever), we must have at least some criteria by which to judge "rightness" or "wrongness"; that is, an alternative model that predicts better or worse than the model being examined.

The greatest hope of any search for alternative models is always to find one that passes a greater number of significant invalidation tests than the original. Failures are almost as useful as successes, however. Each alternative considered and rejected on the basis of available evidence eliminates one way of modeling the impact problem that might well have been acceptable but is now known to be wrong. The general goal of the comparison exercise is to generate two lists from the alternative models considered: models rejected, and models possibly useful for prediction. The characteristics of these lists – specifically, the range of alternatives considered, the plausibility of the rejected models, and the variability in results of the remaining (unrejected) models – will strongly influence our degree of belief in the eventual impact predictions. This degree of belief is one of the most significant pieces of information communicated to the decision makers. We will first discuss these properties of alternative models and then outline some specific ways of generating candidate alternatives.

PROPERTIES OF ALTERNATIVE MODELS

Range

The greater the range of the models considered, the more confident we will be that the ones offering adequate explanations of historical data are in fact good models on which to base future predictions. By a wide range of models, we mean models that involve a variety of different assumptions about how the causal mechanisms are represented. For predicting effects of salmon enhancement, for example, one might consider a model that assumed that salmon populations were largely limited by mechanisms operating during their stay in fresh water, or an alternative one that emphasized mechanisms in the marine environment.

Clearly, one of the most valued and effective traits a manager can possess is his ability to see (and therefore to model) a problem from a wide range of perspectives. In practice, most interpretations (i.e., models) offered for a problem tend to be shaped by habitual ways of thinking, and effective "new looks" are most difficult to establish. Consensus-breeding techniques are your enemy in this situation, and imagination is your only sure friend. A few technical crutches for broadening the range considered are discussed below, in the section on generating alternative models.

Plausibility

Clearly, if we cannot (or cannot be bothered to) imagine any alternatives, then we might as well not have a model at all. This is just the same as saying "any model will do, none predicts better than others." Equally clearly, however, it is not the sheer volume of alternatives considered by the end of the study that counts. If we go out on the street and ask the first ten people (or ten consultants) for their opinions (i.e., models) on the relationships of age structure and land tenure to erosion in Obergurgl, their predictions should not affect our belief in the model one way or another. What counts is not the number of silly or trivial alternative models discarded, but rather the number of plausible ones. The real payoff comes when we can generate alternative models that give credible performance for all our historical tests. Critically designed experiments may allow rejection of some of these models, adding substantially to the credibility of those remaining.

Variability

When a broad range of models has been considered, a set of plausible alternatives identified, and a number of these rejected on the basis of available evidence, there will generally remain several different models. Any (or all, or none) of these might provide a realistic basis for predicting future impacts, but we have no way of choosing among them. To the extent that all the remaining alternatives give the same predictions, there is no problem. If the alternatives give different predictions, then there exists a problem of choice under uncertainty. You may elect to reduce the uncertainty through further data collection and experimentation or as part of your management program (Chapter 10), or to consciously gamble on the basis of other factors influencing your belief in one or another of the alternatives. Finally, you may seek to change the development or management program so as to minimize the variability and uncertainty of impact predictions. These are problems of evaluation and choice rather than invalidation *per se* and will be taken up again in the next chapter. One invalidation issue does remain, however.

Almost all parameters in almost all environmental or ecological models cannot be fixed exactly. It is often convenient, nonetheless, to treat them as though they were fixed throughout most of the analysis, using mean or, occasionally, extreme values for model predictions. Before these predictions can be "believed," however, it is necessary to examine their sensitivity to realistic variation in the parameter values. Such variability in parameter values is to be expected as a result of measurement errors or future variation, and if the predictions change radically as a result, then these predictions must be treated very cautiously during assessment.

Some authors (e.g., Miller, 1974) claim that the most "valid" ecological models are those with predictions that are least sensitive to changes in parameter values. But both ecological systems and the models that realistically reflect them may in fact be acutely sensitive to small differences in their structure or parameters (Gilbert *et al.*, 1976). In the budworm and many other insect–plant systems, for example, it is clear that differences of a few days in temperature-dependent development rates can determine whether a potential host plant species is fed upon at all by a particular defoliating insect. Thus, the question is, given a set of best estimates and measurements of parameter values, how sensitive the resulting model's predictions are to changes in those parameters.

The techniques of sensitivity analysis are well known and have been applied to a number of impact assessment models (Ackerman *et al.*, 1974; Hamilton *et al.*, 1969). It should be noted, however, that simultaneous variation of the parameters in question is necessary to give reliable results. A good example of this is given in a study by Scolnik (1973) on the Meadows world model. Conventional analysis had shown the model's predictions of population boom and collapse to be stable to small perturbations in many parameters. But when several parameters were simultaneously varied over ranges of less than 10 percent, the results changed dramatically, giving an increase of populations to a density that was maintained thereafter. Since simultaneous variation of the parameters is to be expected in the real world, the model's predictions of catastrophe are not necessarily credible.

An opposite result was reported by Herrera *et al.*, (1976), who examined the agricultural sector of the Latin American World Model for sensitivity to small simultaneous variation in the parameters. In this case, the model predictions were found to be stable and therefore comparatively believable, even in the face of a search for "worst case" combinations.

Where acute sensitivity to small changes appears to be a true property of the system under study and not simply an artifact of the model, the only recourse is to seek management policies and programs that can tolerate the range of possible variation.

GENERATING ALTERNATIVE MODELS

At one extreme, the notion of alternative models can be approached by conducting independent workshops from independent data bases, independent assumptions, and independent perspectives, each generating an independent set of hypotheses or models. However, a multiworkshop model approach is usually prohibitively inefficient and expensive, and a more practical view of the alternative model issue is necessary.

The most obvious set of alternative models to consider are those implied by the issues left unresolved or the components deliberately excluded during development of the process model (Chapter 4). Recall that during model development explicit lists were kept of (a) those things that were left out of the analysis because of bounding considerations and (b) the functional relationships and parameter values for which reliable data were least available or disagreements most acute. We now construct alternative models for comparison with our original by adding the suspect factors initially left out and exploring the most likely alternative functional forms and parameter values. This process creates a number of "plausible" alternative models, fairly similar in structure and predictions to the original. Some will be rejected on the basis of comparisons between their predictions and available data; others will be retained for use in the evaluation exercise.

For example, in a lake model we have worked with, it was thought necessary to calculate nutrients added to the water by zooplankton and fish excretion. However, when these calculations were added to the simpler model, virtually no difference was seen in the overall system behavior because the amounts of excreted nutrients were an insignificant fraction of the total nutrient inputs from the watershed. In another model, it was thought that caribou feeding on snow-covered lichens during winter did not cause intraspecific competition. However, when the effect of feeding behavior on the trampling and packing of snow in the surrounding area was added to the model, very different results were obtained. In fact, one of the most critical parameters in the model turned out to be how much food was made unavailable through compaction of snow per unit of food eaten (Walters *et al.*, 1975).

The models produced by examining the workshop bounding and choice decisions may well span a fairly narrow range of alternative structures. In order to expand that range so as to better assess the limits of credibility, it is necessary to develop more extreme alternatives of model structure and to explore their predictive consequences. Our experience suggests that if the initial model is in fact a very good representation of reality, then most of its extreme structural variants are likely to make very bad predictions. But only by actually verifying that this is the case can we develop a confident belief in a given model's credibility.

The method for generating these extreme structures is essentially that of systematically adding entire functional components or processes to a basic version of the model and removing others. In the Obergurgl study we examined the consequences of such functional components as the effect of ski-lift construction on farming or on the perception of erosion by summer tourists. In the budworm analysis very substantial insights were gained from the alternative models developed by adding vertebrate predation and removing dispersal processes. In fact, the addition of predation effects produced such markedly superior predictions that the "best-guess" model was revised accordingly. The detailed budworm case study (Chapter 11) further shows how the qualitative, simplified model forms discussed in Chapter 6 can be used to facilitate the generation of extreme types of model structure.

When you have finished the invalidation procedures, you will not have a valid model, you will not have eliminated all uncertainties, and you will not even know probabilities. However, you will have a critical understanding of the weaknesses and strengths of available models that is extremely valuable. You will be able to meet criticisms that "such-and-such was left out" by saying why and what difference including them would have made. Most important, by understanding both the extent and limits of your models' predictive capabilities, you will be able to proceed with the design and evaluation of development proposals in the most responsible manner possible.

8 Evaluation of Alternative Policies

The invalidation process generates one or several models that elicit the greatest degree of belief. These models can then be used to predict impacts and to compare different ways of management. Some traditional environmental assessments consider only a single proposed development or management scheme. We argue that alternative development programs should always be considered because there may be other ways to achieve the desired goals while avoiding some disadvantages of the original proposal. Thus, the process of choosing between alternative development schemes becomes analogous to choices faced in resource management problems in general, such as choosing between managing a population by setting kill quotas or by directly controlling hunting effort.

Before going further, we should clearly define our usage of some terms that have rather varied meanings in practice.

Actions Specific deeds available to the manager of some environmental system. For example:

Harvest trees

Release x cubic feet of water from a reservoir

Spray insect pests

Build a fish hatchery

Policies Rules by which these actions are initiated. They state at what time or under what conditions actions are taken. For example:

Cut all trees above a given age

Spray insects when populations surpass a certain density

Release enough water from a reservoir to maintain a given minimum flow downstream

Indicators Measures of system behavior in terms of meaningful and perceptible attributes. For example:

The number of trees of harvestable size
The crop loss due to insects
The stored volume of a reservoir
The costs of a program

Preferences The trade-off rates between one indicator and another.

Objectives Desired goals in terms of indicators. For example:

The reservoir to remain at least 90% full
The catch to sport fishermen to stay above 1965 levels
The cost of management to grow at a rate less than the national budget

One should remember that decision structures are hierarchical, and what is a goal at one level in the structure may be a policy at the next higher level. For example, a manager of a fishery of a given species has a harvest goal that he attempts to achieve by regulating the number of days open for fishing, the allowed gear types, and so forth. But his harvest goal is only a part of the policy designed at a higher level to achieve a broader goal of maximum sustained yield over many stocks.

We view evaluation as the entire iterative process of combining actions into policies, using a model (or some other predictive device) to enact the policies and generate time streams of indicators, and using objectives to choose among the different time streams of indicators.

The traditional view of evaluation assumes that there is a given set of management objectives and decision preferences. It sets out to characterize these in a quantitative fashion, to reduce them to a single measure, such as a cost–benefit ratio, and then to rank several policies from "best" to "worst" according to this measure. The rankings are then presented as a list to the decision maker. However, this traditional outlook is static and fundamentally inadequate for adaptive environmental management and assessment.

The approach we have used treats evaluation as an essentially adaptive communication process. It assumes that neither policies nor objectives are immutable and that the critical assessment and modification of both is one goal of the analysis effort. It therefore concentrates on those aspects of evaluation that promote understanding rather than on the numerical products – products that all too easily become goals in themselves.

So defined, adaptive evaluation takes on a broad and varied character with which we shall not deal in any systematic fashion in this book. Rather than presenting a superficial overview, we have chosen to discuss in detail two fundamental aspects of adaptive evaluation – namely, indicator generation and an informal process of policy comparison. These we view as both essential and feasible steps for every assessment. In addition they constitute the foundation of attitudes and understanding upon which any critical application of more subtle evaluation concepts must be based.

Utility analysis and objective functions, discounting and intertemporal trade-offs, uncertainty, and conflict resolution are some of the many evaluation topics you will *not* find treated here in any depth. We *do* feel that they are important – often critically so – and we have therefore included a brief review of some of our own experience toward the end of this chapter. The case studies document this importance in more detail and illustrate some of the benefits and pitfalls inherent in the various techniques. This experience has left us with strong biases regarding the opportunities for use and abuse of commonly advocated numerical evaluation techniques. In the last section, the more obvious of these biases are explicitly stated along with a few key references to further reading on the subject. It is essential to emphasize, however, that we believe that no one, including ourselves, is yet equipped to write a general "how to" manual for applying the more complex techniques of evaluation to environmental assessment and management. The issues involved are subtle in the extreme. You will need expert help, and the experts will disagree profoundly on each subject. This is not necessarily a bad thing, provided that you can use the disagreement to stimulate dialogue and communication. Here, perhaps more than in any other aspect of environmental management and assessment, it is the adaptive process rather than the numerical product that should be your preeminent concern.

INDICATOR GENERATION

The first requirement of evaluation is a suitable language or vocabulary to describe objectives and the outcomes that result from applying given policies. Up to now we have dealt with this issue rather informally, usually describing the output of assessment and modeling activities in terms of fundamental "state variables" such as number of fish or proportion of trees over a given age. But socially relevant and responsible evaluations cannot be based on the behavior of these elements alone. State variables must be translated into a broader set of indicators relevant to those who make, and those who endure, the ultimate policy decisions. Indicators can usually be broken down into a few broad but overlapping classes – e.g., ecological, economic, recreational. Several examples are given in the case studies, and a typical list drawn from the budworm analysis is shown in Table 8.1.

Appropriate indicators for evaluation are readily generated in any assessment problem, provided that an essential constraint is understood: there is no "comprehensive" list of indicators, and there is no "right" set of indicators for any problem, ever. This is the same issue encountered earlier in our discussion of choosing variables to include in a model. There we stressed the importance of bounding many variables *out* of the dynamic model to make it parsimonious and more understandable.

Evaluation is also essentially a model formulation process in which we develop ways to prescribe "better" policies. Therefore, attempts to include everything as an indicator will likewise result in an incomprehensible and misleading monstrosity, rather than an aid to assessment. This attitude is implicit in the "looking outward"

TABLE 8.1 Examples of Indicators of Known Interest Taken from the Budworm Case Study

Socioeconomic Indicators

Profits to the logging industry
Profits as a proportion of total sales
Cost per unit volume of harvested wood
Cost of insecticide spraying
Unemployment rate reflected by the proportion of mill capacity utilized

Resource Indicators

Volume of wood in trees older than 20 years
Volume of wood in trees older than 50 years
Volume of wood harvested
Proportion of total volume harvested
Volume of wood killed by budworm
Mill capacity
Total forest volume

Environmental Indicators

Visible damage due to budworm defoliation
Damage due to logging operations
Age class diversity of the forest
Number of high quality recreational areas
Insecticide impact in terms of fraction of province sprayed

approach to modeling presented in the chapter on orchestration (Chapter 4). Indicators, like variables, are included in the analysis when knowledge of their behavior is essential if the model is to respond to somebody's major policy choice or design question. When there is no client or potential user demanding the indicator, it is usually best to omit it from consideration. Of course, this presents a danger of leaving out something important and perpetuating habitual viewpoints, just as it did in the modeling work. One must use judgment and occasionally err on the side of inclusion. But, as we will argue below, implicit or explicit simplification to a few indicators is ultimately necessary for comprehensible comparison of alternative policies and objectives. There is consequently little to be gained from amassing huge lists in order "to be safe."

The "looking outward" criterion for indicators cuts two ways, however. It is not uncommon to find that an indicator that is clearly relevant to policy choice simply cannot be predicted with available models (e.g., the types of gear that will be used on fishing boats or the world demands for wood pulp). Sometimes the models can be changed, but often this is not feasible. The only defensible response in this situation is to record the indicator explicitly in a list of "things left out" and to weigh its significance and bearing on the policy choice question independent of the model part of the analysis. This might be accomplished by mobilizing expert opinion, by interfacing with other models or experience, or by some other means of resolution. An excellent example of the second approach is provided by Baskerville (1976). He used the budworm–forest model presented in the case studies to describe the effects of various management policies on forest harvests and inventory. The significance of these predictions for employment and industrial profitability was then evaluated through an independent economic analysis, using the model's forest inventory data as inputs.

INITIAL COMPARISONS OF POLICIES

Once the basic indicator set has been defined for an assessment problem, each decision maker can select those indicators of personal interest and compare their performance under alternative policies. Although there are rigorous techniques for making such comparisons, we find that simple visual inspection of the projected time series of the indicators is often a powerful and unambiguous first step in the evaluation process. Sometimes it is clear that certain policies dominate – they are better in all respects. More commonly, some policies will exhibit obviously desirable outcomes for a few indicators and indifferent or undesirable outcomes in others. For example, certain reservoir discharge policies will keep downstream water flow rates high for trout, but will also create a large, recreationally undesirable band of muddy lake shore.

Traditional static evaluation procedures seek to provide a common denominator or metric for ranking such complex alternative outcomes (cost–benefit ratios, dollar values, utilities, and so on). But we have found it useful to highlight the *differences* among indicators, at least initially, and to use these differences as starting points for policy modification and improvement. If we use the "laboratory world" of the assessment model, policies with complementary strengths and different weaknesses can be combined in an iterative, experimental effort. In this manner it is often possible to achieve more uniformly desirable indicator performance through "hybrid" policy design. A great deal of exploration of alternative policies can be made in this manner without worries about formal schemes of indicator combination or the rendition of objectives into numerical form. Furthermore, the process of policy comparison through direct reference to the individual indicators is the least ambiguous evaluation technique available. What it lacks in refinement is more than compensated for by the clear communication of relevant information.

As an example of this approach, we return to the budworm management policy evaluations mentioned earlier. Extensive experimentation with the system model and interviews with relevant decision makers identified five of the indicators listed in Table 8.1. as primary. The values assumed by these indicators in a simulation of the management policy historically used in New Brunswick are given in Figure 8.1. In an attempt to improve this policy, new spray and harvest rules were developed

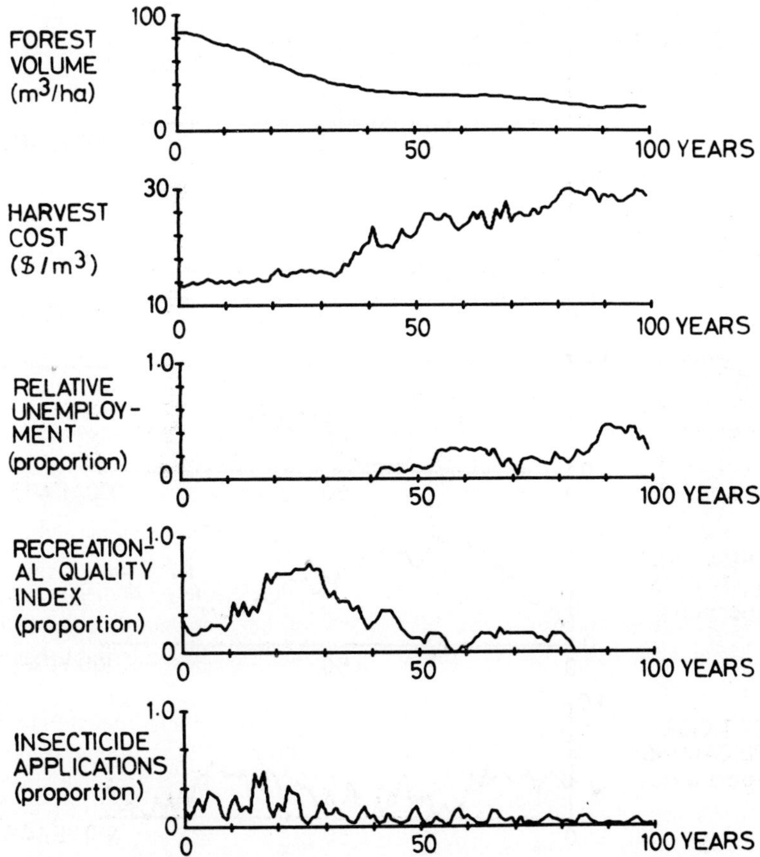

FIGURE 8.1 Value of indicators that resulted from the historical budworm management rules.

and then tested on the simulation (see the case study section for further details). The results, presented in Figure 8.2, show improvement in some indicators, notably total forest volume, profits to the logging industry, and recreation, but a somewhat worse situation with regard to employment and insecticide spraying. Without performing any but the most trivial analysis, we can say that it would be nice if a policy could be found that preserved the gains of this alternative policy, but repaired its failures.

A modification of the alternative policy was next designed, explicity tailored to decrease spraying by cutting down trees threatened by budworm. The results in Figure 8.3 show that spraying frequency is indeed reduced, but at a cost of even more irregular employment due to the sporadic antibudworm harvest. The "good" forest volume, harvest cost, and recreational performance have been reasonably

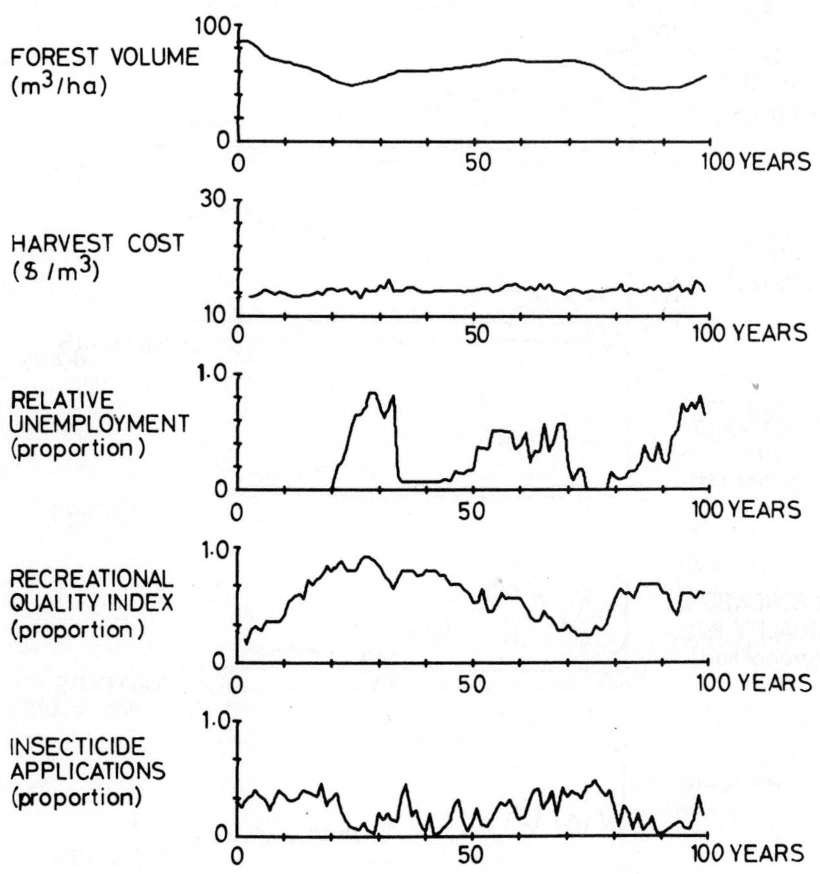

FIGURE 8.2 Value of indicators resulting from proposed management rules: first alternative.

maintained, however. Since any preventive harvest scheme seemed likely to incur this disadvantage, we searched elsewhere and attempted to reduce spraying by adding a hypothetical but realistic budworm virus to the model. As shown in Figure 8.4, this succeeded in reducing spraying substantially without radically increasing unemployment. Forest volume was better than with any other policy, and recreation was superior to any but the antibudworm harvesting policy.

At this point detailed utility analyses (quantitative statements of preference) could be made to identify the "best" of these four policies (see the next section). A good deal of careful study would have to be made of implementation costs and feasibility as well as of model reliability before such rankings would be meaningful. But to insist at this stage on a formal ranking would be to miss the whole point of adaptive evaluation. The benefits of the exercise just described are not

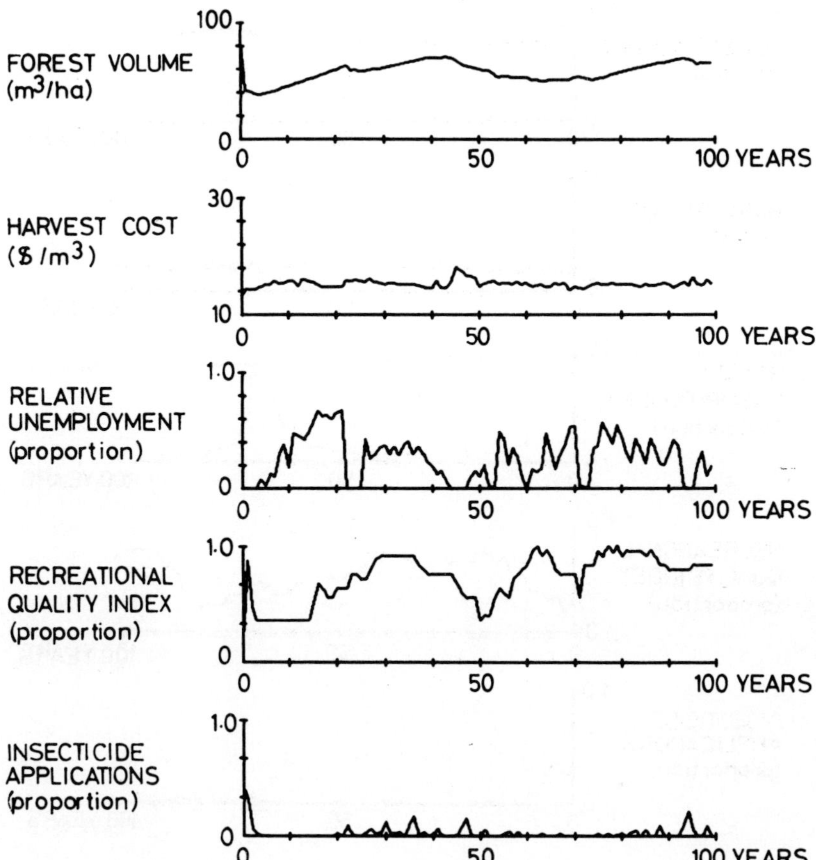

FIGURE 8.3 Value of indicators resulting from proposed management rules: antibudworm harvest.

found in the development of a ranking scheme, but rather in the design of policies for meeting specified objectives through creative exploration of policy alternatives.

FURTHER COMPARISONS

When the number of alternative policies becomes large, the problem of comparison and evaluation can hamper creative policy design. When the decision maker, or any interested party, embarks on a policy evaluation process, it is critically important that the trade-offs and compromises between competing policies (in terms of alternative indicator patterns) remain as visible as possible. If the evaluation process is too quickly given over to some numerical methodology, then important

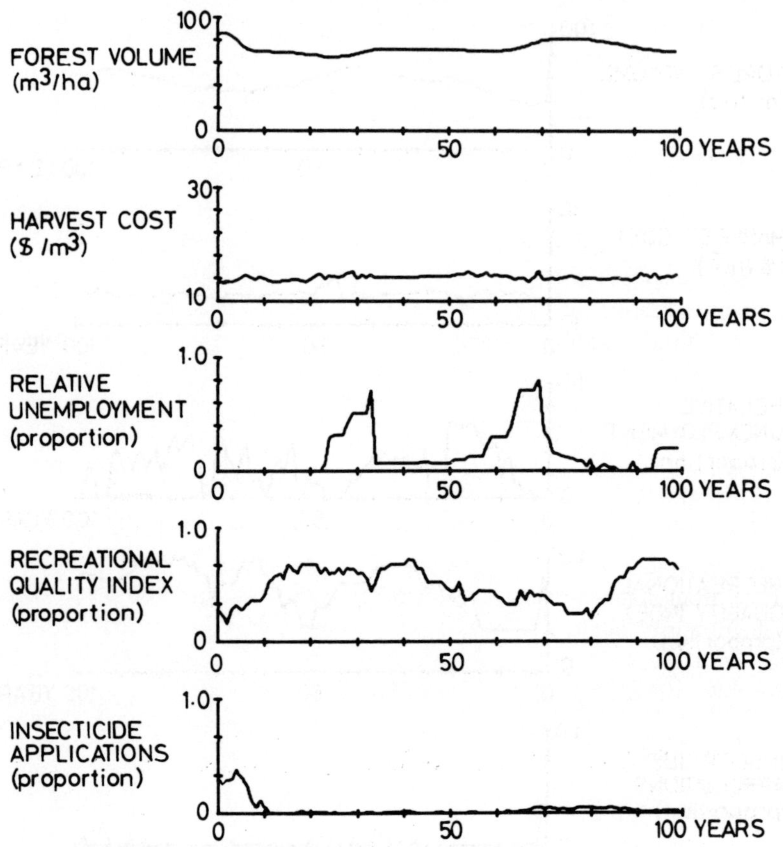

FIGURE 8.4 Value of indicators resulting from proposed management rules: virus addition.

opportunities for the exploration of preferences and discovery of objectives will be missed.

One approach to promote the dialogue between a manager, his problem, and groups that would influence policy involves a condensed graphical presentation of indicator values in a form that allows any user to have "hands on" access to the evaluation. The technique is, in effect, a "management slide rule" that can physically be pushed and pulled and moved about to reveal the consequences of different policies. This technique, sometimes called nomogram or isopleth diagram, is described in Gross *et al.*, (1973) and Peterman (1975). Examples of its application are given in the case studies and Appendix A.

Because the use of nomograms is integrally linked with the whole topic of communication, we defer explicit outline of their construction and use to the next chapter. It is sufficient to note here that they have proved extremely useful for policy evaluation. With these nomograms the manager can explore the consequences of different acts by manipulating the graphs himself. He can add political, economic, and other constraints, identify trade-offs, and begin to evolve realistic compromise policies. Done jointly with a number of interest groups, this becomes a powerful instrument for constructive dialogue and even conflict resolution. Because several indicators can be treated simultaneously using this technique, managers have found it an effective aid in learning to appreciate and creatively manipulate the intricate relationships among policies and indicators (Peterman, 1977a).

These graphical methods for preliminary comparison of policies and their resultant indicators quickly point out to the user (be he analyst or decision maker) the need to articulate goals and preferences clearly in order to make meaningful comparisons among the alternatives. More often than not, the methods provide all the technique necessary for evaluation in the adaptive management process. Under certain conditions, however, more quantitative considerations may be justified. We discuss some of the associated issues below.

As promised earlier, we now introduce some of the more subtle problems of evaluation by way of example. We emphasize that the techniques discussed in this section do more harm than good if employed superficially or uncritically. Expert advice from someone who appreciates or can be taught the needs of adaptive evaluation is mandatory. If this is not available (or believable), you will do best to stay with the solid and straightforward techniques already discussed. They are probably sufficient for most evaluation needs, anyway.

UTILITY ANALYSIS

When there are numerous indicators of interest, a quantitative method for defining preferences may be necessary. Utility analysis permits an individual (or an interest group) to define two things: first, the "satisfaction" or "utility" gained from different values of an indicator; and second, the trade-offs between indicators. In the case study of salmon fisheries, for example, a nonlinear saturating relationship was typically found to reflect the utility for different amounts of sport catch (Figure 8.5). (This is the case because adding 100,000 fish to the catch when the catch is small increases utility more than adding 100,000 fish when the catch is very large; demand becomes saturated.) There are formal questioning procedures to help a person define such utility functions (Keeney, 1977; Keeney and Raiffa, 1976) and these procedures can be repeated for all indicators of interest. It is also possible through another series of questions to determine trade-offs between indicators. For example, one could ascertain how much of a decrease in *utility* of commercial fish catch would be traded for a 20 percent increase in *utility* of native Indian fish catch.

In the salmon study the resulting quantitative description of objectives differed among interest groups such as commercial fishermen, sports fishermen, packing companies, and fisheries managers (Hilborn and Walters, 1977). These utility

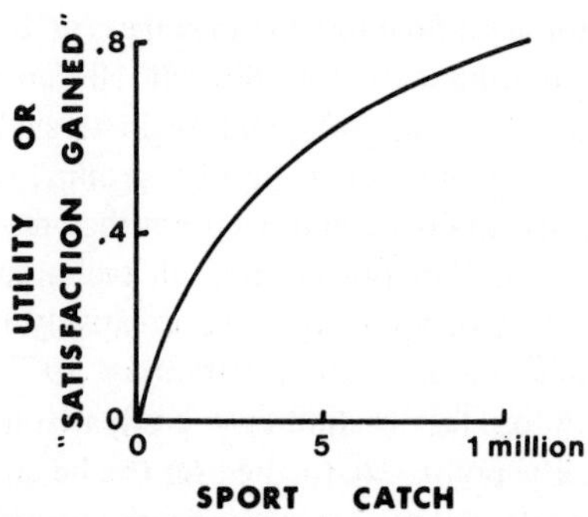

FIGURE 8.5 Example of a utility function for sport catch.

functions were then used in conjunction with appropriate indicators to determine which of the alternative management schemes would give the highest utility to each interest group. However, objectives are never fixed forever; new concerns may arise and interests may shift (witness the sudden importance of environmentalist viewpoints in recent years). While it is possible to deal with changing objectives (see the following section), the assessment team and the recipient of its report should recognize the dangers of ranking policies on the basis of fixed quantitative utility functions. By far the greatest benefit of the utility analysis process in our studies has been the triggering of dialogue about goals within and among interest groups (Hilborn and Walters, 1977; Hilborn and Peterman, 1977). Often, people are stimulated to articulate or at least think about their goals much more clearly than before, a useful result in itself.

More extensive utility analyses were conducted with affected decision makers in the budworm studies (Bell, 1975a, b). Again, the important result was not the production of some ultimate utility function but rather the creation of dialogues among the various decision makers, and especially between them and the analysts (Baskerville, 1976).

UNCERTAINTIES

Three major kinds of uncertainty are relevant to the evaluation process, and we will briefly discuss possible directions for each. Again, there are no simple solutions.

First, there is the uncertainty in objectives, which can change over time. A policy that was determined to be best for achieving one objective might be totally inappropriate for some new objective. Thus one must perform an analysis of the sensitivity of each policy to specified changes in objectives.

Just as we suggested a wide-ranging approach for formulating alternative models in earlier chapters, we also recommend consideration of extremely different future objectives here. Model results can be evaluated with these different objectives to identify preferred policies. A delicate issue may arise from such an exploration. A certain policy may be the least sensitive to a plausible range of objectives, but that policy may produce slightly worse indicator values than another policy. Which policy should be chosen? There is no fixed answer to this question; the decision maker must rely on his judgment of the likelihood that objectives might change.

The second sort of uncertainty arises from model assumptions. If several alternative models with different assumptions emerge from the invalidation process, then evaluation of alternative policies should be made with each of these different models in turn. If one policy comes out best under all assumptions, there is no additional problem. If, however, "best" policies are different under alternative assumptions, then the decision maker must again rely on that all-important measure of "degree of belief." When the degree of belief is not significantly different for the different assumptions, critical experimentation or data collection becomes necessary.

Third, there will always be some deviation from desired results. For example, a policy designed to result in a fish catch of 140,000 may actually result in 185,000 fish being caught, or a desire to maintain a minimum water flow from a dam of 400 ft^3/sec may actually result in a flow of only 300 ft^3/sec. The question is, "How significant are these deviations?" If the desired fish catch was near the overexploitation point, there might be serious consequences in terms of the indicators. The assessment model can be used to explore the effects of these "control errors," but only in a fairly haphazard way. Again, only a wide exploration of different possibilities can help minimize the likelihood of later surprises.

TIME HORIZONS AND DISCOUNTING

Finally, there is the problem of treating time in evaluations. Should the indicators produced by each policy be examined over a 10-year period or over 100 years? Should these yearly values simply be averaged, or should some years be discounted more heavily than others?

These issues are critically important in determining which policy alternatives will seem most appropriate for selection. We illustrate in Chapter 11 several policies that look good for controlling budworm in the short run but are clearly disastrous when their longer term consequences are included in the evaluation. In another study, Fox and Herfindahl (1964) re-evaluated 178 water resource development projects undertaken in 1962 by the U.S. Army Corps of Engineers. These projects represented a combined initial investment of over $3 billion and were all characterized by benefit–cost ratios of 1.0 or more when evaluated at the prevailing prescribed discount rate for federal project costs of 2.6 percent. Fox and Herfindahl re-evaluated the projects at discount rates of 4, 6, and 8 percent and found that the project adoption decision was reversed (i.e., the new benefit–cost ratio dropped below 1.0) for 9 percent, 64 percent, and 80 percent of the projects, respectively.

Similarly powerful cases for the dominating influence of time stream aggregation assumptions may be found in Baumol (1968), Krutilla (1969), and Koopmans (1974).

The theoretical literature on discounting and intertemporal evaluation in general is a perennial mess. Good examples of the prevailing arguments are assembled in Joint Economic Committee (1969), Layard (1972), and Lind and Greenberger (in press). We do not pretend to address the technical issues here, other than to note that there are excellent formal grounds for *not* applying the same discount rate ("market" or "social") to all evaluation problems (see, e.g., Feldstein, 1964). Our own biases and experience argue strongly that – subject to certain technical constraints of consistency – the choice of the "appropriate" time horizon or discount rate for evaluation is essentially a political or even ethical question. There simply is no extrinsically defined "technically correct" answer to questions like "How many fishermen should be put out of work today in order to increase the chances that their children will still have a healthy fishery available?"

Our own approach to this dilemma is to treat the discount problem as one of temporal preferences – i.e., of the trade-offs that a given decision maker is willing to make between future and present. Just as we earlier suggested discussions with decision makers of questions like "How much of a decrease in commercial catch are you willing to endure for an increase of 20 percent in native Indian catches?" so we now propose to ask those concerned, "How many fishermen would *you* be willing to put out of work today in order to increase the chances that their children will still have a healthy fishery available?" Answers to such questions (which should be more subtly posed – see Keeney and Raiffa, 1976) often suggest radically different time preference rates than those implied by standard discounting assumptions. For example, in the budworm work we found that managers using 5 percent or 10 percent "prescribed" discount rates in their formal economic analyses nonetheless exhibited 20 percent and higher rates when actually asked to choose freely among alternative time streams of indicators. And we doubt that this is an isolated example. The point is not that any of these particular discount rates is "right" or "wrong," but that the discussion of the contradiction forces all participants in the assessment exercise to explore the critical question of time preferences more deeply. Similar discussions are provoked by explicit comparison with the full indicator time streams, as recommended earlier in this chapter. As we have stressed repeatedly, it is only such a process of mutual exploration that can lead to understanding and meaning in the evaluation. To casually consign this fundamental question of values to the untender and unilluminating mercies of an extrinsically defined discount rate seems to us the epitome of unadaptive, irresponsible assessment.

SUMMARY

Every single exercise in adaptive evaluation can and should begin with the development of a set of specific indicators responsive to the concerns of those who will make, and those who will endure, the policy decisions. These should be followed by an explicit graphical comparison of indicator patterns. As we have stressed repeatedly, if you must address the more subtle issues of evaluation, you will require expert assistance. Obviously, you should have no patience at all with consultants hawking "answers" in such an uncertain field. But even the most well-meaning and self-critical experts tend to be bound to their own specialties and techniques.

A recent report by a U.S. study group critically reviews past efforts to apply decision-theoretical approaches to specific environmental problems and provides an excellent perspective for would-be evaluators (Holcomb Research Institute, 1976). There are several good texts on applied decision theory in which you can read about these formal approaches to evaluation. We have found those by Raiffa (Raiffa, 1968; Keeney and Raiffa, 1976) to be the most readable.

Since even good texts tend to concentrate more on strengths than on shortcomings of a field, however, we recommend several papers that provide effective self-defense against overenthusiastic technicians. Liska (1975) has edited a collection of essays on the so-called "consistency" issue. These show that preferences and utility functions of a given decision maker do change over time, and often as a consequence of previous interviews with decision analysts. Lipset (1976) presents strong empirical evidence that "objectives" dear to decision theorists simply do not exist on many issues except as they are elicited by the evaluation dialogue. This, of course, is just what adaptive evaluation hopes for.

The notion that each policy should be associated with a probability distribution of outcomes reflecting uncertainties in the analysis is attractive and probably formally correct. Decision theory is well adapted to coping with such probability distributions. Unfortunately, people are not. Slovic and Lichtenstein (1971) summarize a body of evidence that suggests that a probabilistic assessment of utilities is most unlikely to lead to meaningful evaluations, even in the simplest cases.

In retrospect, it should be clear that the real problem of evaluation is not one of technique, but of meaning. The ultimate goal is not to produce a set of numerical rankings, but to understand the strengths and weaknesses of alternative policies' performances. For it is on the basis of such understanding that meaningful, adaptive steps can be taken toward policy modification, improvement, and eventual implementation.

9 Communication

Effective communication is essential if environmental analysis is to have an impact on decision making. Our experience is that at least as much effort must go into communication as goes into the analysis. This has been confirmed by several other studies (Ackerman *et al.,* 1974; Ford Foundation, 1974; Holcomb Research Institute, 1976).

Individuals involved in doing an environmental assessment are generally not involved in the decision making. They are instead an advisory body that formulates and presents conclusions to the decision-making body. An analyst who wishes to convey the results of a detailed study faces a serious dilemma. The volume of information (data and future scenarios) is usually very large, too large to hope that decision makers will have the time to absorb and assess it. Yet findings that are condensed into an executive summary will carry little weight unless the reader has easy access to the supporting data and analysis.

In order to achieve successful communication, the assessors must clarify *what* information there is and to *whom* it should be transferred. The format or technique of communication depends on the answers to these questions. Several techniques are outlined below, but the general rule is that the sender must present the information in a language that is comprehensive and believable to the receiver.

WHAT INFORMATION?

Four types of environmental assessment information should be conveyed: first, the *data base,* both actual measurements and assumptions; second, the *technical method* used in the analysis and the assumptions of that method; third, the *results* of the analyses; and fourth, the *conclusions* derived from these. These last two have the highest priority. Each of these types of information has two facets:

the actual numbers or literal meaning, and the degree of belief. The believability of the information is by far the subtler and more difficult to convey – but it is certainly equally important.

METHODS OF COMMUNICATION

For illustration, let us assume that the assessment team reports to a single decision maker. Traditionally, a detailed report is produced that includes all the techniques, assumptions, and results, and an executive summary is prepared that is intended to be a set of recommendations for the decision maker. These detailed and lengthy reports are awkward documents that generally defeat their own purpose.

Instead of this traditional method, we have tried some alternative communication techniques, ranging from those requiring a high degree of involvement of decision makers in problem analysis to summarizing statements that only crudely represent the underlying complexity of the problem. From this spectrum we will discuss only four of the techniques we have used.

PARTICIPATION OR INTERACTION (THE WORKSHOP)

Of the communication techniques at the disposal of an impact assessment team, this one creates the most thorough understanding, and it is the most demanding of the recipient. As we discussed in Chapters 3 and 4, the managers should be involved in the original workshops when analysis begins. We have found, especially in the budworm and salmon case studies, that if managers can be involved from the start, they have at least a moderate understanding of the assessment techniques and assumptions. At the same time, they contribute insight and direction to the assessment and thereby develop a commitment.

In addition, at different stages of model construction, managers and policy people can be involved in short (2–4-hour) gaming sessions, where results of different policies are compared. The opportunity to sit in front of a graphics computer terminal and interactively try out alternative model assumptions or management options has several unique advantages. First, the decision maker gains an understanding of the underlying structure that generates particular predictions. When an unexpected result emerges from a run of the model, he can question the analysis team to discover what assumptions produced this result. This process makes the decision maker a member of the analysis team instead of an observer and gives him some understanding of the model itself. Secondly, by altering model assumptions, he can see how sensitive the predictions are to changes in these assumptions, to uncertainties in the data, and to uncertainties in the implementation of the policies. This leads to the third benefit, which provides a sense of the degree of belief that should be placed in the results. As more assumptions are explored, an appropriate level of confidence in the results is established. Finally, and perhaps most important, rapid interactive gaming with the model permits the decision maker to try out new alternative management schemes, which forces him to realize that the management alternatives are not necessarily limited to a few well-defined options. Thus he is encouraged to try new and unusual options and to begin to approach problems in an adaptive way.

It should be noted that such workshops will probably have value even if assessors use predictive methods other than simulation models. Any opportunity for the decision maker to analyze the predictive techniques' assumptions is beneficial. We emphasize that our experience in several case studies shows that the more decision makers can be involved *during* the analysis, the easier the transfer of information will be at the end. When the top-level manager is not available for workshop participation, we must turn to other communication methods.

NARRATED SLIDE PRESENTATIONS

At the other end of the spectrum there is an approach that requires little time or effort on the part of the receiver, but that does require considerable preparation by the sender of the information.

The basic premise of a narrated slide presentation (35-mm projection slides and an accompanying soundtrack on recording tape) is that technical language, mathematical formulations, computer programs, and even underlying theoretical concepts can be translated and condensed into a readily digestible form.

In the past it has been very difficult to communicate the technical methods and assumptions to a manager. Managers often are either not fluent in or comfortable with the "language" involved or else their time constraints are severe. Frequently, the evaluation technique has remained mysterious to them, and the credibility of recommendations resulting from the technique is low. In order to address these problems, we have prepared and used 10 different narrated slide shows (Bunnell and Tait, 1974; Bunnell, 1976) on subjects ranging from ecological and management history to actual models, techniques, and even ecological theory. Figure 9.1 shows a brief segment of the slide presentation of the spruce budworm simulation model.

The slide presentations usually last 10–25 minutes, yet they convey a great deal of information. They are short and to the point, they do not overwhelm with numbers or confuse with jargon, and they hold the attention of the audience. We have examined the usefulness of this approach by distributing evaluation questionnaires after slide shows. Audiences evaluated the usefulness to themselves (Figure 9.2*A*) and indicated for which other occupational groups they thought the slide shows were suitable (Figure 9.2*B*). Of all the types of viewers, our intended audience (decision makers and managers) was the group that found the material most useful. In addition, to our surprise, a much broader audience also found the shows informative. This suggests that narrated slide shows of this type may be useful in educating and involving the public.

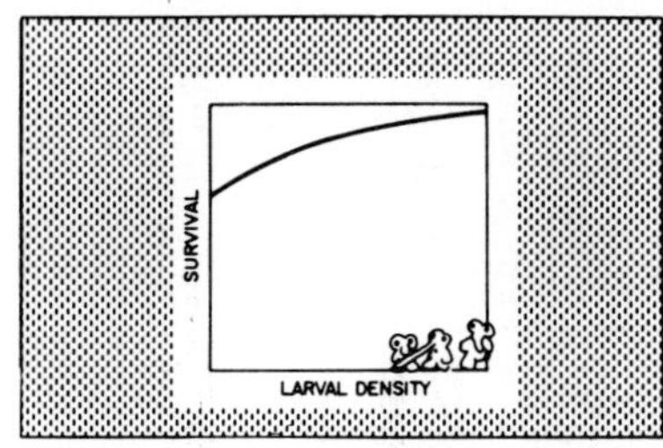

25. Larvae may be killed by disease or by parasites.
As the larval density increases, a larger proportion manages to survive death due to parasites or disease. This is because the number of parasites is limited by other factors. Parasites can affect only a certain number of budworm.

26. When there are lots of budworm, the percent survival is high.

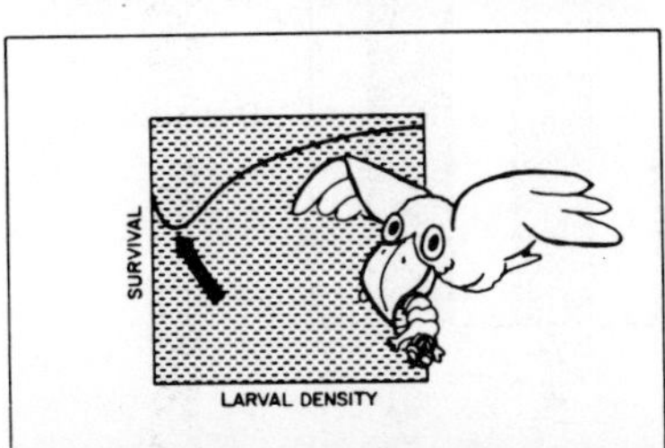

27. Birds eat larvae. There are several kinds of avian predators such as warblers, thrushes, ovenbirds, and finches. The model simulates the combined effect of all the birds. Like parasites, the birds cannot keep up to increases in the larval population. A higher percentage of larvae survives when there are lots of larvae.
An interesting feature of the bird predation pattern is the depression in the survival curve at low larval densities. The lowest survival occurs just above the lowest density – when larvae get extremely scarce, the birds cannot find them.

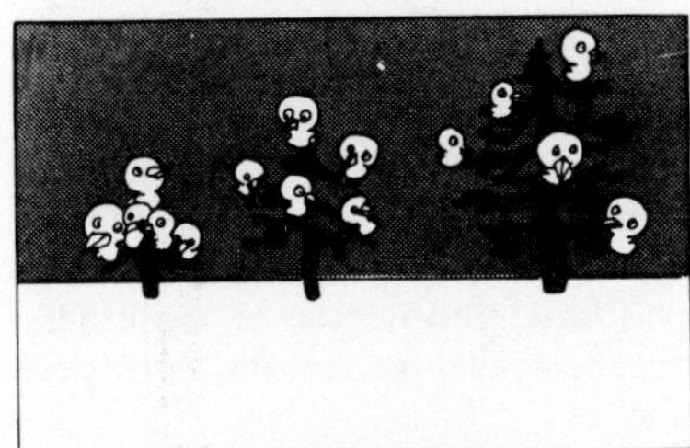

28. The ability of birds to find larvae is also influenced by the size of the tree on which the budworms and birds are living. When the trees are small, the birds are concentrated and their feeding impact is high. As the trees grow larger, the birds spend their time searching among more branches and the budworms have a better chance to escape.

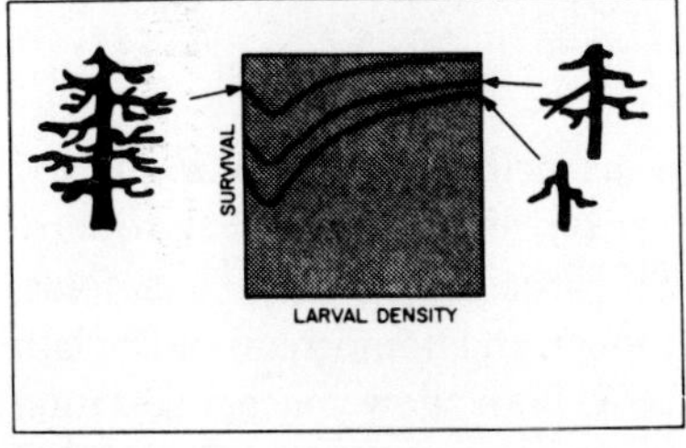

29. Thus, the size of the trees influences the ability of budworm to survive predation by birds.

FIGURE 9.1 Sketches and narration from a segment of the "Spruce Budworm Model," a 10-minute slide–tape presentation (Bunnell, 1976).

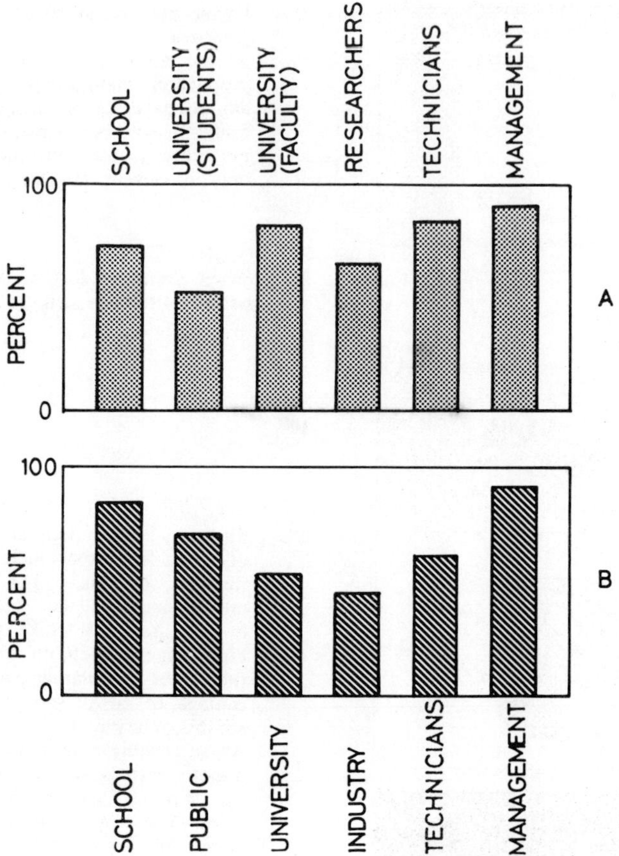

FIGURE 9.2 Audience evaluation of the usefulness to themselves (*A*) and to other interest groups (*B*) of the slide–tape presentations on the spruce budworm (Bunnell, 1976). Respondents (sample size = 139) indicated degree of usefulness in each of the potential categories; the histograms show average results. Zero percent indicates not useful, 100 percent extremely useful.

SUMMARIZING GRAPHICS

Between the two ends of the spectrum (lengthy participation in workshops and exposure to condensed slide presentations) are a variety of techniques that organize information. Two such techniques have proved particularly useful: manifolds, which reveal the essential inner workings of the model, and nomograms or isopleth diagrams, which condense simulation model outputs. Both allow conceptualization of complex phenomena. Nomograms furthermore permit gaming through manipulation of possible alternatives.

Manifolds

Equilibrium manifolds (described in Chapter 6) are extracted from a descriptive model. They represent the system's dynamics in a concise form and give an intuitive sense of how the model works. Manifolds are conceptually very simple, but because of their nontraditional nature, understanding them requires a modification of the viewer's perspective. People encountering a description of a system in the manifold format frequently go through a period of saying "So what?" followed by a feeling of revelation and understanding as a large number of apparently disparate observations fall into a logical structure. Because of this, it seems worthwhile to simplify the model into manifolds to communicate some of its characteristics.

Nomograms, or Management Slide Rules

In Chapter 8, the technique of nomograms, or isopleth diagrams, was mentioned as one way of permitting the decision maker himself to perform some evaluation of management alternatives. We re-emphasize the merits of this graphical technique in this chapter because of the method's proven value as an effective communication device. The communication of information takes place while the decision maker is using the nomograms. In order to illustrate this clearly, it is necessary to explain briefly how nomograms are created. (A more detailed discussion is presented in Appendix A.)

Nomograms are constructed from several runs of the same simulation model during which two management options are varied over some range. For example, in a deer management model the decision options might be percent of the population to be harvested and sex ratio of the harvest (Table 9.1). Each simulation run calculates the value of several variables or indicators that are relevant to decision makers – for instance, "annual harvest" or "long-term numbers harvested." Results of these several simulation runs are then plotted on graphs, one graph per indicator variable, whose axes are the two management options (Figure 9.3). Contours of values are then drawn through the values on the grid points (Figure 9.4). After this contouring, isopleth diagrams of several indicators are reduced in size and pasted onto a single page (Figure 9.5).

The nomograms, which now represent a considerable compression of numerous simulation results, are then ready to be used by the decision maker. Two benefits immediately emerge merely by inspection of the response surfaces (Gross *et al.*, 1973; Peterman, 1975). First, they provide a graphical information system that summarizes some of the data relevant for decision making. Second, limits of the system can easily be determined. For example, in step 3 (Figure 9.4) it can be seen that it is not possible, with the two management options shown, to achieve an annual deer harvest of more than about 325 animals for the herd modeled.

TABLE 9.1 First Step in Construction of a Nomogram

	Management Actions		Indicators		
Simulation Run No.	Proportion Males Harvested	Harvest Rate	Annual Harvest	Long-Term Harvest	...
1	0.0	0.0	0	0	
2	0.0	0.2	48	.	
3	0.0	0.4	35	.	
4	0.0	0.6	22	.	
5	0.0	0.8	18	.	
6	0.0	0.99	5	.	
7	0.2	0.0	0	.	
8	0.2	0.2	73	.	
9	0.2	0.4	40	.	
10	0.2	0.6	32	.	
11	0.2	0.8	25	.	
12	0.2	0.99	17	.	
13	0.4	0.0	0	.	
14	0.4	0.2	145	.	
⋮	⋮	⋮	⋮	⋮	
36	0.99	0.99	282		

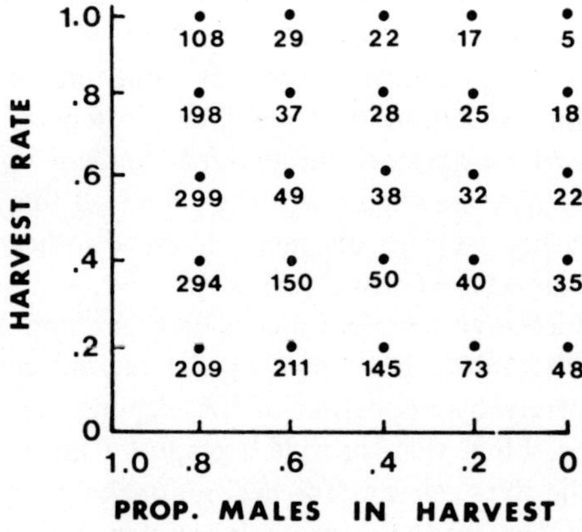

FIGURE 9.3 Second step in construction of a nomogram. See text and Table 9.1.

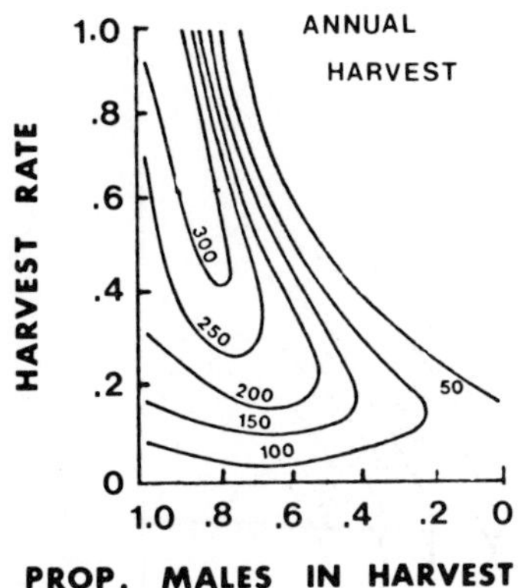

FIGURE 9.4 Third step in construction of a nomogram. See text.

The major benefits from the isopleth diagrams emerge when a clear plastic overlay is used with pointers indicating identical coordinate locations on all graphs. One position of the overlay pointers is shown by the + s in Figure 9.5. The position corresponds to a harvest rate of 60 percent and a proportion of 85 percent males in the harvest. It is then simple to read off the values of the various indicators. By moving this plastic overlay, the user can "experiment" with alternative management actions without touching the computer; the computer work has already been done. Trade-offs between indicators can easily be seen when, for a particular pointer position, one indicator is at its desired peak but another indicator is at an undesirable low. The decision maker then can "experiment" with alternative ways of trading off those indicators, until some satisfactory compromise is reached.

This "experimental" aspect of the nomograms has earned this method labels such as "management slide rule," "desk-top optimizer" or "ouija board." The use of this method in the budworm, salmon, and Guri case studies is described in more detail in Chapters 11, 12, and 14, but, in short, nomograms have proved to be an extremely effective way for decision makers to perform part of the assessment in a brief time and to understand some of the assessment's limitations.

GRADED SERIES OF COMMUNICATION DEVICES

For any particular assessment, the choice of components in a graded spectrum of reports or presentations is dependent on the methodologies used. A series of messages or packages is made available so that detailed and thoroughly explained forms lie at one end, and simply illustrated and briefly explained forms at the other. With such a graduated series of information packages the receiver can locate a starting point that suits his background and his time constraints. Anything toward the simpler end provides him with a summary, and anything more detailed substantiates and makes believable the simpler presentations.

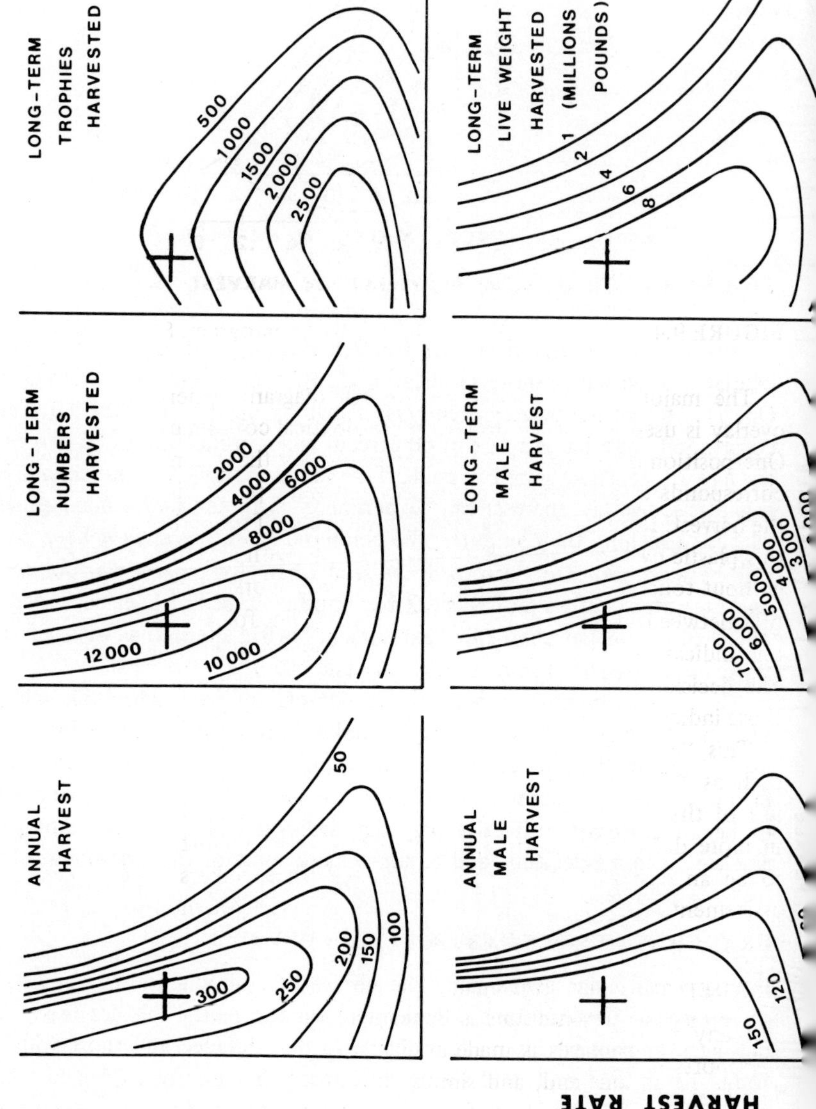
ANNUAL HARVEST
300
250
200
150
100
50
LONG-TERM NUMBERS HARVESTED
12 000
10 000
8000
6000
4000
2000
LONG-TERM TROPHIES HARVESTED
500
1000
1500
2000
2500
ANNUAL MALE HARVEST
150
120
LONG-TERM MALE HARVEST
7000
6000
5000
4000
3000
LONG-TERM LIVE WEIGHT HARVESTED (MILLIONS OF POUNDS)
1
2
4
6
8
HARVEST RATE

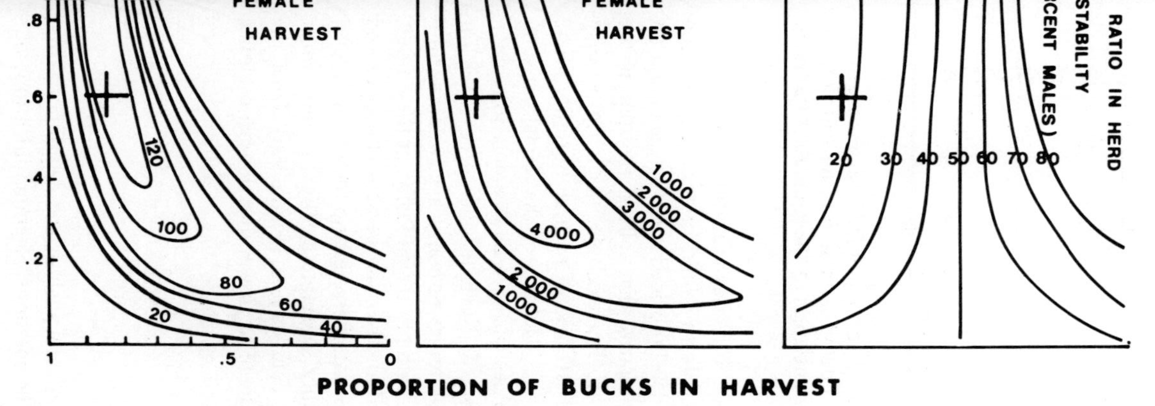

FIGURE 9.5 Fourth step in construction of a nomogram. A sample nomogram for a deer model demonstrating simulated responses of nine different indices, given varied harvest rates and proportion of bucks in the harvest. The X on each graph indicates the value of that particular indicator given the combination of the two management options (after Gross *et al.*, 1973).

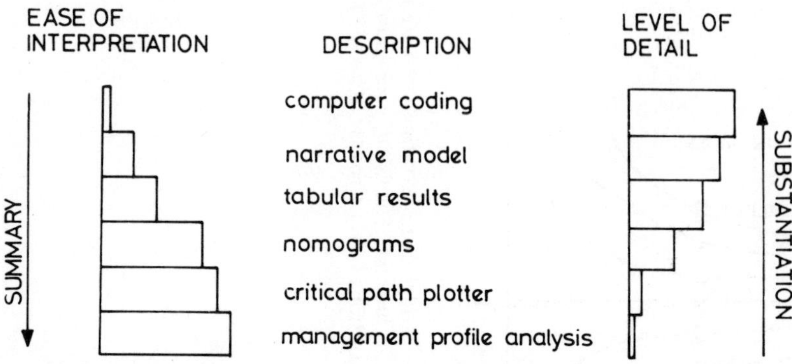

FIGURE 9.6 Graded series of descriptions used in explaining deer management models. The individual may enter at the level of detail suitable for him and proceed either to a summary or to a more detailed substantiation of the program. (Redrawn from Gross *et al.*, 1973.)

The Colorado Cooperative Wildlife Research Unit has used this approach successfully in explaining deer management models to administrators and decision maker (Gross *et al.*, 1973). The most detailed level provided is the actual computer program or coding. This is summarized by a narrative that follows the steps in the program and the results generated at each step. For example, the narrative may read, "In year 5, 50 male deer were harvested, 10 died of natural mortality, there were so many deer in each of the age classes, etc." Results of the model are summarized in tabular form, and from these tables (using several simulation runs), nomograms or isopleth diagrams are constructed. Next, feasible alternatives for moving from the present system state to some target several years away are summarized in yet a higher level, called a "critical path plotter." Finally, at the crudest level, there is a very brief summary of the alternative management strategies and their predicted consequences. The most important characteristic of this multilevel information system is that each level is visibly substantiated by the next most detailed one and summarized by the next less detailed level (Figure 9.6). Thus, the decision maker can easily consult any level of detail to answer questions or establish the validity of recommendations.

CONCLUSION

Communication is the bridge between environmental analysis and decision making. The strength of this bridge depends upon the methods of communication; our experience suggests two important criteria. First, communication should begin as soon as the analysis begins. Second, a variety of techniques of communication should be employed: the diversity of peoples' perceptions should be matched by a diversity of communication material. This material should span several levels of detail, so that decision makers can examine the analysis at any level appropriate to their interests and training. Most important, communication takes time.

Communication should be the sole responsibility of at least one member of a six-person staff. The others should spend up to one-third of their time in interactive communication. Note that this is not public relations. Rather, it is a vital aspect of environmental analysis and decision making. If the goal of the analysis is to produce better environmental decisions, then communication requires as much creative design as the analysis itself.

10 An Underview

Traditionally, a book that has spent nine chapters outlining and advocating a new perspective and a novel operational approach deserves a strong concluding chapter. So if you are expecting such a grand finale, you should be warned that there is none. To have provided such an ending would have been deceptive – creating the tidy but false impression that we have left no loose ends to our story. Unfortunately, our exposition of a new adaptive style of environmental assessment and management has left some important unresolved issues in its wake. These issues were raised in the first two chapters and remained an implicit backdrop thereafter. Therefore we end Part I by reviving these issues because we feel strongly that they must be woven into the mental framework of those who deal in policy, especially where environmental concerns are paramount. We also bring these issues back to the surface to emphasize the need for new conceptual and methodological tools to address them. In the meantime, they are reminders that our "solutions" are not ultimate and that we must operate without all the answers.

All of these unresolved issues relate in one way or another to the theme of *uncertainty*. We believe these issues to be philosophically important; our view of the world is inseparable from our view of uncertainty. We also believe these issues to be pragmatically important – first, because uncertainty is real and, second, because these issues need continual attention, creative conceptualization, and active research before useful procedures and techniques can emerge.

The phenomenon of uncertainty was raised in the opening chapters as a central theme. Although the word did not appear regularly in the middle chapters, it was implicit in our descriptions of an adaptive approach to environmental problems. As we return now to that theme, we emphasize that we have no theories or conclusions to report – only our concerns and speculations.

PREDICTION IS NEVER PERFECT

The future is uncertain. Few would disagree with this in principle; the debate, if any, would involve definitions and criteria. Moreover, environmental assessments are not, and cannot be, predictions in any real sense. First, we cannot measure everything, and, what is more, we should not try. The things left unmeasured will also be affected by man's interventions, and these effects will cause change in those things that are being studied. Initial bounding and selection of key variables aim to minimize this effect but cannot eliminate it.

Second, no amount of observation prior to a project will reveal what impacts the project will eventually have. Almost by definition, the impacts will be the consequence of disturbances that are unlike any the natural system has yet experienced. To some extent lessons can be learned from similar situations, and conclusions can be drawn from the general responses of disturbed ecological systems. But the post-project system is a new system, and its nature cannot be deduced simply by looking at the original one. If the project planning and development sequence fundamentally incorporates adaptive assessment throughout all of its stages, then the ecological response of both the new and old systems will be studied.

If assessment continues into the future, then prediction loses its status as a goal, and assessment merges into environmental management. Prediction and traditional "environmental impact assessments" suppose that there is a "before and after," whereas environmental management is an ongoing process.

If assessment techniques cannot make true predictions, then what are they for? Is assessment simply swallowed into the larger activity of environmental management? The activities described in the preceding chapters comprise a procedure of adaptive assessment, but their aim is no longer prediction of what will happen or even what will most likely happen. Environmental assessment should be an *ongoing investigation into*, not a *one-time prediction of*, impacts.

The people making environmental assessments often are the first to admit that their conclusions are not certain. But if they attribute their doubt to a lack of time, money, and manpower, then they have missed the point. Attempting to close the gap on imperfect predictions detracts from a proper focus on the consequences of the inherent uncertainties that will always remain. If prophecy is impossible, then go for understanding.

LIVING WITH UNCERTAINTY

As uncertainty is a very broad concept, it is useful to think of three classes of uncertainty. The analyses used for assessment and the strategies adopted for management will be different for each.

The first class involves those events that can be predefined, that have known direct effects, and that have known probabilities of occurrence. The coin toss is a didactic example, while varying weather patterns are an example with environmental significance. Statistical analyses, the study of stochastic processes, the subdiscipline of decision theory, and many other applied methodologies are founded on this class of uncertainty. It is natural that analytical advances should start here – when you know the probability distribution, a large proportion of the uncertainty is resolved.

The second class of uncertainty involves those events that are imaginable and at least partially describable, but for which neither the outcome nor the probability of occurrence are known. Nuclear reactor failure exemplifies this class of uncertainty, and the continuing scientific controversy highlights the absence of a conceptual or analytic framework for this class.

Many "natural" examples are either not entirely convincing or of minimal ecological importance. Being struck by lightning comes to mind. Earthquake and drought have large social importance, but with observation and experience, these events can move into the first class.

The situations that are rapidly dominating this class involve man-made interventions such as the development of a nuclear power economy, a possibility that currently enjoys a moderate degree of public attention. Climate modification, recombinant-DNA research, and heavy metal and synthetic chemical discharges are other relatively new items joining a rapidly expanding list. Two features make these "advances" potential horrors. First, they each introduce a perturbation into the environment that is unique in the evolutionary history of the biosphere. And second, modern technological and industrial capacity permits such perturbations to take place rapidly on a global scale.

The third class of uncertainty contains all those events for which we have no experience (or have forgotten) and events involving unknown processes of unknown functional form. Examples are to be found in the historical record; imagine, for instance, the character of a simulation model of disease had it been built before Pasteur.

Assignment of events to one or the other of these classes depends on what is "known," that is, on a changing constellation of ideas – new things being added while others are forgotten. A possible correlation appears between class and time scale. Things that occur on a "human time scale" (minutes to years) are more likely to fall into the first class.

The relationship of uncertainty and variability to the functioning of ecological systems received its prime emphasis in Chapters 1 and 2. The subsequent focus on the procedures of the adaptive approach that we recommend adds new elements for consideration. In an environmental analysis there will be things we know about but choose to exclude and things we do not know about and thus have no choice but to exclude. The distinction, though sounding simple, does have meaning. The former can be checked as discussed in Chapter 7. The latter should not be ignored simply because nothing can be done about them. Residual uncertainty should influence our decisions and policies now; it certainly will influence our world later. Watt (1974) accurately describes this "*Titanic* effect": when uncertainties are wished away and not planned for, the crises that follow are all the more intense.

Environmental decisions are made in a social setting. Of all the uncertainties of human and social behavior, the one of paramount significance to environmental policy is the shifting nature of individual and social preferences. The profound changes in policy stemming from the rise of environmental awareness in the late 1960s are more than obvious. The point to remember is that other equally radical shifts in social goals will occur in the future.

Even the relatively objective activity of environmental assessment is influenced by social preferences. The attributes selected as important for consideration, the time horizon chosen, and the treatment of alternatives are a few of the characteristics colored by public opinion. Emphasis can range from protection of unique scenic areas to smog to endangered species to the socioeconomic environment of the world's citizens.

In order to live successfully with uncertainty, our environmental management institutions must maintain their responsiveness to change. The ecological systems that have persisted have been those that were resilient enough to absorb the unexpected and learn from it. Our institutions, too, need a similar ability to cope. Institutions, like biological systems, learn to handle change by experiencing change. And as with other things learned, this ability will be forgotten if the experience is not occasionally reinforced. Insulation from small disasters leaves one ill-prepared and vulnerable to larger ones.

MONITORING AS "POSTDICTION"

The final draft of an environmental impact statement is stamped "approved," and then the bulldozers move in. Unfortunately, this has been the case too often. A major operational change required to shift assessment from its traditional role into meaningful environmental management is the continuation of assessment activities during and after the period of construction. Such an extension of activity requires the addition of a monitoring capability. At the very least, monitoring provides an opportunity to attempt an invalidation of the analysis that has already been done. Prediction may not be possible, but some postdiction is.

The choice of what to monitor presents many of the same problems that were faced in the choice of what to include in the original assessment. The easy solution would designate the key variables of the assessment as the quantities to monitor. However, such a choice would ignore some of the understanding gained in the analysis and would miss some opportunities to increase the scope of that understanding. Monitoring provides an opportunity to pursue model and assessment invalidation and to solidify our degree of belief in the investigation to date. This objective requires a testing and probing of our analysis that cannot be accomplished without stepping beyond the previously selected key variables and relationships.

Not all key variables are equally important. Some will have been found to be strongly implicated in possible future impacts. Others will be accompanied by larger uncertainties in the form or magnitude of their relationships with other variables. And some will be a combination – strongly implicated, but sensitive to the range of variation in our estimates. A monitoring plan should address these differences between variables.

A model or an analysis is characterized as much, if not more, by what is left out as by what is put in. Invalidation and monitoring have an obligation to "look outward" and include the excluded factors in some way.

Is this an open invitation to monitor everything possible? Clearly not. Limitations of time and money and the sheer incomprehensibility of masses of complex data call for restricted and focused monitoring. The question to ask is, "*What would I do with the information if I had it?*"

Some monitoring will also be needed to mitigate impacts. Almost all human activities have some impact on the environment. Some impacts will be acceptable prices to pay, and the project will proceed. However, we may wish to "fix up" a particular unwanted impact. For this, the monitoring and corrective actions are more focused than in the broader management problem, but the same general procedures and concerns apply. Mitigation often appears as a separate and distinct activity rather than as one component of good management. This distinction lies very close to the dichotomy between "externalities" and "internalities." Those undesirable effects that are mitigated are perceived as "side effects," as if they were somehow merely inconvenient intrusions from outside. But undesirable effects are an inherent part of the total problem, and management should treat them as such. Even the word "mitigation" reflects a perceived realm of responsibility: mitigation is left to other public agencies or is performed under legal obligation.

The above observation does not reject mitigation as an important activity. The development plan should include the mitigation of some impacts just as it should include steps to avoid others. There will always be impacts inseparable from the development itself that require remedial action – land recovery after strip mining and reforestation after logging, for example. Fiering and Holling (1974) discuss some of the properties and constraints of restoring a dynamic system to a desired condition.

Monitoring provides us with one other useful payoff – lessons for the next time. Future environmental investigations stand a better chance of improvement if monitoring and retrospective analysis contribute to the common experience. A catalogue of things that went wrong and impacts that were "surprises" could be a useful tool in future assessments (see, e.g., Dasmann *et al.*, 1973). Some of the same mistakes could be prevented. But the big take-home lesson is that the unexpected is to be expected.

ADAPTIVE MANAGEMENT

Adaptive management is not really much more than common sense. But common sense is not always in common use. Many industrial and engineering concerns routinely practice adaptive management. In developing a new product, not all the final details are planned and fixed before the first action is taken. Activities such as pilot projects, test modeling, and market surveys are all efforts to use information from the first stages to adapt the final outcome to greater advantage.

The extensions of relevance here are the inclusion of environmental considerations among the criteria for project adaptation and the integration of the assesment and planning processes. Such integration requires mechanisms that allow the assessment to continue along with the project evolution and mechanisms that allow the project to adapt in response to ecological considerations.

No particular set procedures will accomplish this task. But there are types of questions that can be asked: Are there times in the development plan when changes can be made and new directions followed? Will the analysis be able to respond at the right time with the information needed to influence the project development? Absolute replies to these questions are not possible, but the mere act of asking reorients the perspective from one of assumed certamty to one of prepared responsiveness.

Adaptive management can take a more active form by using the project itself as an experimental probe. In this context we place an explicit value on ecological information. A deliberate alteration in the project or the sequence of its stages may reveal detrimental ecological effects that can be avoided in the final form of the project. In many cases such alterations will be "inefficient" in a traditional sense, but a judgment must be made concerning the longer term value of the information to be gained. An explicit attempt to use the project itself can be used to address one element of the uncertainty surrounding environmental responses. Walters and Hilborn (1976) and Peterman (1977b) propose this strategy for the management of fishery stocks.

A note of caution should accompany these last proposals. There is small hope of gaining useful information by arbitrarily perturbing the environment or trying some action just to see what happens. Experimental probes of the type suggested here should be addressed to specific questions about environmental response. Experiments without clear questions are likely to give ambiguous answers.

Incrementalism is a very similar trap: Build a small dam and everything is fine; build a large dam and everything goes belly-up. The inherent nonlinearities, thresholds, time delays, and spatial redistributions of ecological systems may completely hide the potential effects that would result from a larger intervention. Small may be beautiful, but big is not simply several smalls (Holling, 1976).

FORECLOSURE OF OPTIONS

Without uncertainty in ecological behavior and without uncertainty in future societal preferences, finding the "right thing to do" would take on an entirely different character. However, along with these two very real sources of uncertainty comes the trap of irreversibility. Will the ecological system head off in an unanticipated and undesirable direction that is not amenable to recovery? In terms of the descriptions of Chapter 2, will the system be flipped into an entirely new equilibrium region? Or, on the other hand, will a project that is acceptable now be viewed as intolerable in the future?

Recovery and future flexibility present very real issues. We cannot always require a complete return to starting conditions or complete freedom to reach any other conceivable condition. But we can try to keep from getting locked into any one situation. No guarantees exist, but to ask honestly what options are being foreclosed reorients the planning and development process and makes dead ends less likely.

Besides the vagaries of nature and the swings of human preferences, decisions taken now have consequences for decisions to be taken in the future (Walters, 1975a). All decisions change the environment in which future decisions are made, but a pathological aspect arises when a particular decision sets up a sequence of following decisions from which there is no retreat. Developments involving large capital expenditures are especially apt to follow this one-way path.

Adaptive assessment should look ahead to identify at least some of the *de facto* future decisions that are being made by our present actions.

DESIGNING FOR UNCERTAINTY

Unless big disasters can be completely eliminated (which we take to be impossible), there remains the problem of designing our institutions and artifacts to cope with their occurrence. Occasional small disasters offer an important learning opportunity, but the choice between several small and one large calamity is intuitive at best. Nevertheless, we propose that some amount of change and uncertainty is necessary and healthy in order to maintain responsiveness and resilience.

Some systems are inherently more capable than others of absorbing insults and changes without losing their integrity. We would like to be able to conclude with a list of design principles that point the way, but, unfortunately, we do not know what those principles are. We do, however, believe there is one axiom that underlies any design for uncertainty. This axiom states: There exists a serious trade-off between designs aimed at preventing failure and designs that respond and survive when that failure does occur, (Holling and Clark, 1975).

We have no definitive picture of how this latter sort of system would look, but it probably would not be accomplished by the traditional means of maximizing engineering and economic efficiency. Our research into sources of persistence in ecological systems is beginning to point in some likely directions. Undoubtedly, some further lessons could be learned by examining the response and reactions of different societies to hazards and other disruptive forces. The anthropological literature should yield some clues how differing cultural structures react under stress.

Examples are few and a theory is lacking, but this will continue to be the case until we learn to see the world in a new perspective – a perspective that recognizes adaptability and responsiveness rather than prediction and tight control, and a perspective that actively views uncertainty as a fundamental facet of environmental life rather than as a distasteful transition to attainable certainty.

Part Two

Case Studies

In Part I we described the individual elements of the adaptive approach, drawing on appropriate case study material to illustrate our arguments. Part II treats the same issues, but shifts the perspective to that of the case problems *per se*. Each of the next five chapters documents one of the specific applied problems that figured in the development and testing of the general approach outlined so far. Because this approach evolved as a direct result of the studies, no one study represents what would be an "ideal" case of adaptive management or assessment. But together, these studies document the usefulness of the approach.

Each of these five case studies was developed by a different subset of the authors, together with their colleagues at each of their home institutions. The material presented was coordinated and prepared by the following individuals:

C.S. Holling, "The Spruce-Budworm/Forest-Management Problem," Chapter 11
R. Peterman, "Pacific Salmon Management," Chapter 12
C.J. Walters, "Obergurgl: Development in High Mountain Regions of Austria," Chapter 13
Jorge Rabinovich, "An Analysis of Regional Development in Venezuela," Chapter 14
J. Gross, "A Wildlife Impact Information System," Chapter 15.

11 The Spruce-Budworm/ Forest-Management Problem

The spruce budworm case study reported here covers a period from 1973 to 1976. It involved scientists and managers from the Canadian Forest Service, the New Brunswick Department of Natural Resources, the Institute of Resource Ecology at the University of British Columbia, the International Institute for Applied Systems Analysis near Vienna, and the Engineering and Applied Sciences group at Harvard.

The goal of the study was to develop and test many of the strategic approaches to ecological policy design reported in this book. The procedures and results are reported at length in a manuscript in preparation, and we summarize parts of the work here in order to illustrate the interrelationships among problems of policy design, management, and adaptive assessment in a specific context.

INTRODUCTION

The boreal forests in North America have for centuries experienced periodic outbreaks of a defoliating insect called the spruce budworm (*Choristoneura fumiferana*). In any one outbreak cycle a large proportion of the mature softwood forest in affected areas can die, with major consequences to the economy and employment of regions that are highly dependent on the forest industry. An extensive insecticide-spraying program initiated in the Canadian province of New Brunswick in 1951 has succeeded in minimizing tree mortality, but at the price of maintaining incipient outbreak conditions over an area considerably more extensive than in the past. The present management approach is particularly sensitive to unexpected shifts in economic, social, and regulatory constraints and to unanticipated behavior of the forest ecosystem.

Many major environmental problems in the world today are characterized by similar basic ingredients: high variability in space and time, large scale, and a troubled management history. Because of their enormous complexity, there has been little concerted effort to apply systems analysis techniques to the coordinated development of effective descriptions of, and prescriptions for, such problems. The budworm–forest system seemed to present an admirable focus for a case study with two objectives. The first, of course, was to attempt to develop sets of alternative policies appropriate for the specific problem. But the more general purpose was to see just how far we could stretch the state-of-the-art capabilities in ecology, modeling, optimization, policy design, and evaluation to apply them to complex ecosystem management problems.

Three prinicipal issues in any resource environmental problem challenge existing techniques. The resources that provide the food, fiber, and recreational opportunities for society are integral parts of ecosystems characterized by complex interrelationships of many species with each other and with the land, water, and climate in which they live. The interactions of these systems are highly nonlinear and have a significant spatial component. Events in any one point in space, just as at any moment of time, can affect events at other points in space and time. The resulting high order of dimensionality becomes all the more significant as these ecological systems interact with complex social and economic ones.

The second major challenge is that we have only partial knowledge of the variables and relationships governing the systems. A large body of theoretical and experimental analysis and data has led to an identification of the general form and kind of functional relations existing between organisms. But only occasionally is there a rich body of data specific to any one situation. To develop an analysis that implicitly or explicitly presumes sufficient knowledge is therefore to guarantee management policies that become more the source of the problem than the source of the solution. In a particularly challenging way, present ecological management situations require concepts and techniques that cope creatively with the uncertainties and unknowns that pervade most of our major social, economic, and environmental problems.

The third challenge reflects the previous two: How can we design policies that achieve specific social objectives and yet are still "robust"? Policies that, once set in motion, produce intelligently linked ecological, social, and economic systems that can absorb the unexpected events and unknowns that will inevitably appear. These "unexpecteds" might be the "thousand-year" drought that perversely occurs this year, the appearance or disappearance of key species, the emergence of new economic and regulatory constraints, or the shift of societal objectives. We must learn to design policies in a way that shifts our emphasis away from minimizing the probability of failure and toward minimizing the cost of those failures that will inevitably occur.

Rather than repeat the details of the budworm case study here, we shall emphasize the lessons learned as we attempted to develop and test the methodologies and concepts mentioned above. These lessons tended to expose the fairy-tale nature of many of the most treasured assumptions of ourselves and our collaborators.

We have preserved the better fables to remind us of our errors, and have replaced them in practice with our own "counterfables." These provide a convenient focus for the discussion that follows.

DYNAMIC DESCRIPTION

Fable 1 Policy design should begin with an analysis of the institutional and decision environment.

Counterfable 1 Policy design should begin with a dynamic description of the physical and biological system.

If our goal were to analyze and prescribe for a specific problem in a specific region with specific institutional constraints, then clearly an analysis of the institutional and decision environment would have the highest priority at the very beginning of the case study. But our goal was not that. Our goal, rather, emphasizes transferability of concepts and methods to a constellation of problems occurring in various regions in various nations. It is true that to give focus we concentrate initially on a specific problem with the name budworm–forest, and on one particular region – the Province of New Brunswick in Canada. This is just a pragmatic necessity to give concreteness and allow for testing in a real-world situation. As the steps of transfer begin to take place, it becomes necessary to examine specific institutional settings in a number of different regions and nations. This represents analysis of the implementation phase (level $N-1$) suggested in Table 11.1 and Figure 11.1.

With our approach, in order to make transfer a reality, the initial emphasis must be on those elements of the problem that are truly general, for it will be those parts

TABLE 11.1 Elements of Ecological Policy Design

Systems Level	Analytical Element	Function
N + 1	Hypothetical overview (embedding)	Consequence check for larger societal implications
N	System description	Specification and dynamic description of causal structure for the system under study
N	Policy prescription	Specification of a strategic range of alternative objectives for the system and development of corresponding policies
N	Policy evaluation	Comparison of alternatives through an array of indicators, focussing on the unknown, the uncertain, and missing components of the descriptive analysis
N – 1	Implementation	Consequence check for detailed practicality and operational feasibility.

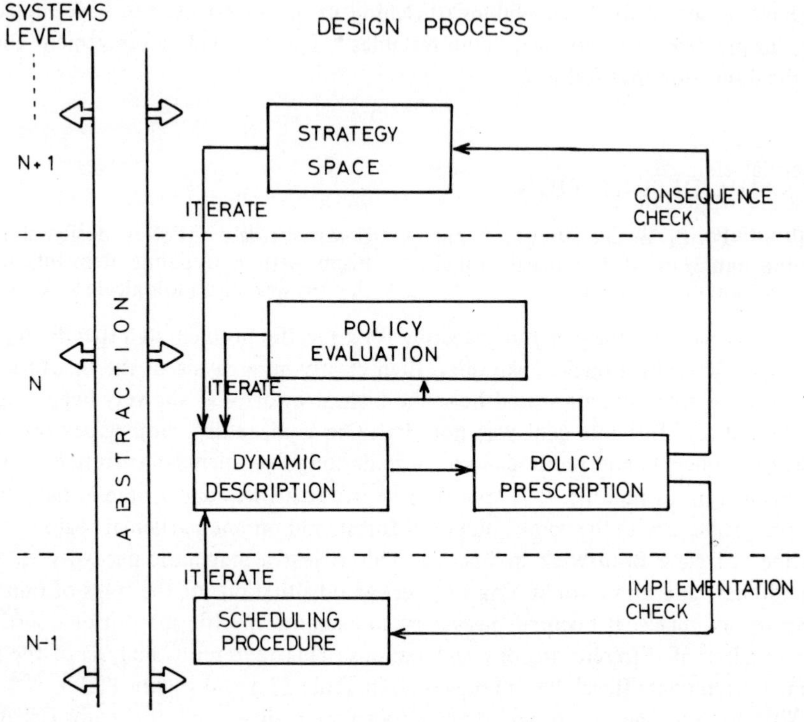

FIGURE 11.1 The process of ecological policy design.

that are independent of problem, of region, and of nation. This focus on generality is not possible in an analysis of institutional or decision behavior. The state of knowledge in those fields is still primitively rooted in specific examples. In contrast, the state of knowledge of ecological systems and of ecological processes allows for well-tested analyses that have generality beyond the specific focus. With the need to facilitate transfer, the first requirement is to develop an effective and validated dynamic description of the ecological parts of the problem. At this stage, the aim is to develop a simulation model that can be used as a kind of laboratory world with some confidence that it will be responsive to the exploration of a variety of different policies and their consequences.

BOUNDING THE PROBLEM

Fable 2 A complex system must be described by a complex model in order to respond to complex policies.

Counterfable 2 A simple but well-understood model is the best interface between a complex system and a complex range of policies.

Any dynamic descriptive model represents an abstraction of reality. The initial steps of bounding the problem determine whether the abstraction will represent that part of reality that has relevance to the issues raised. Any ecosystem management problem is comprised of an immense array of interacting variables, conflicting objectives and competing actions. A major effort is demanded to abstract the essential elements. Our rule is to be as ruthlessly parsimonious and economical as possible while retaining responsiveness to the management objectives and actions appropriate for the problem. The variables selected for system description must be the minimum that will capture the essential qualitative behavior in both time and space.

BOUNDING OBJECTIVES

It could logically be argued that the bounding process should be dictated by the policy or management objectives. If the intent of the budworm case study were to analyze only the New Brunswick problem, then it might indeed be possible and valuable to start with a definition of their management objectives. But again, to re-emphasize, New Brunswick was only chosen as a pragmatic convenience – particularly because of its troubled management history and the availability of committed collaborators in both research and management agencies. With our primary focus on transferability, an initial emphasis on the objectives of New Brunswick would have quickly constrained the range of uses and the generality of the analysis. It would have led, perhaps, to an emphasis on developing a regional econometric model and to an institutional analysis with the ecological dynamics implicitly and inflexibly appended.

The budworm has evolved over the centuries to contribute to forest renewal and maintenance of species diversity. Its status as a problem depends upon the particular social and economic conditions and objectives in any region. In New Brunswick the budworm was considered only a natural curiosity until the pulp and paper industry, which developed in the 1930s, found it had to compete with the budworm for fiber. New Brunswick's economy is now largely dependent upon the forest industry, and the province's objectives are social and economic.

Other regions have very different objectives. For example, the Canadian Province of Ontario has a much more diversified economy, and the forest industry makes minor use of budworm-preferred species. Here, objectives relate to recreation within provincial and national parks. In the United States, the budworm is a serious problem in Maine, where peculiarities of land use and ownership make for a complex set of sometimes conflicting social, economic, and environmental objectives. Moreover, even though objectives might be defined rigorously within a single region, they will likely change over time. As an example, recall that the recent concerns for the environment were scarcely recognized 10 years ago. Hence, we argue that an initial primary focus on objectives is inadequate to give guidance for creating a useful tool for policy design.

We recognize five aspects of the budworm problem that exist to some degree in all environmental management situations – these aspects are social, economic, resource, recreation, and environmental. Any attempt to integrate all these into a model that would respond to a diverse set of policies would produce an analysis as complex and mysterious as the real world; such an analysis would be useless for policy purposes. Clearly, some things must be left out, and our transfer goal dictates that we leave out those things that are regionally specific. It is the resource and environmental aspects that are selected for their generality with respect to other problems, regions, and nations.

These considerations of objectives, based on the need for generality and transfer, define the primary system that will be analyzed: the forest ecosystem. A model of the forest can then be designed to generate indicators of social, economic, and recreational interest that will interface with the mental and mathematical models of specific regions and specific policy issues. Moreover, these indicators can be combined to provide a variety of objective functions that become part of the optimization effort.

BOUNDING POLICIES

The core of the descriptive analysis focuses on the forest ecosystem, but it must, from the outset, be responsive to realistic alternative policies. The specific policies, or actions, that have been or could be applied are almost infinite – the use of insecticides, biological control agents, genetic manipulation, tree harvesting and planting schemes. Moreover, the actions that now seem to be economically impractical might, with future developments, become highly feasible. But the whole range of actions feasible now and in the future fall into essentially three classes – control of the insect, harvest of the trees, and manipulation of the forest through planting. The descriptive model must allow intervention with any of these classes of action at any moment in time and any point in space.

The steps of bounding that focus on objectives and management actions must precede the actual modeling steps. Otherwise, the descriptive analysis would inexorably lead to an exercise in modeling as a goal in itself. The rules for the final bounding of the problem require decisions about the number of ecosystem variables, the temporal horizon and resolution, and the spatial extent and resolution.

BOUNDING VARIABLES

An ecosystem of this complexity has many thousands of species and potential variables. Our understanding of the dominant budworm–forest dynamics is sufficiently detailed, however, that the system's relevant behavior can be captured by a limited subset of variables, each of which serves a key role in determining the major dynamics of the forest ecosystem and its resulting diversity. These key variables are summarized in Figure 11.2.

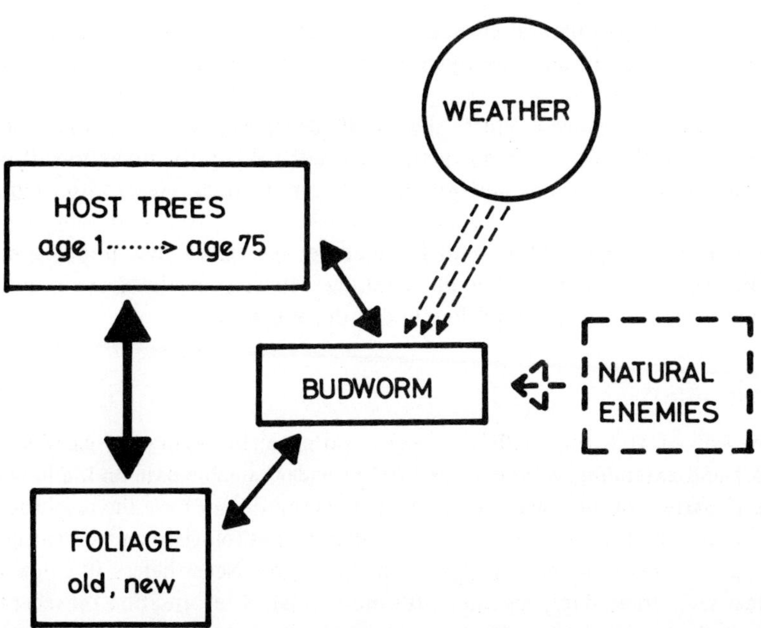

FIGURE 11.2 The key roles or variables and their interrelations in the natural ecosystem. The principal tree species (birch, spruce, and balsam fir) have a dynamic interaction of their own, which is altered by the presence of budworm, which consumes some spruce but primarily balsam. The budworm is in turn affected by a complex system of natural enemies and a stochastic weather variable. Only budworm, balsam, and weather are treated as explicit dynamic variables.

The principal tree species are birch (*Betula* sp.), spruce (*Picea* sp.) and balsam fir (*Abies balsamea*). They have a dynamic interaction of their own that is dependent on the influence of budworm. Balsam is highly susceptible to damage, spruce less so, and birch not at all. Our rule of parsimony and our strategic level of interest dictate that we include only the budworm host, balsam, as a dynamic variable. It is this species, as well, that provides the principal source of pulp to the mills of New Brunswick.

The amount of balsam fir is a quantitative, or extensive, measure. We must couple with it a qualitative, or intensive, measure to account for tree condition. This property is closely linked with foliage condition and retains the memory of past stress. The particular behavior characteristics of budworm and balsam require that this variable be split into two components, which we call old and new foliage in the model.

Between outbreaks the budworm is rare but not extinct, its numbers being controlled by natural enemies such as insectivorous birds and parasites. A key feature of this control is that there exists an upper threshold of budworm numbers that, once exceeded, allows the budworm to "escape" predation and multiply unchecked. Although natural enemies are an important feature whose effect must be included, it seemed unnecessary to introduce them as dynamic variables at the outset.

Outbreaks cannot occur unless the forest has recovered sufficiently from the previous outbreak to provide adequate food and habitat for budworm. If warm, dry weather then occurs, budworm survival can increase enough to trigger an outbreak.

From the thousands of potential candidates we select five as being critical dynamic variables for capturing the essential behavior of the system: the host tree, two aspects of foliage condition, budworm, and weather.

BOUNDING TIME

An analysis of tree rings (Blais, 1968) covering eight regions of eastern North America and extending as far back as 1704 provides valuable data on the long-range temporal pattern of outbreaks. These data, however, do not have the resolution and sheer volume of the time series data familiar to hydrologists and climatologists. Hence, any formal time series analysis is inappropriate. Nevertheless, in a qualitative but clear way, these data, together with more detailed information on recent outbreaks, indicate a distinctive 30–45-year period between outbreaks, with occasional periods of 60 to 100 years (Figure 11.3). Between outbreaks the budworm is present

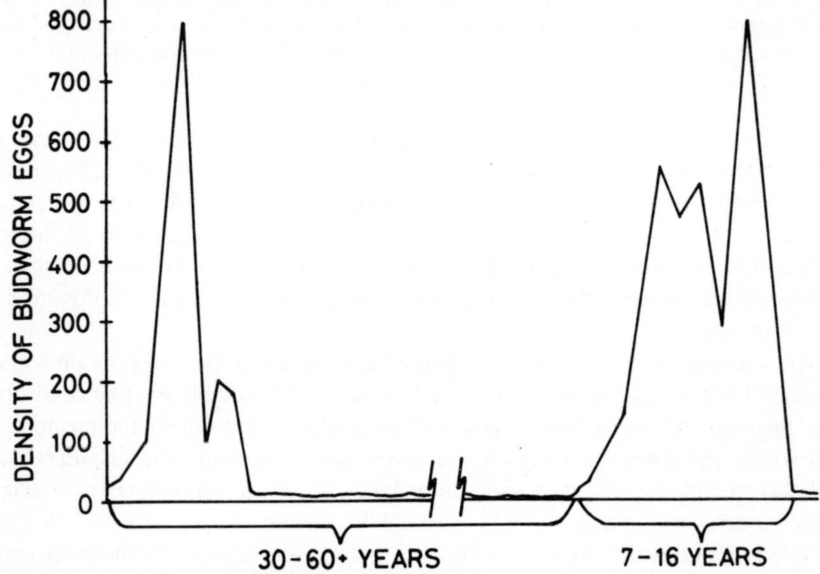

FIGURE 11.3 The pattern in time. Representative historical pattern of spruce budworm outbreak. There have been four major outbreaks since 1770. The density measure of budworm is what would occur on a typical balsam fir branch.

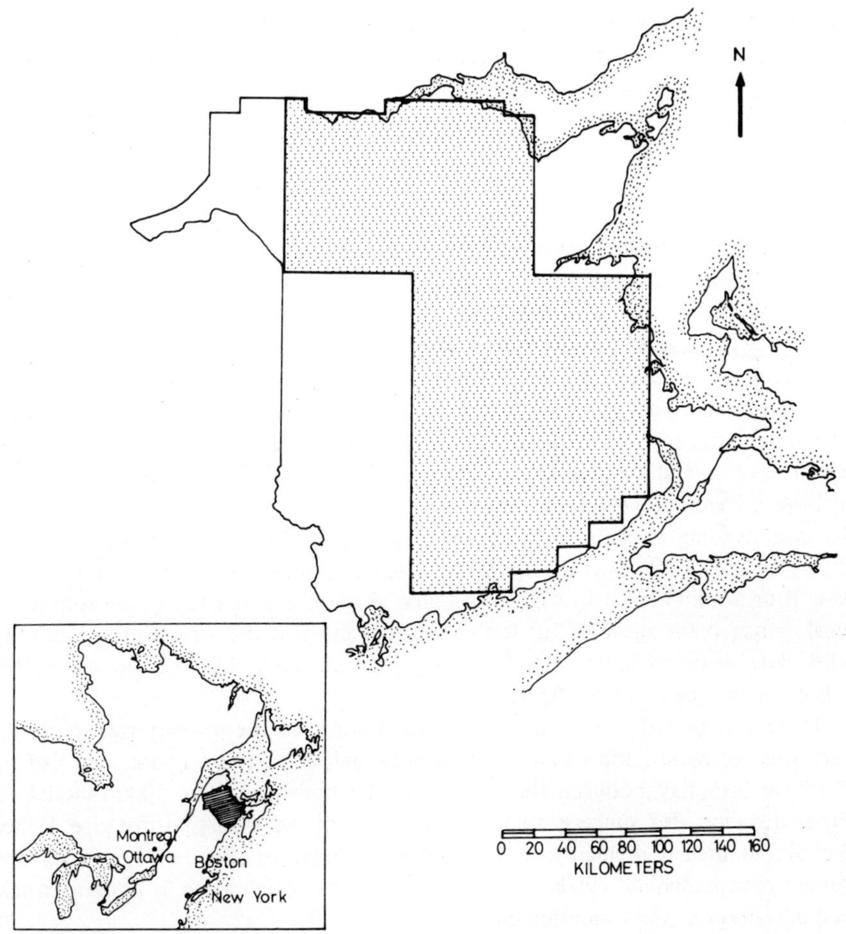

FIGURE 11.4 The study area used by the model in relation to the Province of New Brunswick, Canada.

in barely detectable densities which, when appropriate conditions occur, can multiply explosively by three orders of magnitude within 3 or 4 years. Once initiated in a local subregion, the outbreak can spread over thousands of square kilometers and finally collapse only after 7 to 16 years, with attendant high mortality to the forest. Because of the pattern of outbreaks shown in Figure 11.3, the minimum time horizon required is one that can completely contain two outbreak cycles – that is, 100 to 150 years.

The time resolution that will capture the dynamics of the system is 1 year – this matches the generation time of the budworm, as well as the planning sequence for management. Seasonal events within the year can be implicitly represented. This time resolution, though natural for the budworm, adds a technical complication to our representation of the forest because we must consider the age distribution of the trees. Therefore, we are forced to subdivide the balsam variable into 75 separate age classes.

BOUNDING SPACE

The distinctive pattern in time is paralleled by one in space. Typically, the historical outbreaks spread from the points of initiation to contaminate progressively larger areas. Collapse of the outbreaks occurs in the original centers of infestation in conjunction with severe tree mortality. The result is a high degree of spatial heterogeneity in forest age and species composition.

As with many pest species, the budworm has very strong dispersal capabilities. The modal distance of dispersal is about 50 kilometers from one location, but distances of several hundred kilometers have been recorded. It was thought essential to have a minimum total area that would encompass about five times this modal distance, leading to a modeled region of about 63,000 km^2. The particular area chosen in this study was a 50,000 km^2 area containing much of the Province of New Brunswick (Figure 11.4). The peculiar shape is a pragmatic concession to the local management agencies but it also includes most of the area from which validation data were available. A buffer zone approximately 80 km wide around this area compensates for edge effects.

There is high variation in the spatial distribution of the primary tree species, of harvesting activities, and of recreational potential, in part as a consequence of the historical interplay between the forest and the budworm. The 50-km modal dispersal distance also suggests a spatial resolution of less than that distance. Hence, the overall area is divided into 265 distinct subregions (Figure 11.5), each containing approximately 190 km^2. Again the exact configuration is chosen to take best advantage of the validation data.

SUMMARY

The decisions on bounding the problem are as follows:

Objectives: Models for resource and environmental subsystems with indicators relevant to the social, economic, and recreational subsystems

Policies: Budworm control and forest management

Key variables: Host tree species (with age structure), foliage condition, budworm, and weather

Time horizon: 100–150 years

Time resolution: 1 year with seasonal causation

Spatial area: 50,000 km^2

Spatial resolution: 265 subregions of 190 km^2

	01	02	03	04	05	06	07	08	09	10	11	12	13	14	15	
01	1				2	3	4	5	6							2
02	7	8	9	10	11	12	13	14	15	16						3
03	17	18	19	20	21	22	23	24	25	26						4
04	27	28	29	30	31	32	33	34	35	36						5
05	37	38	39	40	41	42	43	44	45	46						6
06	47	48	49	50	51	52	53	54	55	56						7
07	57	58	59	60	61	62	63	64	65	66						8
08	67	68	69	70	71	72	73	74	75	76						9
09	77	78	79	80	81	82	83	84	85	86						10
10	87	88	89	90	91	92	93	94	95	96						11
11						97	98	99	100	101	102	103	104	105	106	12
12						107	108	109	110	111	112	113	114	115	116	13
13						117	118	119	120	121	122	123	124	125	126	14
14						127	128	129	130	131	132	133	134	135	136	15
15						137	138	139	140	141	142	143	144	145	146	16
16						147	148	149	150	151	152	153	154	155	156	17
17						157	158	159	160	161	162	163	164	165	166	18
18						167	168	169	170	171	172	173	174	175	176	19
19						177	178	179	180	181	182	183	184	185	186	20
20						187	188	189	190	191	192	193	194	195	196	21
21						197	198	199	200	201	202	203	204	205	206	22
22						207	208	209	210	211	212	213	214	215	216	23
23						217	218	219	220	221	222	223	224	225	226	24
24						227	228	229	230	231	232	233	234	235	236	25
25						237	238	239	240	241	242	243	244	245		26
26						246	247	248	249	250	251	252	253			27
27						254	255	256	257	258	259	260				28
28						261	262	263	264	265						29
	G	H	I	J	K	L	M	N	O	P	Q	R	S	T	U	

FIGURE 11.5 Numbering and indexing system for the 265 subregions, or "sites," in the study area. Each site is a bit less than 11×16 km in dimension, including an area of about 190 km^2.

This bounding of the problem determines the number of state variables, which in turn determines whether subsequent prescriptive steps, such as optimization, are feasible. Table 11.2 summarizes the final decisions made on the number of state variables required. Even though the previous steps of bounding may seem to have led to a highly simplified representation, the number of state variables generated is still enormous. The 79 variables in each site are replicated 265 times to give a total of 20,935 state variables. Thus even this drastic simplification, accomplished through a parsimonious bounding exercise, leads to a system that

TABLE 11.2 Number of Variables per Subregion

Susceptible trees (balsam and spruce, by age)	75
New foliage	1
Old foliage (retains memory of past stress)	1
Budworm	1
Weather	1
TOTAL	79
(Other variables included implicitly)	
Total number of variables in full region of 265 subregions = $79 \times 265 = 20{,}935$	

is enormously complex for policy relevance. We present approaches for reducing this complexity in a later section, drawing heavily on the repetitive nature of the dimensionality introduced through age class and spatial considerations. The critical role of stringent "bounding" criteria will then be evident. Highly complex descriptive models need not and should not form the basis for even the most complicated policy analyses. Parsimony is the rule.

CAUSAL RESOLUTION

Fable 3 The goal of description is description.

Counterfable 3 The goal of description is explanation.

If description for its own sake were our only purpose, then there would be little need for a detailed understanding of causation. A multivariate statistical model would be sufficient to capture and describe historically observed patterns of behavior. In fact that is what was done in Morris's (1963) classic study of the budworm problem in New Brunswick. The very best of sampling procedures were applied over a 15-year period in a large number of locations, and a multivariate statistical descriptive model was developed. But there are two problems. The first is that ecological systems often have key frequency behaviors that are fully represented not by years but by decades or even centuries. As already shown in Figure 11.3, the basic temporal pattern of this system demonstrates periodicities of 30 years and more. It is hardly conceivable that there would ever be an extensive enough range of data to allow for a full description using statistical methods. At best, they provide an effective way to mobilize whatever data are available to point to those processes or variables that most contribute to the variance.

The second problem is that policies will develop that can move the system into regimes of behavior it has never experienced during its evolutionary history. Considerable understanding of causation is necessary to develop some confidence that the predicted behavior will actually occur in these unfamiliar circumstances. A finer level of resolution in the hierarchy of causation is demanded. Yet, clearly, one can go too far and become encumbered by microlevels of explanation and detail that defy comprehension. Modeling at too coarse or too fine a resolution level characteristically occurs when a system is not well understood. But a considerable amount is known of the structure of ecological systems. On the basis of a rich history of experimentation, theoretical analyses, and empirical field studies, the structure of key ecological processes is known not only in some detail but in a framework that has generality. This information and understanding can be aggregated to produce general and well-tested modules of key processes like growth, reproduction, competition, and predation.

Consider, for example, predation. This process has been examined in great detail (Holling, 1965). It is comprised of three necessary and sufficient subprocesses – the instantaneous rates of predator attack, of competition, and of changes in predator numbers. Each of those subprocesses can be further disaggregated into its fundamental components – some of which occur universally and others of which occur in particular situations only. The great diversity of predation types emerges from the many ways these nonuniversal components are combined.

The actions and interactions of these components have been experimentally defined and analyzed, and a finite number of qualitatively distinct kinds of predation have been identified (Holling and Buckingham, 1976). For example, prey density can affect the instantaneous rate of attack in four and only four qualitatively different ways. Moreover, a simple, rigorous equation has been developed whose four limiting conditions generate each of these types. Equally important, the sufficient biological conditions can be precisely defined so that the most general of information is sufficient to classify any specific situation. Such equations therefore represent the "modules" that can be used as building blocks for ecological models, much as an engineer uses the gravitation equation in his calculation of ballistic trajectories.

Hence our rule of thumb is to disaggregate the model first into the constituent processes that together affect growth and survival. These processes are then disaggregated one step further into their fundamental subprocesses. The principal purpose in choosing this level of causative resolution is to increase our confidence in predictions obtained under novel policies. However, four additional and equally important benefits emerge that directly relate to our emphasis on transfer and dealing with the uncertain and unexpected.

First, transfer implies that someone is receiving the analysis. In many ecological problems the recipients include biologists and scientists with a highly sophisticated and detailed understanding of the mechanisms involved in a specific problem. Without disaggregating to the level suggested the model will, quite legitimately, be seen as not at all credible. Moreover, there would be no way for the analysis to be responsive to the questions and knowledge that typically are focused on distinct processes.

Second, the organized disaggregation to the module level provides an organized way to mobilize existing data concerning partially known processes. The predation process again provides a good example. It happens that avian predators are an important determinant to the frequency behavior of the budworm–forest ecosystem. And yet their action becomes evident only when densities of the prey are extremely low. The densities are so low, in fact, that it is impractical to sample with any reasonable degree of precision and accuracy. But once we can define the qualitative type of avian predation involved, the demands for data are dramatically relaxed. In this example the form of the equation is known with considerable certainty, and only two parameters have to be estimated. Even scarce information can be assembled to, at the minimum, identify possible predator classes and then determine maximum and minimum ranges for the parameters of each class. Subsequent sensitivity analysis then determines whether parameters within this feasible range can maintain the fundamental behavior seen in nature.

Third, modeling at this level of causation provides an effective way to deal with critical unknowns. In the example of predators mentioned above, an evaluation of alternative policies must consider their sensitivities to unexpected changes in that process.

Finally, some of the major advances in coping with the unexpected and unknown are found in the techniques of adaptive management (Walters & Hilborn, 1976). The key here is that, when models are uncertain, management acts can generate information that can contribute to the understanding of the underlying mechanisms. If the models have been conceptualized at a coarse level of resolution, the experiments of adaptive management can require considerable time or extensive geographical areas to obtain results. This is impractical for management agencies with short time horizons and aversions to large-scale trials. However, by disaggregating the model to the subprocess, or module, level, "quick-and-dirty" experiments are immediately suggested that can yield results quickly in a localized and focused manner.

The goal, then, of description is not description but useful explanation.

INVALIDATION

Fable 4 The purpose of validation is to establish the truth of the model.

Counterfable 4 The purpose of invalidation is to establish the limits of model credibility.

If the focus of interest were on developing a microtactical model suitable for day-by-day predictions, then a detailed quantitative validation would be demanded. But the model described here is aimed at strategic-level regional planning with projections produced over large spatial areas and long periods of time. Detailed quantitative validation of such a model is not only inappropriate, it is, in one sense, quite insufficient.

The budworm problem, though prototypical in other respects, is a rare example of a resource system with considerable amounts of quantified data. These data exist for each of 265 subregions from 1953 to the present. Not all state variables were measured, but at least there are detailed insect density data. Data of this extent are rare, but even so they are still quite inadequate. They pertain only to one set of conditions: the historically managed world. During this period, the system was constrained to operate within a narrow regime of behavior and no data are available for other behavioral modes. It would certainly be feasible, though utterly wrong, to tune the model to fit these data. Given a sufficient number of parameters, any temporal or spatial pattern of behavior can be matched. A much more significant kind of validation has a qualitative emphasis, which, despite the qualitative nature, is more demanding. The emphasis is not on specific site-by-site and year-by-year quantitative agreement for particular situations, but more on a general agreement of patterns in space and time in a wide variety of situations. It is better viewed as an effort to invalidate the model.

The first requirement of the qualitative validation is to match the patterns in time suggested in Figure 11.3. That figure summarizes extensive qualitative information concerning the behavior of the system under no management. Under the same conditions, the model replicates this pattern with considerable accuracy, even to the point of typically generating 30–45-year periods between outbreaks and the occasional slip into a period of 60+ years (Figure 11.6). Moreover, not only is the

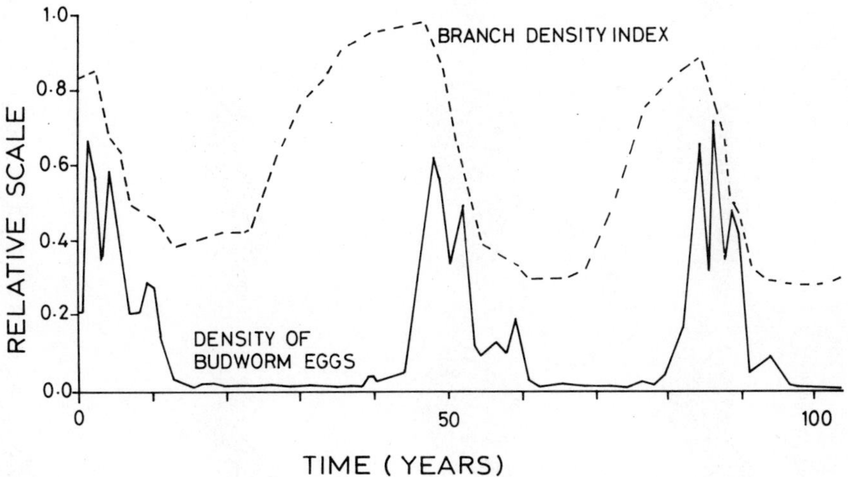

FIGURE 11.6 Typical outbreak pattern generated by model with no management or harvesting imposed. This represents mean conditions in 265 subregions of the simulated province, starting with initial conditions known to exist in 1953. Budworm densities are in 1,000 eggs/10 ft² of branch area. The Branch Density Index is a relative scale that closely parallels average forest age and forest volume. Compare Figure 11.3.

A
YEAR 0
EGG DENSITY
1
2
3
4
YEAR 5
6
7
8
9
YEAR 10
11
12
13
14
YEAR 15
16
17
18
19

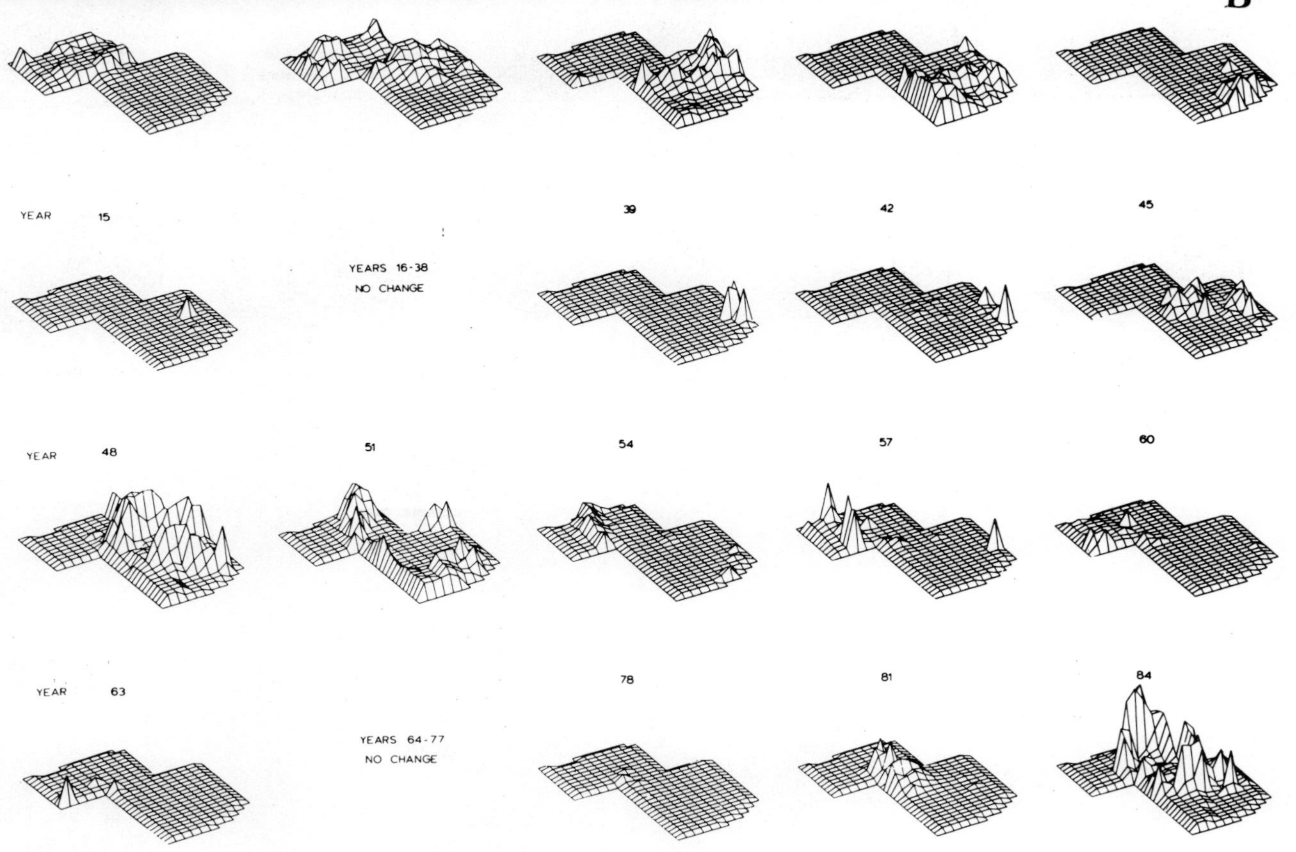

FIGURE 11.7*A* and *B* See page 161 for caption.

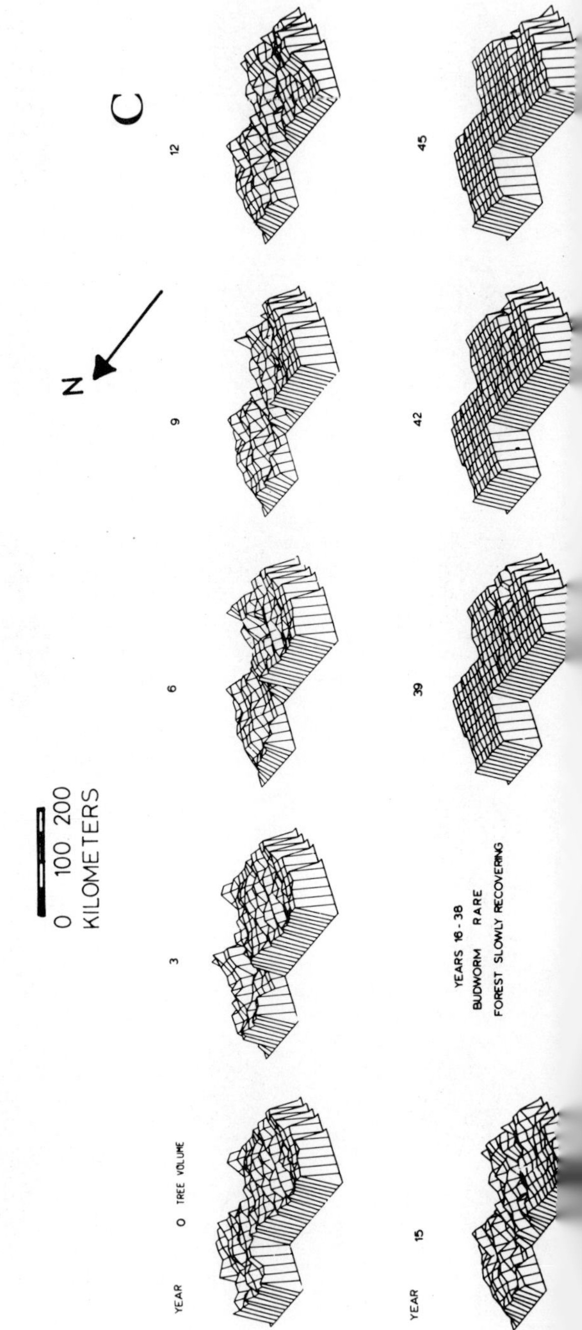
C
N
0 100 200
KILOMETERS
YEAR 0 TREE VOLUME
3
6
9
12
YEAR 15
YEARS 16 - 38
BUDWORM RARE
FOREST SLOWLY RECOVERING
39
42
45

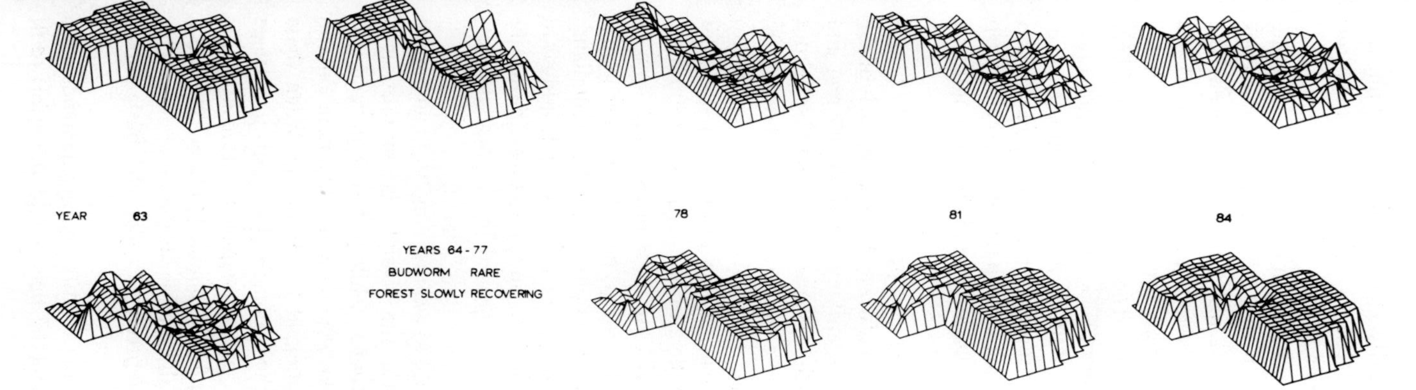

FIGURE 11.7 Spatial behavior of the budworm–forest model under conditions of no management. The horizontal (x,y) coordinates of the figures are spatial map locations corresponding to Figure 11.5. The vertical (z) coordinate represents density of budworm eggs or tree volume. The orientation and scale of Figures 11.7A and B are the same as in Figure 11.7C. Figure 11.7A shows, year by year, the spatial spread of a typical single outbreak. Figures 11.7B and 11.7C show the spread of, and recovery from, three outbreaks over an 84-year period beginning with conditions known to exist in 1953. The typical "boom-and-bust" outbreak cycle of Figure 11.3 can be seen clearly.

temporal pattern reproduced, but the local density changes are well within the observed range. Pattern in space is also reproduced. An example of a model run showing this spatial behavior is presented in Figures 11.7.

The second level of invalidation compares the patterns of behavior with the historically managed system. In this run, as in all runs, all biological parameters have been determined by independent data, and we insist they remain fixed. The only "tuning" allowed is of the initial conditions (where they are ambigious) and the management rules (harvesting trees and spraying insecticide) applied in the simulation model. The result is shown in Figure 11.8. The initial conditions in year 0 are those observed in the Province of New Brunswick in 1953. The dominant behavior predicted is a slowly eroding forest condition and the maintenance of a semioutbreak. This is precisely what has been observed historically. The key point is that the spraying policies employed, while tending to keep the forest green and so preserving the forest industry, do so at the expense of maintaining semioutbreak conditions, highly sensitive to policy failure.

The first 23 years of this simulation run represent the period 1953 to 1975, for which detailed information is available concerning budworm densities in each of the 265 subregions. Again, the pattern agreement is striking. In both the real and simulated world the outbreak starts in the north, collapses there and throughout much of the province, re-emerges in the central regions and, toward the late 1970s, spreads dramatically throughout the whole region.

The third level of invalidation requires the identification of distinct patterns of behavior occuring in the different regions within the area of the pest's distribution. In northwestern Ontario, for example, outbreaks are more intense and tend to occur at intervals of 60 or more years, rather than the typical 30–45-year period observed in New Brunswick. Another pattern has been observed in Newfoundland. Before the recent conditions of persistent outbreak on the mainland, budworm outbreaks were extremely rare in Newfoundland. Recently, however, outbreaks have occurred, and the suspicion is that they are triggered by dispersing insects from mainland regions.

The principal differences in these regions relate to weather conditions and initial conditions of the forest. In northwestern Ontario, for example, the proportion of susceptible host trees is lower than New Brunswick, while in Newfoundland it is greater. Moreover, relative to New Brunswick, the weather in northwestern Ontario is more favorable to budworm and in Newfoundland less favorable. When these simple changes are introduced into the model, the regionally characteristic patterns of behavior emerge. The model does generate periods between outbreaks under northwestern Ontario conditions of 60 years, and Newfoundland has no outbreaks, unless triggered by dispersal. This kind of invalidation is all the more convincing because these regional differences were not appreciated when the basic model was developed.

These three kinds of qualitative invalidation place more rigorous demands upon the descriptive and predictive capability of the model than would any effort to fit

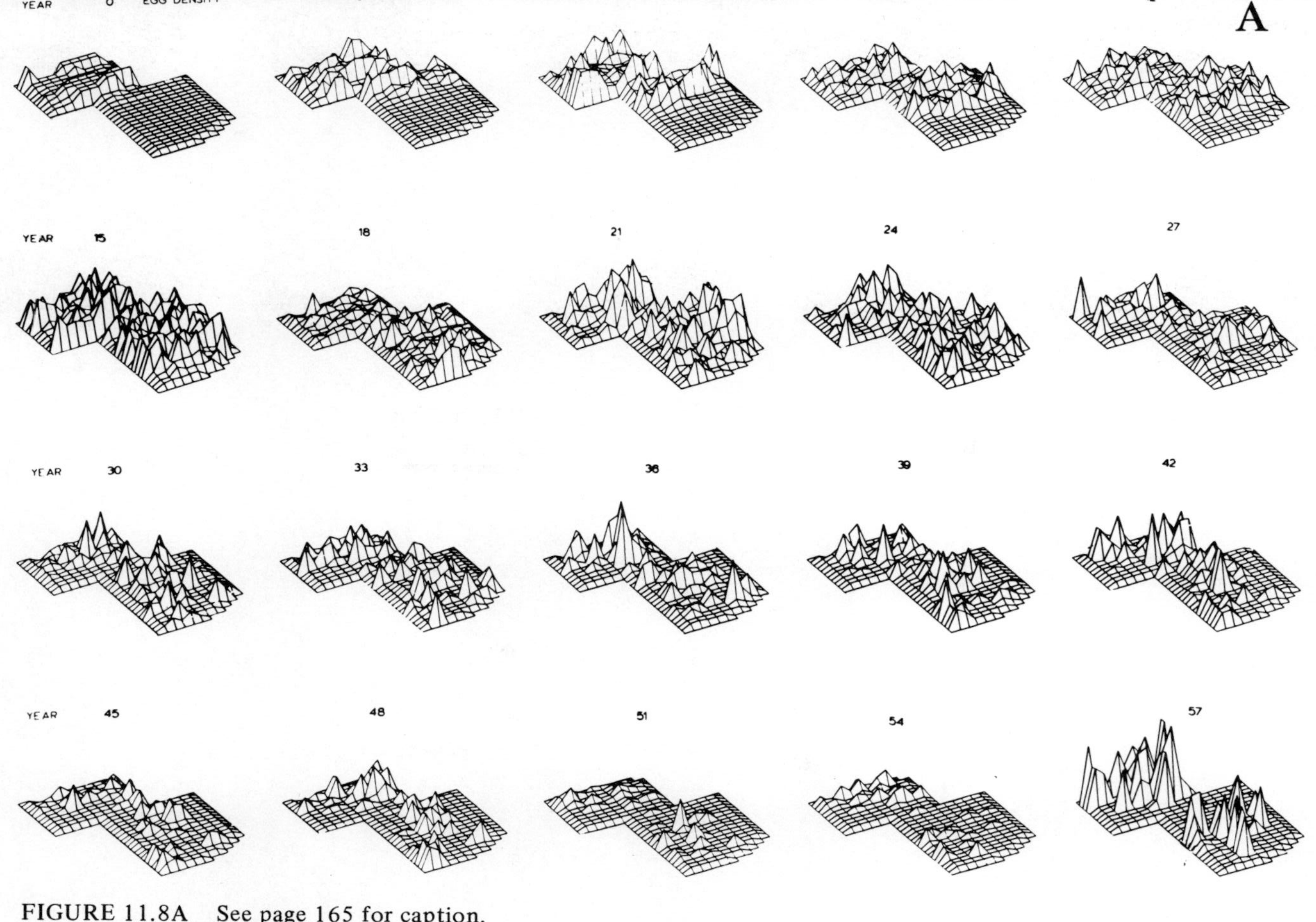

FIGURE 11.8A See page 165 for caption.

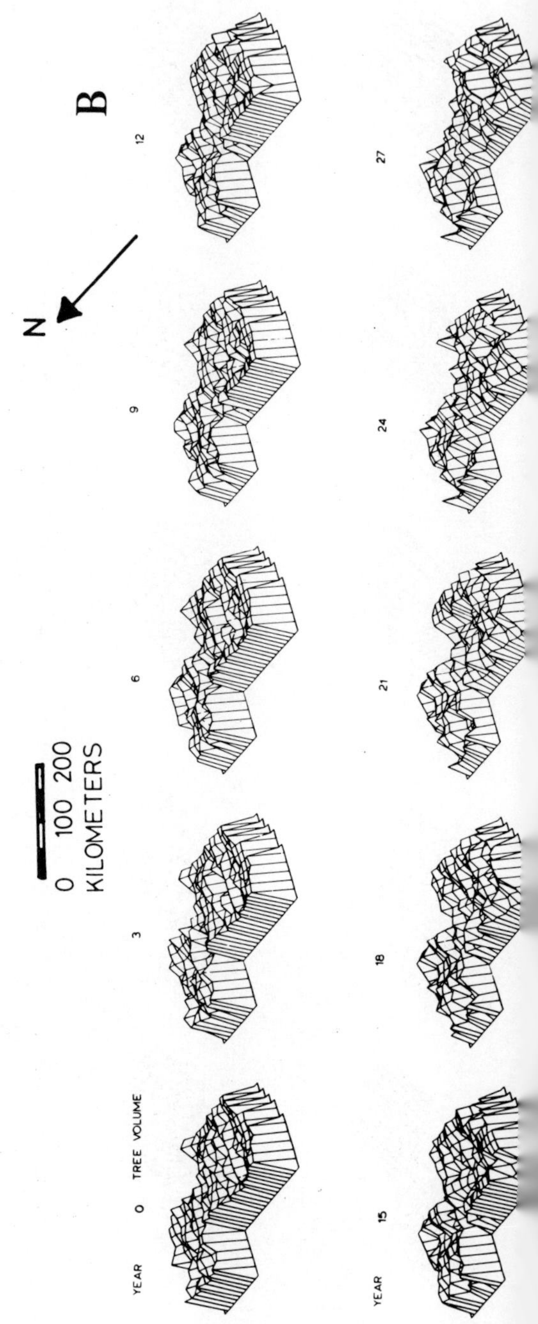

B
N
0 100 200
KILOMETERS
YEAR 0 TREE VOLUME
3
6
9
12
YEAR 15
18
21
24
27

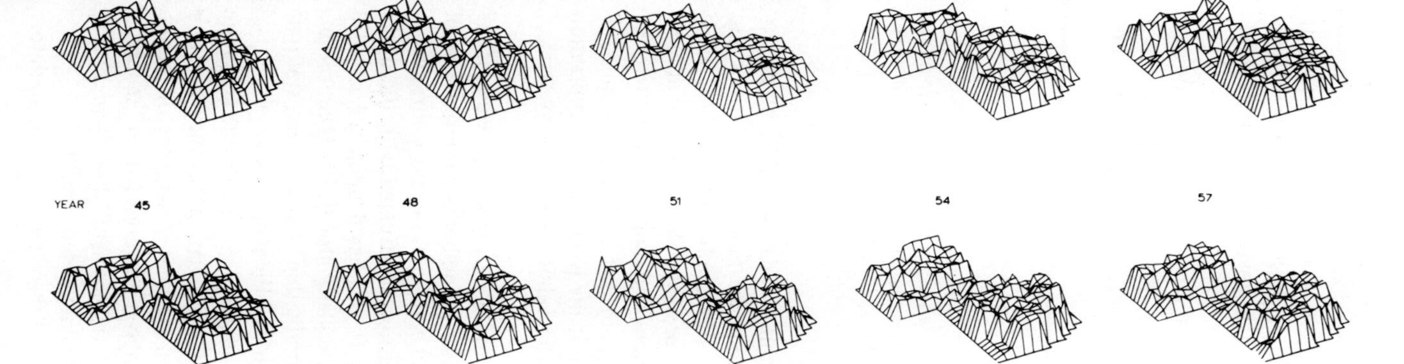

FIGURE 11.8 Spatial behavior of the budworm–forest model under historical harvest and spraying rules. The coordinates are as defined for Figure 11.7. The orientation and scale of Figure 11.8A are the same as in Figure 11.8B. Figures 11.8A and 11.8B show patterns of egg density and tree volume, respectively, beginning with conditions known to exist in 1953. Compared to Figure 11.7, the management policies can be seen to preserve trees, but at the expense of creating permanent semioutbreak conditions, highly sensitive to policy failure.

a specific time series. By focusing on patterns in space and time, it is feasible to mobilize the qualitative information on a variety of extreme behavioral modes associated with various regional conditions and historical management actions. It is this broad spectrum of qualitative matching that established our degree of confidence in a model that must explore policies that will inevitably move the system into unfamiliar regions of behavior.

The goal of invalidation for a strategic model is to produce degrees of confidence that the user can weigh subjectively, as he might weigh public opinion. But a minimum is qualitative agreement of patterns of behavior. A quantitative fit to one set of space–time data is quite insufficient.

SIMPLIFICATION AND COMPRESSION

Fable 5 The descriptive phase of applied systems analysis ends with the systems model.

Counterfable 5 The descriptive phase of applied systems analysis does not end until the systems model has been simplified for understanding.

Even the most ruthlessly parsimonious and credible simulation model of an ecological system will be encumbered by many nonlinear functional relations and many state variables. The explosive increase in the number of variables when spatially heterogeneous systems are considered presents the "curse of dimensionality" in its more intractable form. Compressions and simplifications therefore are essential, in part to encapsulate understanding, in part to facilitate communication in the transfer process, and in part to exploit the potential of optimization techniques, which are as yet unsuited to cope with nonlinear stochastic systems of high dimensionality.

A powerful approach to this essential stage is-to take a topological view of the system. This links the basic qualitative behavior to the number and interrelation of equilibrium states. It focuses, as well, on our central concern for ecological resilience and policy robustness. Note that the model was not constructed with the initial intent of generating multiple equilibria. Rather it was based upon the detailed knowledge and data available in the literature (particularly Morris, 1963) concerning specific processes of survival, dispersal and reproduction. Nevertheless, multiple equilibria emerge as a consequence of the interaction of these processes.

This is summarized in Figure 11.9, where the population growth rate (the ratio of budworm population in generation $t + 1$ to the population in generation t) is plotted against density of budworm in generation t. These growth-rate or recruitment curves condense all the reproduction and survival functions within the model. As examples, when curves cross the horizontal "replacement" line (representing zero net change in population), a stable or unstable equilibrium results.

The dip in the curve at low budworm densities is the effect of avian predators,

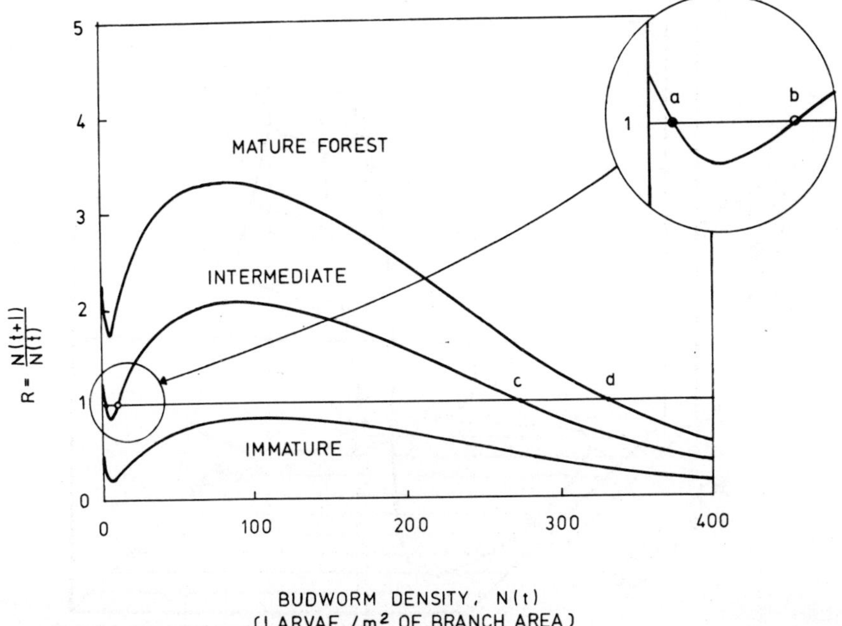

FIGURE 11.9 Growth-rate curves for budworm populations at various budworm densities and three forest conditions. Potential equilibria occur whenever the growth rate intersects the horizontal "replacement" line.

augmented to a degree by parasitism. When the forest is of an intermediate age, a lower stable equilibrium is introduced; this persists until forest conditions improve and the curve rises above the replacement line. An outbreak then inevitably occurs. But an outbreak can also occur by "swamping the predator pit" through an influx of budworm from other areas. The curves generated, for this example, also do not include the stochastic elements of weather, which affect both survival and dispersal. When these are included, we obtain a third trigger for outbreak in the occurrence of warm, dry summers, which can raise a growth rate above the replacement line.

The highest-density crossover point is introduced largely through competition by budworm for foliage. Although it is presented as a stable equilibrium in this figure it is, in fact, unstable because of the response of trees. At these high budworm densities, defoliation is so heavy that trees die and the forest collapses, taking the budworm with it.

A more complete and succinct summary of these multiple equilibria can be obtained by plotting all the equilibrium points in a three-dimensional space representing condensed forms of the three key variables – budworm, foliage condition and branch density (Figure 11.10). This represents an equilibrium manifold of the

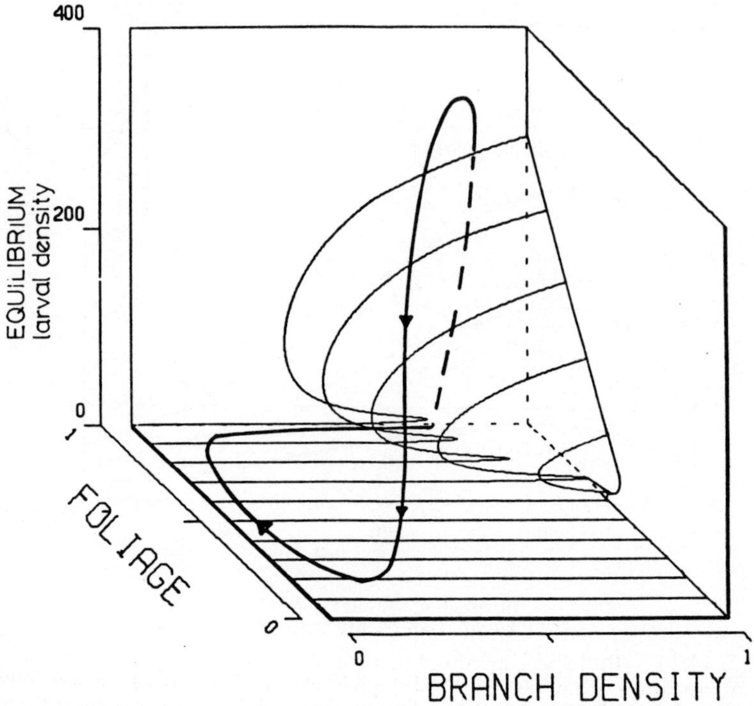

FIGURE 11.10 Budworm manifold (position of all equilibrium levels of budworm) for different amounts of living foliage per branch and different densities of branches per acre. The trajectory shows a typical path through this space, describing one outbreak cycle in an unmanaged world.

kind found in topology and catastrophe theory (Jones, 1975). The undercut portion of this fold is introduced by the effect of avian predators. Such representations provide a particularly revealing way of interpreting outbreak behavior. The temporal pattern of the unmanaged system such as that shown earlier in Figure 11.6 can be understood by following the trajectory over this manifold as shown.

These manifold representations prove to be very helpful in condensing the simulation model. They are also a powerful device for exploring the consequence of changes in key processes or management approaches. As one example, a manifold is shown in Figure 11.11 in which the foliage axis is replaced by a predation intensity axis. When predation is at the level occurring in nature (1 on the scale), the "pit" responsible for the lower equilibrium is pronounced. But as predation is relaxed, the pit gradually disappears along with the reflexively folded character of the manifold. Under such conditions the whole behavior of the system is different. A world is generated with a fairly immature forest and moderate budworm densities that oscillate on an 8–12-year cycle. Since insecticides can affect avian

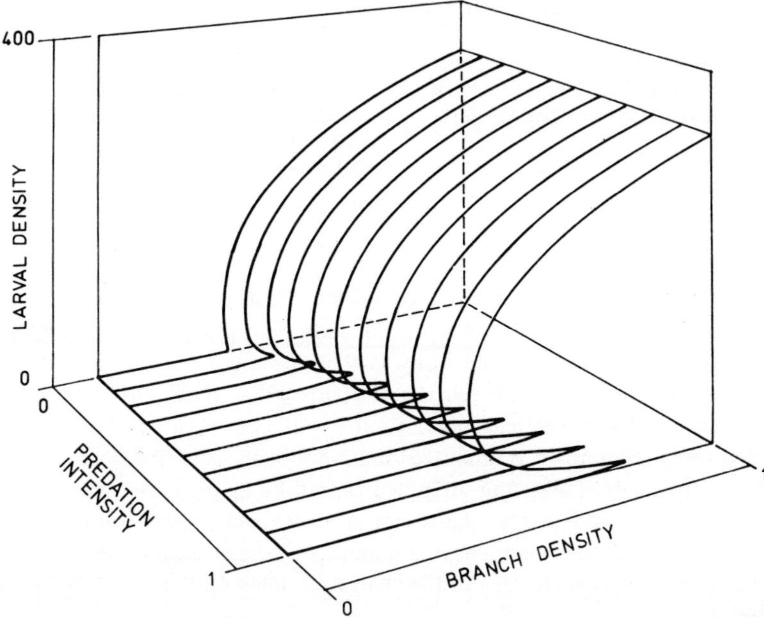

FIGURE 11.11 Budworm manifold at maximal foliage levels for different intensities of predation from 0 to the maximum occurring in nature (1) and different densities of branches per acre.

predators directly through mortality or indirectly by affecting food availability, the significance of this result for management is obvious.

These manifold representations are not only useful in condensing our understanding and providing a guide to key research and management questions, but they also provide a formal approach to defining a small number of distinct states of the system. The budworm–forest system has eight such states that formally define various endemic, threat, outbreak, and postoutbreak states. The movements within and between these states under various conditions can be represented as a matrix of transition frequencies, each of which has a particular benefit or cost attached to it. Moreover, as Fiering (1974) points out, such a representation also provides a succinct "back-of-the-envelope" technique for the initial development of policies.

Finally, it has been possible, by concentrating on equilibrium conditions, to capture the system characteristics in a small set of differential equations (Ludwig *et al.*, In press). Again the emphasis is on qualitative behavior and powerful analytic techniques that can more definitively explore methods of spatial management designed to achieve resilient systems.

Clearly, if the descriptive part of the analysis stops at the development of a simulation model, the clarity of understanding needed for transfer and policy design is seriously compromised.

ATTITUDES TOWARD THE UNKNOWN

Fable 6 Good policy design relies upon concepts and methodologies for the rigorous treatment of the known.

Counterfable 6 Good policy design relies upon concepts and methodologies for the organized treatment of the unknown, the missing, and the intentionally "left out."

Any useful analysis is based on an abstraction of reality. Such analyses therefore will always be incomplete. Attempts to "include everything" result in ambiguity, confusion, and intractability. The irony is that the more rigorous and organized the attempt to abstract a useful portion of reality for analysis, the more tempting it is to presume that those features left out of the analysis are unimportant. The more effectively the known is analyzed, the more likely it is that decisions will be based upon the analysis. But the unknown cannot be ignored, and any attempt to do so is bound to end in the unpleasant surprises and policy failures discussed earlier. For effective policy design, it is therefore critically important to emphasize that what is left out at each stage of the analysis is much more important than what is kept in.

As noted earlier, we must "look outward" from the known to the unknown. If the bounding process has been effectively accomplished, then it should be clear, at least, which known systems or known phenomena have been intentionally left out. It is necessary to look outward to regions connected through dispersal or transportation processes to the managed region. Even the best of management policies designed for one region can have unexpected and disastrous consequences remote from that region. It is necessary to look outward in time as well. The budworm analysis explicitly focuses on a time horizon determined by the slowest variable in the system, i.e., tree regeneration and growth. It does not consider long-term evolutionary changes that can trigger competitive shifts in tree species composition. Similarly, short-term benefits of a management policy might be followed later by unanticipated surprises that, being unanticipated, become crises.

It is also necessary to look "upward" to those "$N + 1$" level phenomena in which the detailed analysis is embedded. In the budworm study we explicitly and correctly left out an econometric model of the province and the logging industry. Yet, somehow, the policies designed must be evaluated within an economic context. Finally, it is necessary to look to the variety of known, uncertain, or even hidden objectives that might be affected by decisions of management.

The methodologies associated with the looking outward approach are mentioned later when we touch on evaluation issues. Now, it is the concept that is important: an organized treatment of what is left out is the minimum requirement for a strategy of creatively managing the unknown.

OBJECTIVES IN POLICY DESIGN

Fable 7 Prescriptive analysis should concentrate upon realistic objectives.

Counterfable 7 Prescriptive analysis should concentrate upon a strategic range of different objectives.

The uncertainties and unknowns encountered in describing an ecological system are almost trivial compared to the ambiguities encountered in defining societal objectives. The objectives that seem so clear at any moment can shift dramatically, as testified to by the recent concern for environmental issues. Moreover, as has been discovered by water resource planners in particular, even the best of policy analyses can founder on initially unrecognized or hidden public objectives. Since societal objectives are hidden, ambiguous, conflicting, and otherwise indefinite, the analyses rarely can accommodate them in a satisfactory manner. Hence the analyses themselves become uncomfortable, intrusive, and divisive sources of confrontation.

In response to this essential ambiguity of objectives, we felt it essential to identify a strategic range of alternative objectives containing a systematically defined spectrum of plausible and not-so-plausible management goals. Any specific example drawn from that spectrum is considered only a touchstone for the analysis and in no sense is a realistic or desired objective. The goal, therefore, is not so much to define objectives that are realistic as to define a strategic range which encompasses specific objectives which may be sought by particular individuals.

At one extreme, the strategic range specifies the classical sort of unconstrained, optimally "efficient" objectives – for instance, long-term maximization of expected profits in the face of known stochastic factors. At the other extreme, and equally unrealistic, are resilient and robust objectives such as those explicitly seeking the maintenance of dynamic variability.

Table 11.3 lists eight strategically defined "touchstone" objectives explored in

TABLE 11.3 Alternative Objectives Explored in the Budworm Policy Analysis

Retain existing management approaches ("historical management").
Maximize long-term profits to logging industry.
Maximize long-term profits to logging industry without exceeding present industrial capacity or operational constraints, and without violating environmental standards regarding insecticide application ("constrained profit maximization").
Maximize long-term profits to logging industry subject to above constraints, simultaneously maximizing recreational potential of forest.
Minimize budworm densities.
Minimize budworm densities while eliminating insecticide applications (e.g., replacing with methods of biological control and/or forest management).
Transform the system's existing temporal variability into spatial variability (i.e., develop a forest in which the budworm functions as a forest manager and the essential dynamic interplay of natural forces is retained).
Eliminate all human intervention, both harvest and budworm control.

the budworm analysis. A corresponding range of policies was designed to achieve each of these alternatives. In an iterative process involving evaluation and comparison, these policies are now being modified, combined, and refined in a realistic policy design dialogue with managers and specific interest groups.

MATHEMATICAL PROGRAMMING AND OPTIMIZATION

Fable 8 The purpose of mathematical programming techniques is to generate optimal policies for management.

Counterfable 8 The purpose of mathematical programming techniques is to suggest interesting starting points for further development in an iterative process of evaluation and design.

Objectives – strategic or specific – specify goals. A central issue of policy design is the identification of management rules or acts (broadly, policies) that will efficiently and effectively promote those goals. We could, of course, seek to identify appropriate policies by simple heuristic gaming with a dynamic descriptive model. This is often a useful approach and is almost always the best way to begin. But except in the most trivially simple cases it is a prohibitively slow, expensive, and inefficient way to develop interesting, much less optimal, policies. The number of possible policy formulations is so large that some formal guidance is necessary to define interesting regions in policy space. A variety of mathemetical programming and optimization techniques have been developed to provide such guidance.

As noted earlier, however, present mathematical programming techniques are just not up to the task at hand. The high dimensionality of ecological systems cripples dynamic programming, while the essential nonlinearities and stochasticities militate against such dimension-insensitive techniques as linear programming and its variants. Drastic simplification of the descriptive model is necessary to obtain any of the benefits of mathematical programming, yet with that simplification all guarantees of real-world optimality for the resulting policies are inevitably lost.

Our response to this dilemma has been to employ a variety of mathematical programming techniques, not to discover *the* optimal policy, but rather to generate interesting probes into policy space – probes that can then be employed in conjunction with the strategic range of alternative objectives as starting points in an iterative process of policy evaluation, modification, and design.

In the budworm study, Winkler and Dantzig (Winkler, 1975) used dynamic programming to calculate age, foliage, and budworm infestation conditions under which trees should be sprayed with insecticide or harvested. They resolved the dimensionality problem by viewing the forest as a collection of single trees, and they handled movement of budworm between trees by assuming that the number of budworm leaving a tree would be exactly balanced by the number arriving from other trees. The analysis resulted in a set of management rules "optimal" for the extreme objective of maximizing long-term logging profits. These rules take the form of policy "look-up" tables telling the manager what to do for any possible condition of his forest (Figure 11.12).

It was essential to test the policies of the Winkler–Dantzig optimization in the full descriptive model in order to determine whether, in spite of the simplifications, it still warranted further investigation. The results were dramatic, as can be seen in a comparison of Figures 11.13*A* and 11.13*B*. The historical budworm outbreak is rapidly smothered and thereafter prohibited by the Winkler–Dantzig policy, and very little budworm-induced tree mortality occurs. But again, we emphasize that this policy must be viewed as an unrealistic but interesting starting point for further modifications, and *not* as a "solution," optimal or otherwise, to the problem. The potential of the modified Winkler–Dantzig policy is still being explored (Holling and Dantzig, 1976; Clark *et al.*, 1977).

As one encouraging example of this potential, the system behavior shown in Figure 11.13*C* was obtained from the policy rules, even after realistic constraints were applied to limit annual tree harvest to existing industrial capacity, to force spraying in large economical blocks rather than on a tree-by-tree basis, and to limit insecticide dosages to those permitted by legislation.

Because each formal technique of optimization forces different compromises, we are also developing and applying other methodologies. One of the more promising has been termed fixed-form control law optimization. In this approach, the functional form of the control law is guessed, utilizing available understanding of the causal mechanisms determining system behavior. Gradient search techniques are then employed to optimize the parameters of the function for a given objective function. Another guess is then taken, and the process continues until sufficiently interesting policies are generated. The great advantage of this approach is that it can cope with a much higher dimensionality than can dynamic programming. In addition, Fiering and his colleagues at Harvard University are exploring optimization techniques that deal explicitly with spatial pattern by applying quadratic programming approaches to a simplified Markov compression of the dynamic descriptive model.

By insisting on a strategic range of alternative objectives and using a variety of optimization techniques to identify interesting policies, a rich menu of possibilities can be defined, each of which then requires systematic evaluation.

THE EVALUATION PROCESS

Fable 9 The goal of evaluation is to rank alternative policies, usually by means of an objective or utility function.

Counterfable 9 The goal of evaluation is to compare and contrast alternative policies in terms meaningful to the policy designer.

Ranking implies a given set of policies, one of which must be chosen as "best" with respect to a given objective. The evaluation process properly includes such questions

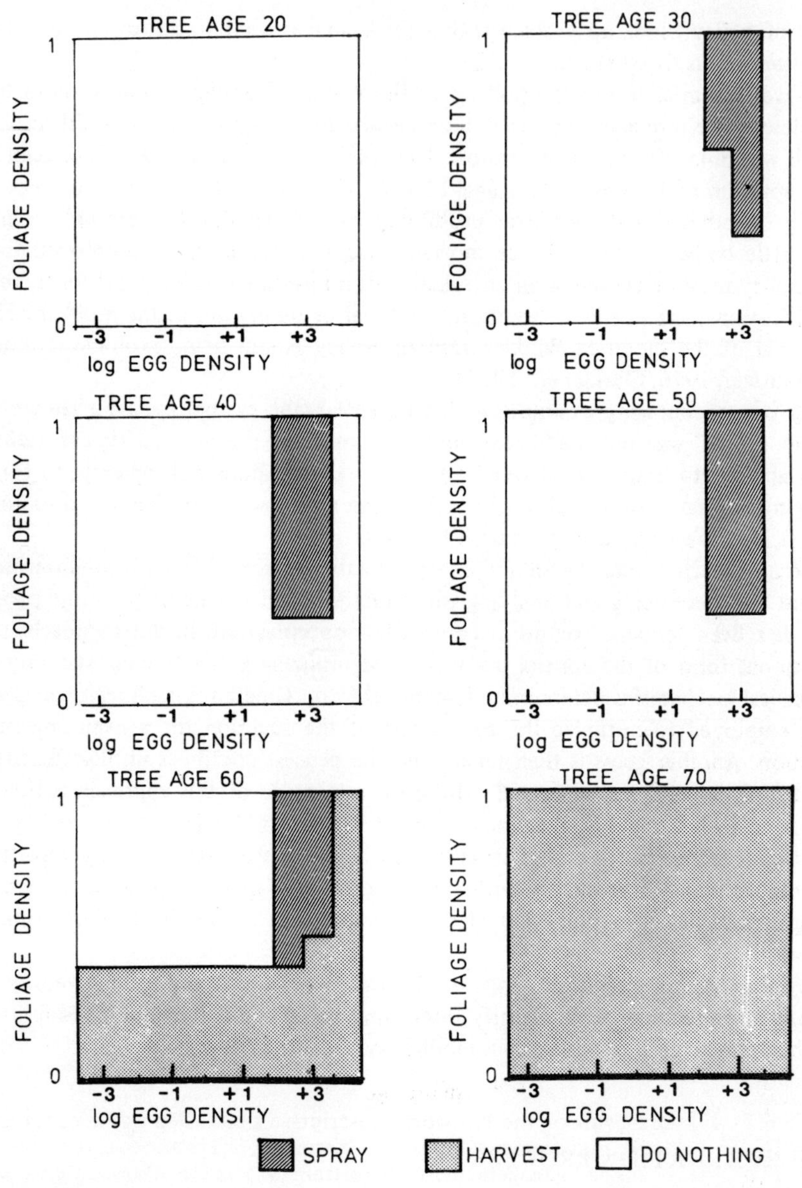

FIGURE 11.12 Representative policy tables generated by the Winkler–Dantzig optimization. A separate table is provided for each age of tree (or, in practice, age of stand). The table tells what management act should optimally be applied to the tree as a function of the tree's present complement of foliage (foliage density) and its resident budworm egg density (here plotted as the logarithm of egg density). Available management options are to do nothing, to spray, and to harvest or log the tree.

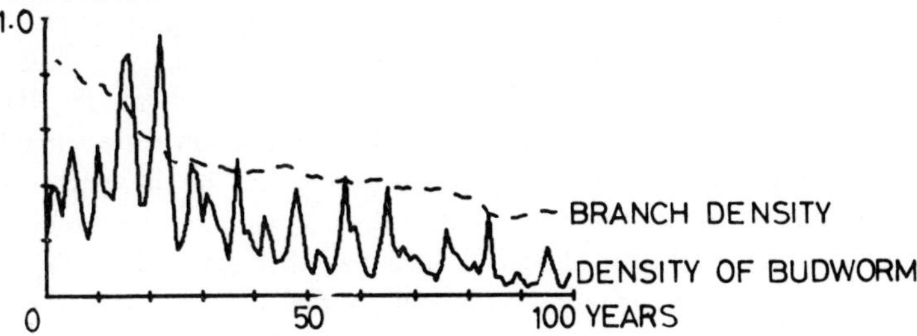

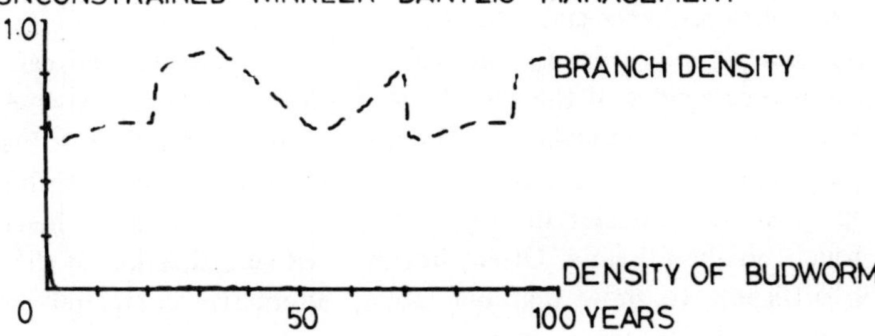

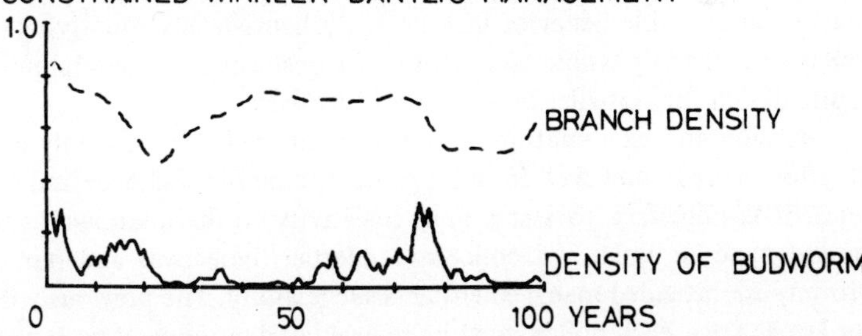

FIGURE 11.13 Behavior of the budworm descriptive simulation under historical and Winkler–Dantzig management rules. *A*, historical management. *B*, unconstrained Winkler–Dantzig management. *C*, constrained Winkler–Dantzig management. Labeling conventions are the same as for Figure 11.6. "Historical" management rules are approximately those in use in 1970; "Unconstrained Winkler–Dantzig" management rules are those developed by a dynamic programming version of the model with no constraints on harvesting or insecticide dosages; "Constrained Winkler–Dantzig" are the same rules with the added constraint that no harvesting was allowed to exceed mill capacity (2,000,000 units) and insecticide dosage was limited to achieve no more than 80% mortality.

of choice but has a substantially broader scope. Our ultimate goal is creative policy design, and for this we require a rich and meaningful language to describe observed and desired policy performance. The "language" employed up to this point has been simply the state variables of the dynamic descriptive model. But socially relevant and responsible evaluations cannot be based upon state variables alone. Rather, we require a broader set of indicators relevant to those who make, and those who endure, the ultimate policy decisions. Further, it is necessary to transform the state variables into indicators in a way that explicitly reflects what has been left out and what remains unknown in the analysis, so that meaningful "handles" can be provided for the integration of other intuition, experience, and expertise available to the user.

The initial step is to develop two comprehensive classes of indicators, one focusing upon the immediate concerns of policy designers, the other on broader questions of policy resilience and robustness.

The first set of indicators is reasonably easy to generate, and can often be partitioned into categories of the sort shown earlier in Table 8.1. At an early stage in the evaluation, a decision maker can choose the particular indicators that interest him and examine the time behavior of each. There are rigorous techniques for comparing alternative policies through their patterns of indicator behavior, and we will touch on these below. Often, however, visual inspection of the indicator graphs is sufficient to show that one policy alternative completely dominates another. This is clearly the case, for instance, when the constrained Winkler–Dantzig forest management policy (Figure 8.2) is compared to historical budworm management (Figure 8.1). Even more important, some of the original policy "touchstones" are likely to exhibit obviously desirable behavior in a few indicators and indifferent or undesirable behavior in others. By heuristically modifying the initial policy rules, it is often possible to combine the best aspects of several policies into a composite design that satisfies most of our objectives.

The generation and examination of indicators of the known are only one part of the evaluation process, however. In order to determine the resilience and robustness of policies, it is necessary to assess their sensitivity to the unknown as well. One predominant type of unknown concerns uncertain objectives and our uncertain ability to impose intended management acts successfully. The previously developed indicator streams for each policy must be re-evaluated in terms of such questions as "What will happen if policies fall short or fail completely?" and "How hard will it be to change objectives or return to a pre-policy situation after the policy is initiated?" The exact form of the "policy failure" questions will change from case to case, but the issue itself is increasingly important.

In the budworm problem, for instance, a policy of insecticide application was adopted in the 1950s to protect foliage and has tended to accomplish that goal. But 25 years of such "success" has left the province in a position where any cessation of spraying would lead to catastrophic outbreak affecting much larger areas than those historically devastated by the unmanaged budworm. With insecticide costs spiraling upward and concern increasing over health and environmental impacts of spraying, the decision makers are stranded in an impossible position with no easy options left. This sort of "option foreclosure" (Walters, 1975a) surprise can and should be avoided by policy evaluation procedures.

Another important class of resilience–robustness problems concerns unknowns and uncertainties in system structure. Many of these issues can be dealt with if system description has focused on developing a topological view of system behavior and, particularly, of equilibrium properties (compare the earlier discussion under "Simplification and Compression," p. 166). It is the number, kind, and size of stability regions that determine qualitative behavior. Shifts in qualitative behavior have similar impact on social, economic, and environmental benefits. Hence, by systematically testing the sensitivity of each policy to shifts in number and position of stability regions, measures of systems resilience emerge. And the point is not of merely theoretical interest. For example, in the Province of Quebec it has recently been observed that budworm parasite densities have increased to unexpectedly high levels. Such acute parasitism would shift the upper equilibrium of the budworm recruitment function. As a test, such a qualitative shift was introduced into the model, and it led to sustained semioutbreak behavior over a wide range of conditions. The parasitism issue was thereby identified as qualitatively important, and steps are now being taken to introduce a parasite component explicitly into the model. But the main point is that new and unexpected processes can appear, perhaps because of management. Tests of topological sensitivity provide a way to evaluate the relative resilience of alternative policies with reference to this class of unknowns.

A comprehensive array of indicators is essential for good policy evaluation. But the more extensive the array and the greater the number of policy alternatives to be compared, the greater the danger of losing meaning in the wealth of numerical detail. For complex evaluation problems some systematic approach to indicator compression is equally essential. A number of concepts and techniques for compression in multiple-attribute problems are available from the field of decision analysis, and Bell (1975b) has brought the more useful of these to bear on the budworm policy design problem.

By far the greatest conceptual and methodological difficulties are encountered in attempts to compress indicators over time. The first inclination is to employ variously weighted time averages of the indicators: means, discounted sums, and so forth. But any such time-averaging scheme implies a particular attitude toward intertemporal trade-offs through which we are willing to relate the future to the present, and the ranking of policy alternatives is exceedingly sensitive to the precise nature of the attitude adopted. Clark and Bell (1976) have argued that standard market-based discounting rates are completely inapplicable to cases of ecological policy design; they recommend instead an explicit evaluation of decision makers' (and, again, decision endurers') intertemporal trade-off functions. The issue is critical and in urgent need of further study.

Even when the problem of absolute temporal compression can be resolved, however, there remains the important but generally ignored issue of local time patterns. Patterns of temporal variability are at least as significant as those of spatial variability and diversity in ecological and social systems, yet such patterns are inevitably lost in temporal indicator compressions. Bell (1977a) has developed new techniques for addressing this problem and has applied them to the budworm policy design problem.

Finally, regardless of what techniques are adopted, compression is a means and not an end. Each step of compression is justified only to the extent that it truly clarifies the problems of design and choice, rather than merely simplifying them. Most compressions will properly end with the indicator array still somewhat disaggregate. The single-valued utility or objective function is rarely a useful goal for the evaluation process.

COMMUNICATION, TRANSFER, AND IMPLEMENTATION

Fable 10 A focus on generality and transferability lays sufficient groundwork for policy implementation.

Counterfable 10 A focus on generality and transferability is necessary for implementation, but it must be complemented by a vigorous involvement of users in the design process.

We have emphasized throughout this volume the necessity of policy design transferable to a wide variety of situations. This has been our prime motivation and justification for focusing on generality at all stages of the analysis. There are numerous advantages to this approach, but it has serious shortcomings with respect to implementation.

Implementation decisions are made in specific circumstances, not general ones. Decisions are shaped by regional constraints, by particular institutional structures, and by unique personalities. A focus on generality sets the stage for implementation, but unless it is followed by effective application to specific situations, the analysis can become simply an academic curiosity.

Hence, close working ties have been maintained with potential policy makers throughout the design process. Three levels of transfer and implementation were explored – one involving federal and provincial agencies in New Brunswick, one involving key institutions within the larger group of provinces and states affected (particularly Ontario, Quebec, New Brunswick, Newfoundland, and Maine), and one involving Japan and several countries in Europe faced with similar problems. In each case, the goal is not to recommend a unique policy, but rather to transfer the concepts, modeling and evaluation techniques, and a list of alternative policy touchstones into the hands of those responsible for and affected by decisions.

The emphasis throughout has been on information packages, communication techniques, and transfer workshops that can be understood, controlled, and modified by the decision maker. For example, a series of integrated audiovisual packages has been prepared (Bunnell and Tait, 1974; Bunnell, 1976) to communicate as succinctly

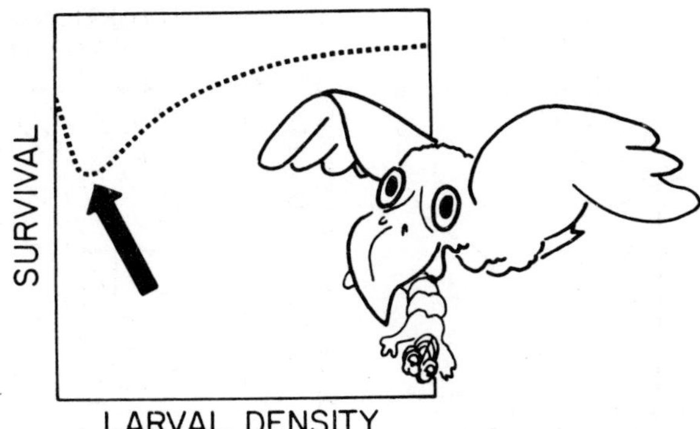

FIGURE 11.14 Communication and policy design. A series of integrated audio-visual packages, employing projection slides of the sort shown above, has been developed to facilitate communication and implementation of the policy analysis.

and meaningfully as possible the features of the problem, the form and philosophy of the models, and the consequences of different policies (Figure 11.14). These are not a public relations exercise, but rather reflect our conviction that the creative communication of inherently complex ideas, stripped of their protective jargon, is as essential and challenging a part of policy design as the analysis itself. Responsible judgment by the decision maker requires understanding of, not necessarily "belief in," the analysis. If this understanding cannot be conveyed, the analyst subverts the decision maker's role with no accountability for the results.

In a similar but more technical vein, graphical techniques (nomograms) have been developed that allow visual evaluation of alternative policies via a kind of management slide rule (Peterman, 1975). Each nomogram is constructed from a large number of model simulations of different policies. The resulting display shows the effect of various intensities of cutting or spraying on a set of policy indicators selected by the user. These are presented as contour surfaces on which the manager can explore the consequences of different acts, add political and other constraints, identify trade-offs, and begin to evolve realistic compromise policies (Figure 11.15). Done jointly with a number of interest groups, this becomes a powerful instrument for constructive dialogue and even conflict resolution (Peterman, 1977a). (See Chapter 9, p. 125, for a discussion of nomograms.)

THE PRESENT STAGE OF IMPLEMENTATION

We followed a sequence of steps very much like those described in Chapter 3. In this example, the core group comprised three of the authors of this book, together with a forest systems ecologist from the federal research laboratory situated in New Brunswick, one of the institutions with formal authority to undertake forest research in that province. Beyond his central contribution to the conceptualization and

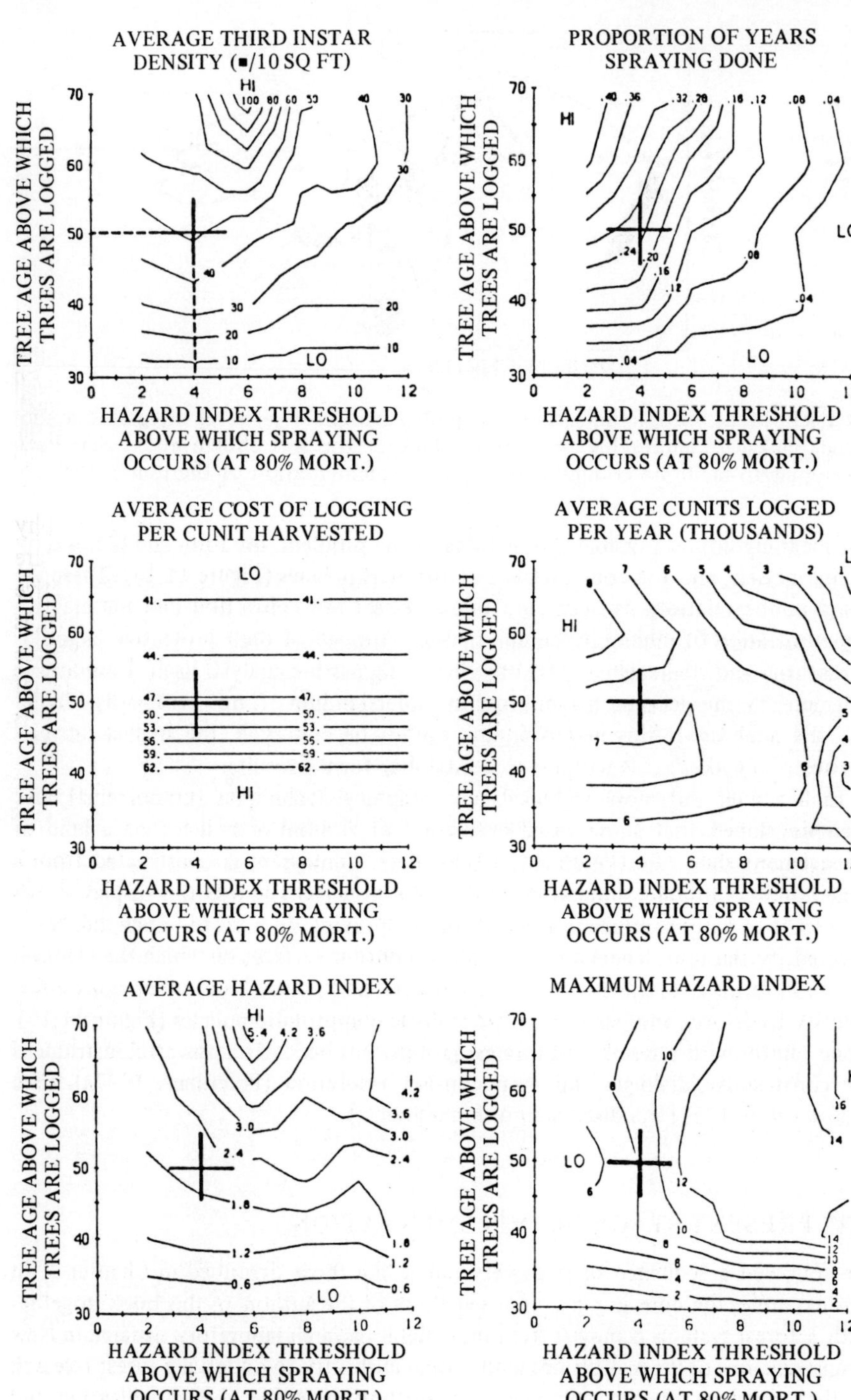
AVERAGE THIRD INSTAR DENSITY (■/10 SQ FT)
TREE AGE ABOVE WHICH TREES ARE LOGGED
HAZARD INDEX THRESHOLD ABOVE WHICH SPRAYING OCCURS (AT 80% MORT.)
HI
LO
PROPORTION OF YEARS SPRAYING DONE
TREE AGE ABOVE WHICH TREES ARE LOGGED
HAZARD INDEX THRESHOLD ABOVE WHICH SPRAYING OCCURS (AT 80% MORT.)
HI
LO
AVERAGE COST OF LOGGING PER CUNIT HARVESTED
TREE AGE ABOVE WHICH TREES ARE LOGGED
HAZARD INDEX THRESHOLD ABOVE WHICH SPRAYING OCCURS (AT 80% MORT.)
LO
41.
44.
47.
50.
53.
56.
59.
62.
HI
AVERAGE CUNITS LOGGED PER YEAR (THOUSANDS)
TREE AGE ABOVE WHICH TREES ARE LOGGED
HAZARD INDEX THRESHOLD ABOVE WHICH SPRAYING OCCURS (AT 80% MORT.)
HI
LO
AVERAGE HAZARD INDEX
TREE AGE ABOVE WHICH TREES ARE LOGGED
HAZARD INDEX THRESHOLD ABOVE WHICH SPRAYING OCCURS (AT 80% MORT.)
HI
LO
MAXIMUM HAZARD INDEX
TREE AGE ABOVE WHICH TREES ARE LOGGED
HAZARD INDEX THRESHOLD ABOVE WHICH SPRAYING OCCURS (AT 80% MORT.)
HI
LO

integration of the work, he performed the essential interfacing role with local scientists, managers, and decision makers. Such a person is essential – but not as a "front-man," but as an integral part of the core group.

The status of the project as of spring 1977 was as follows:

1. Through a series of seven workshops, the models and techniques were subjected to detailed scrutiny by a large community of scientists who have been involved in budworm and forest research. These workshops were held in New Brunswick, Quebec, Ontario, and Maine at major centers of research. The purpose was twofold: to make the effort as transparent as possible and to benefit from the breadth of knowledge that has accumulated, only some of which has been reported. Since these scientists have historically had a major advisory role, their support was essential. The consequence has been the establishment of an interregional research planning function within Canada's Department of the Environment aimed at identifying priorities for research directly relevant to short- and long-term management questions. The research projects emerging will then be implemented in that region that can most quickly and easily respond. The models and policies play a central role in defining this program, and they provide an example of the use of this approach in the research planning process.

2. The models, techniques, and alternative starting policies have been transferred to New Brunswick under the sponsorship of the federal agency and in cooperation with the management agencies of the provincial government. A small staff, including a programmer, were fully trained in the use and modification of this material, and this in itself took several meetings and intense training sessions.

3. A working group of scientists and policy analysts from the federal and provincial agencies was established to tune the model to the very specific needs and constraints of New Brunswick. At the same time, this opened an essential and more formal avenue of communication between the project and federal agency on the one hand and the management agency on the other.

4. The provincial cabinet established and funded a task force, chaired by one of the members of our core group, to evaluate past policies and designs and to explore alternatives. The central core of that analysis was based on the study described here

FIGURE 11.15 A typical nomogram of the sort used in policy design dialogues with managers. (From Peterman 1977a.) All axes are the same, representing two management acts which can be implemented at different levels. "Harvest Age" is the age at which a tree (or stand) will be cut; and "Hazard Index" is an aggregate measure of insect density and defoliation stress above which insecticide spraying is initiated. Each graph represents a single evaluation indicator. Each point in the "policy space" of a given graph is the average value taken by that indicator when the system is run under the corresponding management rules. Any proposed combination of acts can be graphically evaluated by placing the cross hairs at the appropriate level and examining the contour value where they intersect in policy space. By sliding the crosshairs about, aggregate maxima and minima of the contour surfaces can be discovered.

and was recently published (Baskerville, 1976) after submission to cabinet. Significant changes have already occurred in the way the management agency collects and analyzes basic information, and the process we describe is becoming an integral part of their effort to develop different policies.

5. The same process described for New Brunswick is under way in the Province of Quebec, organized by a team consisting of federal, provincial, and university staff.

6. The government of Nova Scotia has placed a ban on spraying budworm, in part because of a newly suspected health hazard and in part on the basis of their interpretation of our analysis.

If our purpose had been to develop an analysis destined for academic journals, we could have completed the exercise within months. But because we have continually emphasized the need to test and transfer these new techniques of ecological policy design, the problem has demanded a much more extensive effort to communicate, modify, and adapt to users in a variety of situations. Only by doing that has it become possible to turn what might have been a mildly interesting scholarly activity into something that has become part of actual policy design and implementation.

SUMMARY AND CONCLUSIONS

Ultrafable We now have all the answers.

ACKNOWLEDGMENTS

In one sense it is presumptuous to thank those directly involved in this study since they were all equal partners in a strange interinstitutional and interdisciplinary experiment. Nevertheless, they deserve the recognition of being as much part of this creation as the authors of this work. The policy people and scientists of Canada's Department of the Environment gave remarkable and consistent support throughout. In particular Gordon Baskerville, Charles Miller, and their colleagues of the Maritimes Forest Research Centre were committed partners in the team, with their flanks admirably protected by Evan Armstrong, Dick Belyea, Murray Nielson, Dick Prentice, and John Tener.

At IIASA, in its pioneering first year, an astonishing group of outstanding people gave their all to something as silly as a budworm – David Bell, George Dantzig, Myron B Fiering, Carlos Winkler, and Howard Raiffa.

The third institution in this effort was the Institute of Animal Resource Ecology, University of British Columbia. Our friends and colleagues Nick Sonntag, Warren Klein, and Zafar Rashid carved off pieces and solved them at times when they saw we were faltering.

12 Pacific Salmon Management

There are six important species of Pacific salmonid in North America: sockeye, pink, chinook, coho, chum, and steelhead. While the age at maturation and the length of time in fresh water differs among the species, they all follow the same basic life cycle: eggs are spawned in streams, young fish spend from a few days to several years in freshwater rearing areas, and juveniles migrate to the ocean and return to their home spawning areas as adults 1 to 3 years later. Most harvesting of salmon occurs as returning adults approach the river mouths. There is a large body of literature on the population dynamics of salmon (reviewed by Foerster, 1968; Northcote, 1969; Wilimovsky, 1962; and Ricker, 1954, 1975). This literature documents the strong dependence of population changes on both within- and between-species interactions such as competitive effects and predation. The data also clearly indicate that salmon population changes are subject to a great deal of influence by such physical environmental factors as stream flows, water temperatures, and silt loads. The strength of these physical environmental influences is reflected by the highly variable data in Figure 12.1, which show population sizes for two species in one river system over a 60-year period.

Because physical factors that may be inherently unpredictable appear to have such an enormous influence on salmon abundance, the management of salmon through the regulation of harvests or salmon production is not a trivial task. Yet there is a very real need for good management in the face of this uncertainty. The salmon-fishing industry on the Pacific coast of North America directly employs over 45,000 people and generates a yearly landed value of almost $200 million to the fishermen (Crutchfield, 1977). Inputs to regional economies are even larger because of multiplier effects. Management of salmon largely consists of (a) changing harvests through gear restrictions or control of lengths of time open to fishing and (b) increasing salmon production and survival through establishment of hatcheries, fertilization of lakes, regulation of stream flows, and so on.

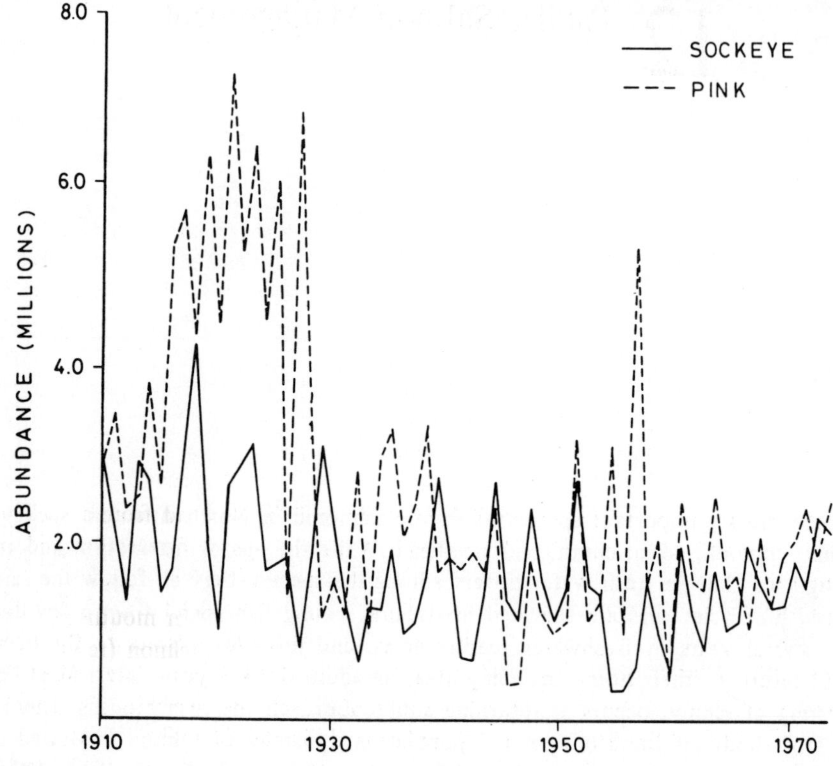

FIGURE 12.1 Historical changes in Skeena River (British Columbia) salmon abundance.

Over the last hundred years there has been considerable accumulation of both theory and practice in salmon management. Nevertheless, major mistakes in management are still being made (such as overharvesting of stocks). There are four main issues that prompted our in-depth examination of salmon management alternatives. First, there has been a drop of approximately 50 percent in catches and populations in British Columbia since the turn of the century (MacLeod, 1977). Second, enhancement of salmon production through establishment of spawning channels, hatcheries, and other facilities is being planned on an unprecedented scale in both the U.S. and Canada. Large-scale construction of facilities began in 1977 in British Columbia with the ultimate aim of doubling the abundance of salmon (MacLeod, 1977), and there is therefore a complex problem of phasing and siting of facilities as well as of managing the resultant stocks. Third, the increase in production that is anticipated after enhancement will exacerbate the already serious problem of overharvesting less productive stocks in a fishery that simultaneously harvests several stocks. Finally, human developments are continually encroaching on salmon spawning or rearing habitats, thereby increasing the importance of proper management of surviving stocks.

HIERARCHICAL NATURE OF THE DECISION SYSTEM

The system in which decisions are made in Pacific salmon management in British Columbia is at least an order of magnitude more complex than in the budworm case described in Chapter 11. In salmon management, many types of decisions are made, ranging from decisions on a very short time scale (day-to-day opening and closing of fishing areas) to those on a long time scale (20-year plan to increase salmon production through enhancement). Decisions are also made over a wide range of spatial scales, from a fisheries officer's decisions about controlling the number of adults reaching specific spawning areas (termed the "escapement") to decisions about integrating the enhancement of different species and different stocks along the whole British Columbia coast. These different kinds of decisions can be viewed as part of a hierarchical decision structure, where information in the form of decisions flows both upward and downward through the levels (Figure 12.2).

Because of this hierarchical characteristic, we attempted to address decision problems at one or at most two levels at a time, while assuming that certain decisions would be made at the other levels. Furthermore, the particular piece of the decision hierarchy we addressed depended on our clients and their needs. In all cases, however, our major clients were members of the Fisheries and Marine Service in the Canadian Department of Fisheries and Environment, and the British Columbia Fish and Wildlife Branch. Both have responsibilities for management, the federal service for marine commercial and sport fisheries and the provincial service for freshwater recreational fisheries.

WHAT WE ANTICIPATED

We felt initially that much of the data necessary to do a thorough exploration of management options already existed and that the application of good systems analysis techniques was all that was needed. We intended to examine existing management alternatives and to create and explore new policies. In so doing, we hoped to promote interdisciplinary communication and to identify critical information gaps as well as directions for future research. The interdisciplinary communication issue was important because many salmon managers now recognize the inadequacies of narrow objectives, such as maximizing economic yield; other biological and sociological considerations are also important (Hilborn and Peterman, 1977; Roedel, 1975).

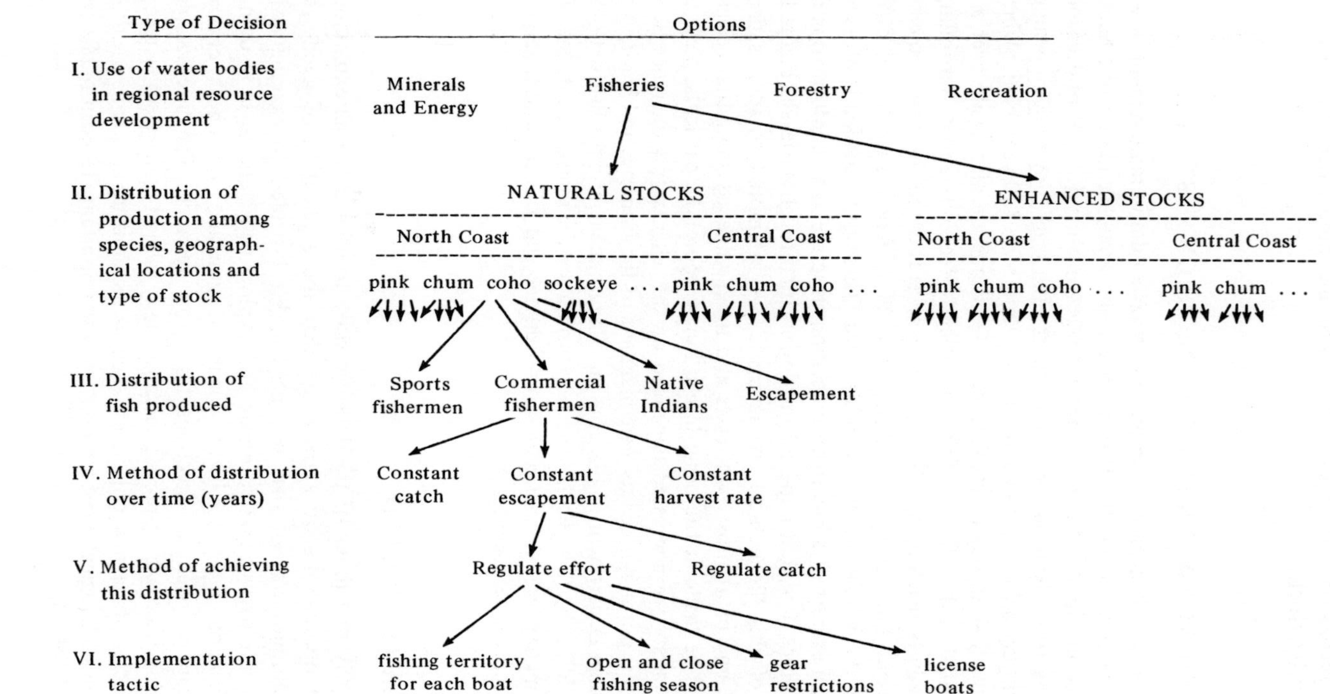

FIGURE 12.2 The decision structure of salmon management in British Columbia. Only parts of this structure are illustrated in detail.

WHAT WE DID

Rather than attempting to describe in detail all the work we have done on salmon, we will present general discussions of management problems we addressed, methods we used, and results we obtained. Fuller descriptions of much of the work can be found in the references given here to our published material. The topics we present illustrate particular issues that are brought up in the main text of this book, or are topics that have had significant impact on our clients. We should note that this work on salmon problems is still in progress.

Our activities can be divided into three general classes: (a) analysis and sythesis of data to provide inputs to the models; (b) development and application of systems methodologies, such as systems simulation models, utility analysis, optimization through dynamic programming, heuristic optimization devices, and catastrophe theory; (c) exploration of new conceptual issues, such as those dealing with uncertainty, multiple equilibria, adaptive management, option foreclosure, and value of information. We will discuss the last two classes of activities in the following pages.

DYNAMIC MODELS

In conjunction with the fisheries management agencies that were our clients, we decided that our systems studies should begin with small, relatively modest problems, and that we should address larger issues only as the usefulness and credibility of the approaches were established. As a result of this decision, our first effort was a short workshop designed to address within-season management questions on one river system, the Skeena River in northern British Columbia. A single fisheries officer is responsible for opening or closing the commercial fishery on a day-to-day basis during the summer. His stated management goal is to obtain a given escapement – that is, to let a predetermined number of fish (determined by data analysis farther up the decision hierarchy) escape the fishery. Therefore, the decision to open or close on a given day is based on several factors: the desired escapement level, the escapement to date, the predicted total run size, the historical average of cumulative run to date, the standard deviation in that figure, to name a few.

We attempted to quantify the conceptual model that the decision maker used to relate all the above factors. The resulting simulation model (Walters and Buckingham, 1975) did not significantly improve on historical achievement of escapements. In part, this was so because the manager used subjectively several factors not included in the model, such as tide levels and river flow rates. In addition, discussions pointed out that the management objective was more complex than achieving a desired escapement. Even when predicted runs were below the desired escapement, some commercial harvesting was permitted, because seasons of no catch were quite undesirable for the fishermen. The decision maker clearly was trading off the short-term value of keeping the fishermen happy against the risk that in the long-term stocks would be severely depleted.

As part of the same initial exercise, several salmon species of the Skeena River basin were included in the model, and the longer term effects of different management actions were simulated (Peterman, 1975). At that time we were exploring management alternatives through gaming alone; no formal optimization methods were applied initially. The broader scope of this exercise, which included calculation of native Indian harvests as well as commercial and sport catches, showed all participants that a clearer articulation of management goals was needed. This need became clear when, for example, two ways of regulating commercial effort were tested; one way resulted in a commercial harvest of 2 million fish and an Indian catch of 50,000, while the other way gave 1.5 million commercial catch and 120,000 Indian harvest. We had no objective method for ranking the two management options because decision makers were using important but unquantified social and economic criteria.

During subsequent modeling workshops, several other salmon models of different geographical scales were built, ranging from simulations of single watersheds (including effects of forestry practices on salmon) to simulations of seaward migration of salmon along the whole coast of British Columbia. In both the early exercises and the later ones, the piecing together of the components of the decision problem made it clear that there were major holes in existing data. Data on many functional relationships had never been measured, and many that had were measured over the wrong temporal or spatial scale for the management questions being asked.

As a result of the relatively poor data, our models were generally not able to capture more than the qualitative characteristics of the natural systems. Therefore, we have viewed our salmon modeling exercises as a means of *guiding* the exploration of management alternatives, of establishing research priorities for the client management agencies, and of deepening our own as well as our clients' understanding of conceptual issues, such as adaptive management, that are on the frontiers of present management practice. In the following sections we will describe selected examples of these topics, and we will end with a discussion of how the results of this work have affected salmon management in British Columbia.

MANAGEMENT OBJECTIVES

As touched on above, our examination of management alternatives was hindered by the lack of precisely stated management objectives. This was true for virtually all of our salmon modeling exercises. This reflects not a lack of judgment on the part of the management agencies but rather a historical lack of stimulus to provide quantified statements of objectives. The decision-making methods practiced by these agencies did not require any more than a verbal statement of objectives. But, as we found in our workshops, these vague goals made it almost impossible for decision makers to make rational, consistent decisions when there was a difficult trade-off to be made.

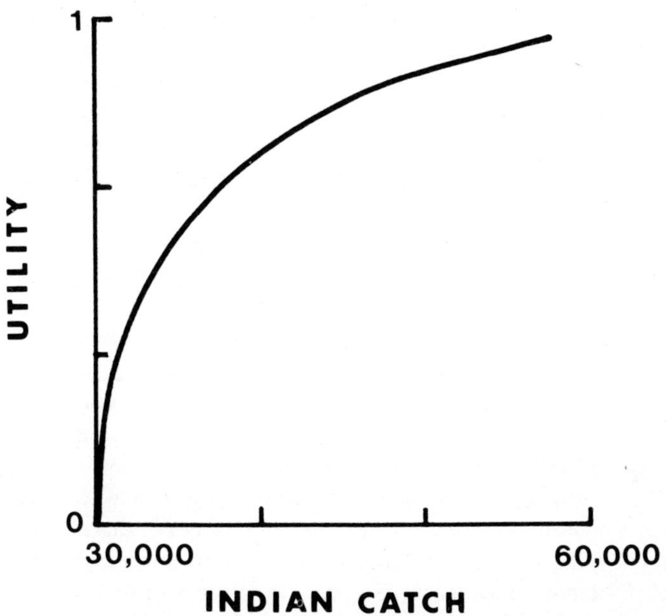

FIGURE 12.3 A sample utility function for an Indian catch indicator.

We began to explore how some decision theory methods could be applied to these problems. In particular, multiattribute utility analysis proved useful. The concept of utility, as discussed by Keeney and Raiffa (1976), recognizes that when 1,000 fish are added to a sport catch of 50,000, there may be a greater increase in "utility," or "satisfaction" than when that same 1,000 fish are added to a sport catch of 1 million. The utility concept thus permits a manager's utility to be nonlinearly related to the value of a particular indicator (Figure 12.3). Questioning procedures have been developed that result in a description of an individual's or an interest group's utility functions. Several studies have confirmed the observation of other workers that measured utility functions are, in fact, nonlinear (Hilborn and Walters, 1977; Keeney, 1977; Keeney and Raiffa, 1976) and therefore that objectives cannot simply be stated in the form "maximize this indicator," or "minimize the weighted sum of these indicators."

Multiattribute utility analysis also allows one to combine the utility functions for two or more indicators, such as sport catch and commercial catch. The particular way in which they are combined is determined again through a set of questions asked of the decision maker or interest group. As a result of the questioning process, the decision maker has an objective means of making trade-offs, or choosing between policies with different outcomes as in the examples described earlier.

As intended, the derivation of utility functions of individuals representing different interest groups did permit a ranking of alternative management schemes from the viewpoint of each group. In one case, we compared several different types of enhancement policies from the viewpoint of three interest groups: sport fishermen, commercial fishermen, and the federal fisheries managers. There was a considerable agreement across interest groups about which single policy was best, but great disagreement about the ranking of the remaining options (Hilborn and Walters, 1977). This study also showed that the rankings made intuitively were different from those made by using utility functions.

But comparison of policies based on utility functions does not provide a definitive ranking of policies. We know that goals or objectives change with time, even for individuals (Hilborn and Peterman, 1977; Holling and Clark, 1975). In fact, it is dangerous to use any quantitative statement of goals as if they were fixed. Therefore, the major benefits of application of utility analysis arose from two other sources. First, the process of questioning forced individuals to clarify and quantify their goals, where they had never been asked to do so before. This somewhat intangible benefit has, according to our clients, led to a better understanding of decision problems by those salmon managers who make decisions, even though few ever use sophisticated methods. Second, there was considerable value in quantifying the utility functions of different interest groups such as the commercial fishermen and sport fishermen in order to provide a focus for discussion and conflict resolution (Hilborn and Peterman, 1977; Hilborn and Walters, 1977). When the utility functions of the two interest groups result in different rankings of alternative management policies, it is relatively easy to answer questions such as, "How much different would the sport fisherman's utility function for sport catch of chinook salmon have to be before he would rank as the best policy the same policy as the commercial fisherman?" In some cases only a slight modification is needed to resolve the conflict.

In conclusion, utility analysis seems to have had as much value during the process of its application as when its product was used.

OPTIMIZATION

In most of our modeling situations, well-defined objectives were not available because they had never been specified. Therefore, "optimal" management policies were determined for a variety of different possible objectives. In this way it could be ascertained over what range of objectives a given policy would be desirable. We used two quite different methods to find such policies: a formal optimization procedure known as dynamic programming and a more heuristic graphical method.

Dynamic Programming

A common question in salmon management is how to achieve a simple objective, such as maximum sustainable yield, for one salmon population. The formal optimization technique of dynamic programming (Bellman, 1961) can be used

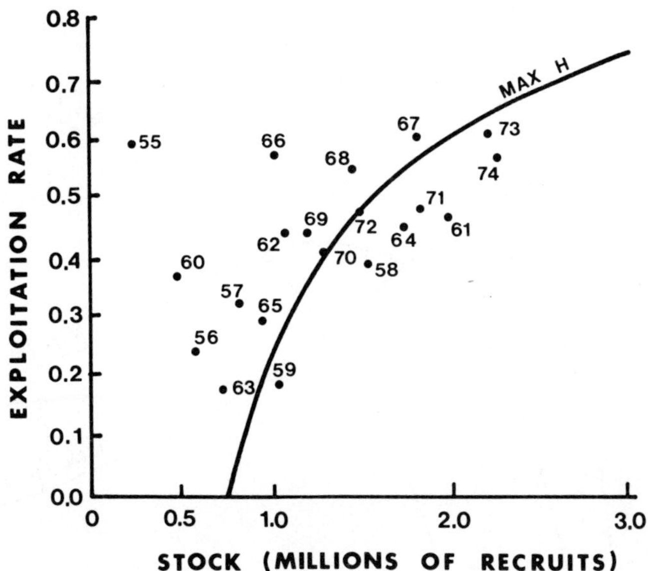

FIGURE 12.4 Harvest rate plotted against stock size. The curve is the relation that would achieve an objective of maximum sustainable yield (Max H). Historical data for Skeena River sockeye salmon are shown for the years indicated. Redrawn from Walters (1975b).

to answer such questions, since the method's requirements can easily be met. A quantitative objective function can be stated along with a dynamic model that describes stock production (Ricker, 1954).

When this optimization method was applied to management of Skeena River sockeye salmon, several significant results were obtained (Walters, 1975b). First, while the stated management objective for this stock was maximizing catch, the management policy that would achieve that goal was quite different from the one applied historically, as reflected by the data (Figure 12.4). When low returning stock sizes occurred in the past, significant harvest rates were allowed even though no catch should have been permitted.

Second, when the management strategies or policies are described in terms of this relation between exploitation rate and stock-size, there are major differences in the shape of the optimal policies for different objectives. If the goal is to minimize the variance in catch around some mean value, then harvest rates at various stock sizes should be very different from those prescribed if the goal were to maximize the catch (Figure 12.5). Finally, even for a simple one-stock system there is a large uncertainty about what the parameters of the production model will be from one year to the next. Historical data are available to estimate the past distribution of parameter values, but there can be considerable leeway in interpreting these data (Walters, 1975b). By using stochastic dynamic programming, it was determined

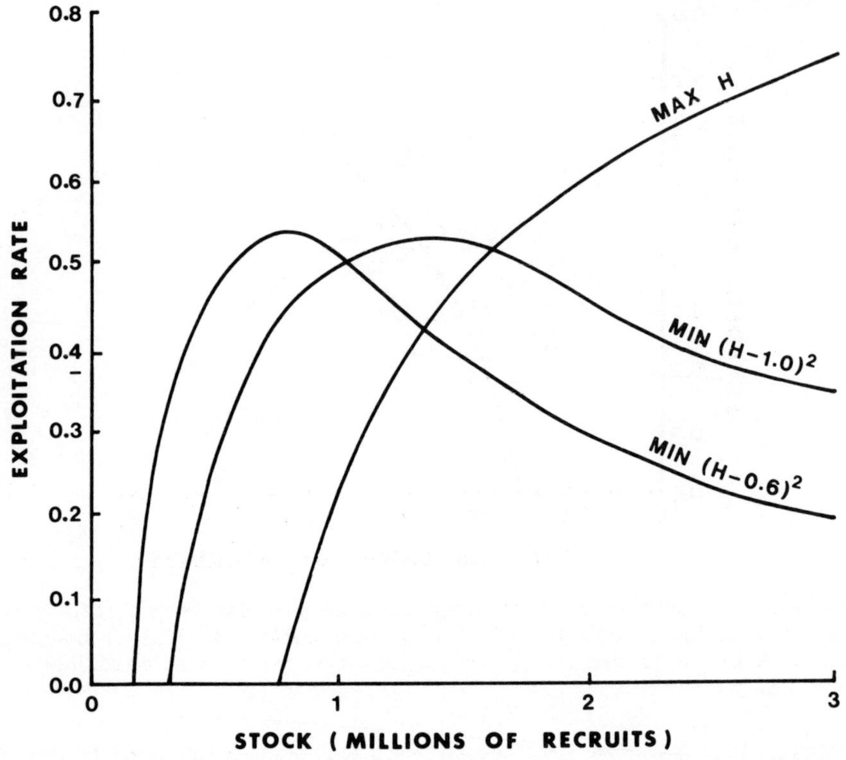

FIGURE 12.5 Optimal harvest strategies that would achieve one of three different management objectives: maximum sustainable yield (Max H); minimization of the variance in catches around a mean value of 1.0 million fish [Min $(H - 1.0)^2$]; and minimization of the variance in catches around a mean value of 0.6 million fish [Min $(H - 0.6)^2$]. Redrawn from Walters (1975b).

how different the optimal management policies were with an "optimistic" and a "pessimistic" interpretation of the production parameter data. Figure 12.6 shows that if the management objective is maximizing the catch, then the optimal harvest rates are almost identical for the "pessimist" and the "optimist." However, if the management goal is to minimize the variance in catches while maintaining a mean catch of 0.6 to 1.0 million, then there is a significant difference in optimal harvest rates between "pessimists" and "optimists." This particular study re-emphasized the need for a clear statement of management objectives, although it did indicate there would be striking similarities in optimal harvest patterns over some range of objectives.

The second study that applied dynamic programming addressed the common problem in salmon management of simultaneous harvesting of several stocks. Since most commercial salmon-fishing gear harvests the fish as they are about to move

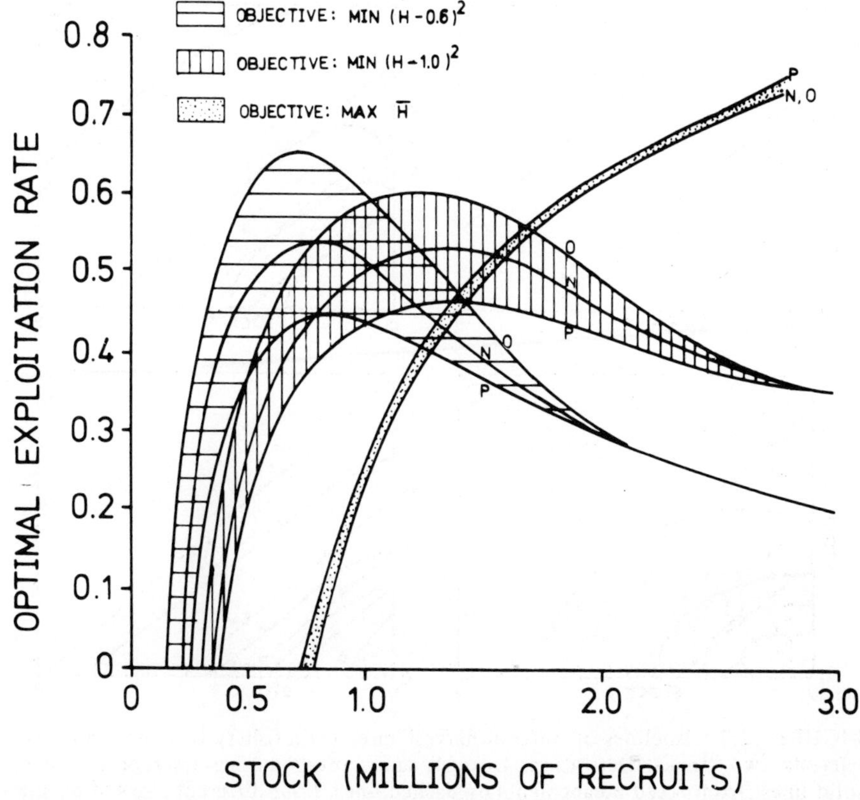

FIGURE 12.6 Optimal harvest strategies for three different objective functions using the optimistic (O), natural (N), and pessimistic (P) probability distributions for the production parameter data. After Walters (1975b).

from salt water into the river mouths, and because different, genetically isolated salmon stocks overlap in the timing of their upstream runs, commercial catches often harvest several stocks at once. This creates serious difficulties because not all stocks that are caught together have the same productivity; a less productive stock may withstand at most a 40 percent harvest rate, for instance, whereas a more productive one may absorb a 70 percent catch. Thus, many harvesting policies, which are aimed at the more productive stocks of a river system, can lead to over-exploitation and extinction of the less productive populations (Ricker, 1958; Paulik *et al.*, 1967). The question is, what is the best compromise harvesting regime if one knows the relative productivities of the stocks that are harvested simultaneously?

Hilborn (1976) explored this question by using a simple Ricker model to describe the population dynamics of stocks and by using stochastic dynamic programming to find the optimal harvest strategies that would achieve an objective

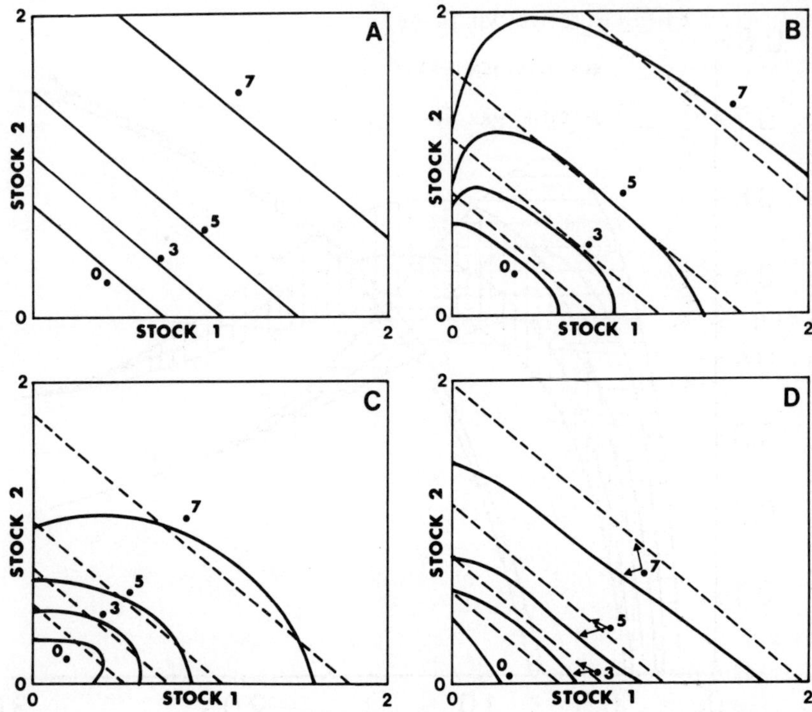

FIGURE 12.7 Isoclines of optimal harvest rates for a fishery that simultaneously harvests two stocks. Derivations from dynamic programming are represented by solid lines, from fixed escapements by dashed lines. Four different cases of production parameter combinations are shown. in Case *A*, both stocks have the same production parameters and the solutions from dynamic programming and fixed escapement are identical. In Cases *B, C,* and *D* the two stocks differ in their production parameters. After Hilborn (1976).

of maximum sustainable yield. Results in Figure 12.7 show that optimal harvest strategies for two-stock situations are quite different from a fixed escapement strategy, the strategy that Larkin and Ricker (1964) demonstrated was best for achieving the above objective for single stocks. Four different two-stock situations are shown in Figure 12.7, one where the two stocks have identical production parameters, and three cases where the two stocks have different parameter values. While we will not discuss the parameters in more detail, the study also demonstrated that the harvest rate isoclines were fairly sensitive to production parameter changes.

Graphical Optimization

As a supplement to the formal optimization procedures just described, we developed and applied more informal, graphical optimization devices that are usable with more complex models (Peterman, 1975). These methods were designed to help bridge the credibility gap between the decision makers, who rarely have an appreciation of the assumptions inherent in formal optimization techniques, and the analysts who do the optimizations. This was done by providing decision makers with isopleth diagrams of different indicators that might be part of their objectives (indicators such as average native Indian catch and commercial harvest of sockeye). In Chapter 9 there is a full discussion of how these isopleth diagrams, called nomograms, are derived. By manipulating a set of crosshairs on these graphs, it is possible to ask many questions that formal optimization procedures also permit, but in a graphical way that is more transparent to the decision maker.

For instance, the response surfaces for four indicator variables are shown in Figure 12.8. These graphs summarize several simulation runs of the Skeena River model mentioned earlier, which calculates changes in pink as well as sockeye salmon populations. These different simulation runs used various combinations of two management options, desired pink salmon escapements and amount of enhancement of sockeye expressed in enhancement units (1 unit = a spawning channel with a capacity of 1,600 spawners). These two management options form the two axes of the nomograms shown in Figure 12.8. By manipulating a set of pointers on a clear plastic overlay, one can read off the values of the four indicators that would result from the respective management options.

A simple example of the "gaming optimization" use of these nomograms is as follows. Assume that a salmon manager wishes only to maximize the average annual pink catch. The crosshairs on the nomograms show that this can be done by having sockeye enhancement anywhere above 100 units and pink escapement below about 0.3 million. However, these two management options give low values for two other indicators, minimum annual pink catch (the lowest catch during the 25 simulated years) and minimum annual Indian harvest. Thus, if these two indicators are an important component of another manager's objective, some compromise policy will be necessary. Figure 12.8 clearly shows that all three indicators cannot be maximized simultaneously. By gaming with the movable set of pointers, some compromise policy can be determined that satisfies both managers.

The minimum annual pink catch graph also demonstrates another interesting result. For levels of sockeye enhancement above 100 units, the steepness of the slope of this indicator surface increases with increasing escapement. This shape of the surface is important because the desired escapement can never be achieved precisely; the realized escapement will end up somewhere near the desired level, but not exactly on it. Such a deviation will result in some altered value of the indicator, and as the desired escapement increases, there is a larger percentage change in minimum annual pink catch caused by that deviation.

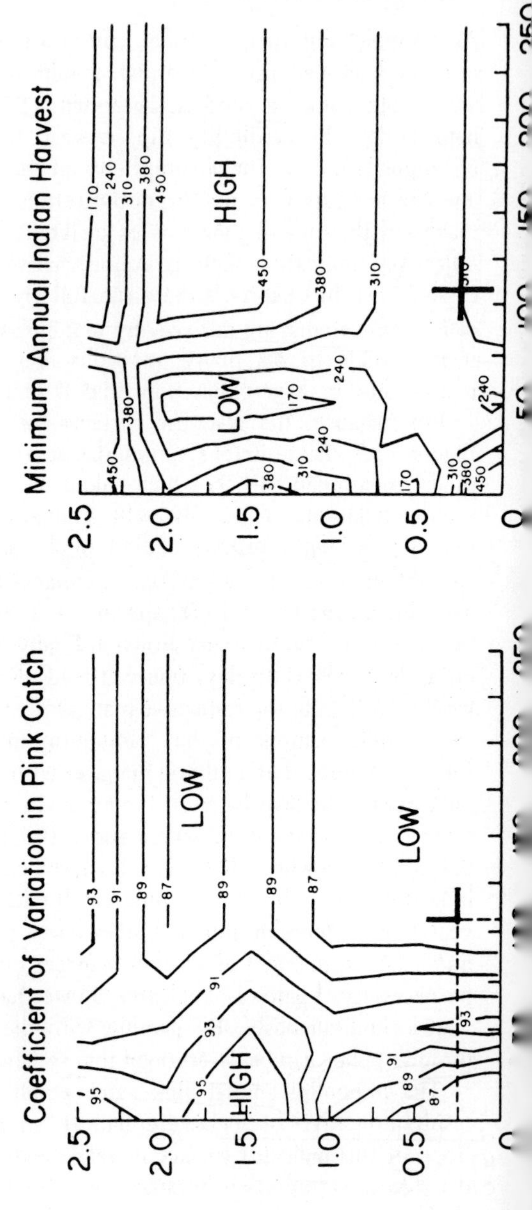

Coefficient of Variation in Pink Catch
HIGH
LOW
LOW
95
93
91
89
87
2.5
2.0
1.5
1.0
0.5
0
Minimum Annual Indian Harvest
HIGH
LOW
170
240
310
380
450
2.5
2.0
1.5
1.0
0.5
0
capement in Millions

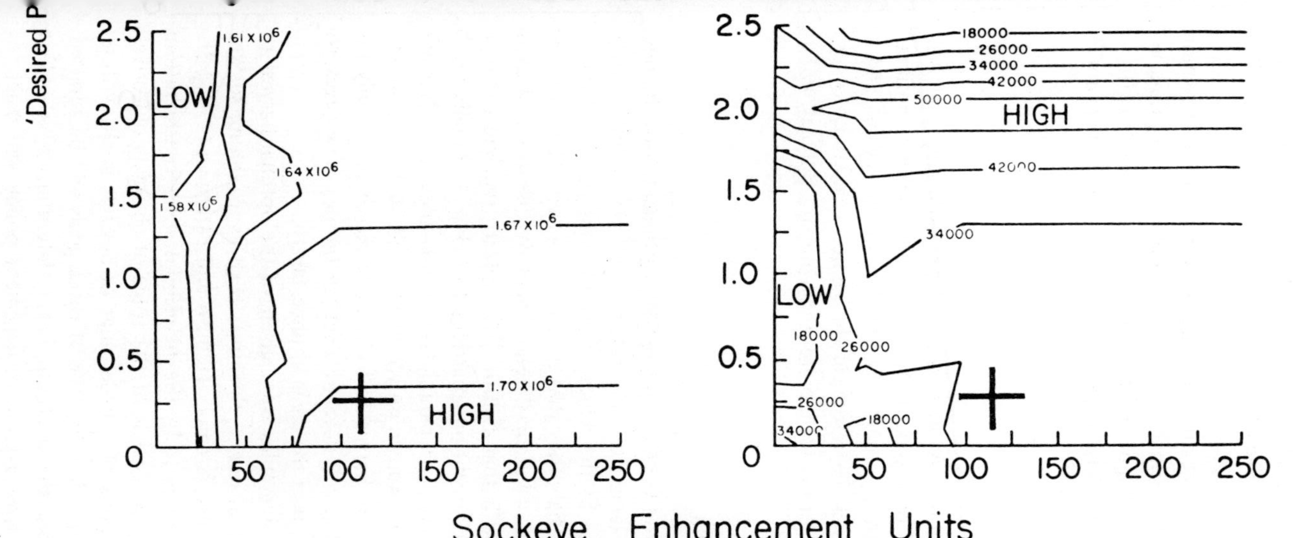

FIGURE 12.8 A sample set of nomograms for four indicators. Cross hairs show the values of the indicators that would result from use of the two corresponding management options shown on the graph axes. Redrawn from Peterman (1975).

Finally, graphical optimizations can be performed by using a set of shaded nomograms as overlays, where the shadings represent the heights on the contour surfaces and the relative importance weighting given to each indicator (see Peterman, 1975, for details).

Unlike the formal optimization procedure discussed in the previous section, nomograms permit the manager to do some "hands-on" comparison of options at a level that is easily understandable to him. Furthermore, the greatest benefits of this graphical evaluation method are derived from the process of its use, not its end product.

Conclusions from Optimization Work

No matter what optimization method is used, whether heuristic graphical techniques or formal methods, salmon managers must *not* take the resulting "optimal" policy as the best option. There are too many uncertainties in the system, and so all predictions are highly conditional. Therefore, in the salmon case study we have viewed optimization merely as a means to explore and compare policies, *not* to prescribe them.

DEALING WITH UNCERTAINTIES

As just mentioned, the major reason we have not pushed optimization techniques too far is that uncertainties loom large from any salmon manager's point of view. Management objectives can change at the whim of government policy or public pressure. There are significant probabilities that a given management action will fail to achieve its purpose (such as a hatchery being swept by disease), and there will be certain costs associated with that failure. Attempts to regulate catch to achieve a desired harvest rate of 50 percent on a particular stock may actually result in 60 percent or 30 percent harvest. The parameters of the underlying dynamic population model for a stock will be known only roughly. And finally, it is known from historical data that if stocks are harvested to below a certain level, only imprecisely determined, the population will never recover. In the next few pages, we discuss how one might approach each of the areas of uncertainty.

In a previous section (p. 190) examples were given of the optimal harvest regimes that were designed to meet different objectives such as maximum sustainable yield or minimization of variance in catch. Hilborn and Peterman (1977) discuss how those analyses could be extended by the inclusion of some considerations from utility theory. A better way to deal with the topic of changing objectives, though, is to explore the implications of a wide range of possible goals, without specific reference to the probability that any one of those goals will be adopted. At best, this exploration can help the decision maker determine how wide a spectrum of possible future objectives a given management policy will meet. At worst, this manager will be ready to respond to changes in goals when they occur.

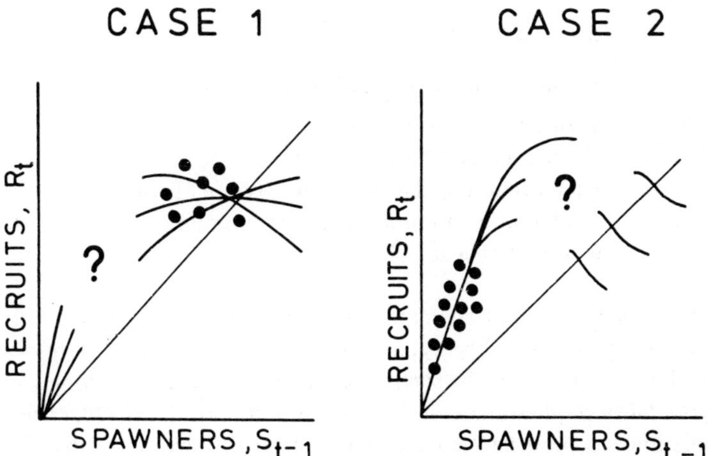

FIGURE 12.9 Management situations that permit simplified adaptive optimization. Case 1: newly developing fishery, β known and a uncertain. Case 2: older fishery with stock depleted below unfished level, a known and β uncertain. After Walters and Hilborn (1976).

Holling and Clark (1975) point out that while the probability of some disaster's occurrence may be very small, the costs of that rare event may be prohibitive and even unacceptable. For example, a pink salmon enhancement facility operating where there are no remaining natural stocks may have a very low probability of producing less than 10% of the normal returning adult population. But the strong dependencies of local fishermen on that enhanced stock may argue against a management plan to double the size of the facility, because the losses that would result if there ever were a failure would be enormous. We included such probabilities and costs of failures in the work, discussed previously, that used utility analysis to rank alternative enhancement policies (Hilborn and Walters, 1977). There it was found that an explicit consideration of costs as well as probabilities of failure affected ranking of policies.

Perhaps the most common source of uncertainty faced by salmon managers is the one associated with the underlying biological model of the population (Walters, 1977). In Figure 12.6 we showed what effect there would be on management policy if different interpretations of the salmon production data were made. In that case, the interpretation of the data depended on which management objective was being sought.

We have also used formal systems analytic methods to address the question of uncertain biological parameters when the observations on the system have occurred over such a narrow range that it is difficult to estimate the parameters of the stock recruitment relation. Figure 12.9 shows two hypothetical situations where this is the case. Let us assume that the underlying stock recruitment relation is of the Ricker (1954) form,

$$R_t = S_{t-1} e^{a(1 - S_{t-1}/\beta) \cdot V_t} , \qquad (12.1)$$

where R_t = recruits (adults) at end of generation t

S_{t-1} = spawners at start of generation t

a = a stock production parameter

β = equilibrium population size in absence of fishing

V_t = a random environmental factor, normally distributed with mean 0 and variance σ^2

To use this model, we need estimates of the two parameters, a and β. In case 1, which is for a relatively new fishery, most data points will be for the unexploited or barely exploited population. In such cases, common in the developing countries, we can get a fairly good estimate of the parameter β. Case 2 is an older fishery where the population has been harvested down to a much lower level than its natural equilibrium. Therefore, it is not possible to estimate β, but a can be estimated from the slope of the data points in the stock recruitment relation. This can be done because S_{t-1} is a very small proportion of β, and Eq. (12.1) reduces to

$$R_t = S_{t-1} e^{a \cdot V_t} , \qquad (12.2)$$

giving e^a as the slope of the relation.

Dynamic programming was used to calculate the optimal exploitation rates for these two cases, given different amounts of uncertainty in estimates of the parameters, and given an objective of maximizing the sum of discounted catches over time (Walters and Hilborn, 1976). Figure 12.10 shows that for case 1, the resulting optimal exploitation rates are a relatively complex function of the stock size and the estimate of the production parameter a especially when the variance in a is large. Results for case 2 are similarly complex, but the general lesson emerging from the study is that under certain conditions it is worthwhile reducing harvest rates to obtain better estimates of the parameter β. Likewise, higher harvest rates can be of value in reducing uncertainty about a when other specified conditions exist.

The final type of uncertainty concerning biological parameters deals with the maximum exploitation rate that can be sustained by a given population. Considerable evidence demonstrates the existence of such limits; numerous populations have sustained increased harvesting up to a certain point, where an increment in the harvest rate has caused population collapse (Holling, 1973). It is possible to calculate the exploitation rate limit for salmon populations if data are available for predation mortality on young salmon (Peterman, 1977b). When predation is severe, a stock recruitment relation similar to the one depicted in Figure 12.11 may exist. The critical characteristic of such a relation is that there are two domains of stability, one at large population sizes and one at small sizes, separated by a boundary, X_0. Once the population crosses this boundary into the lower domain, the stock tends to stay in that domain.

But this boundary population size is not static; it varies with changing

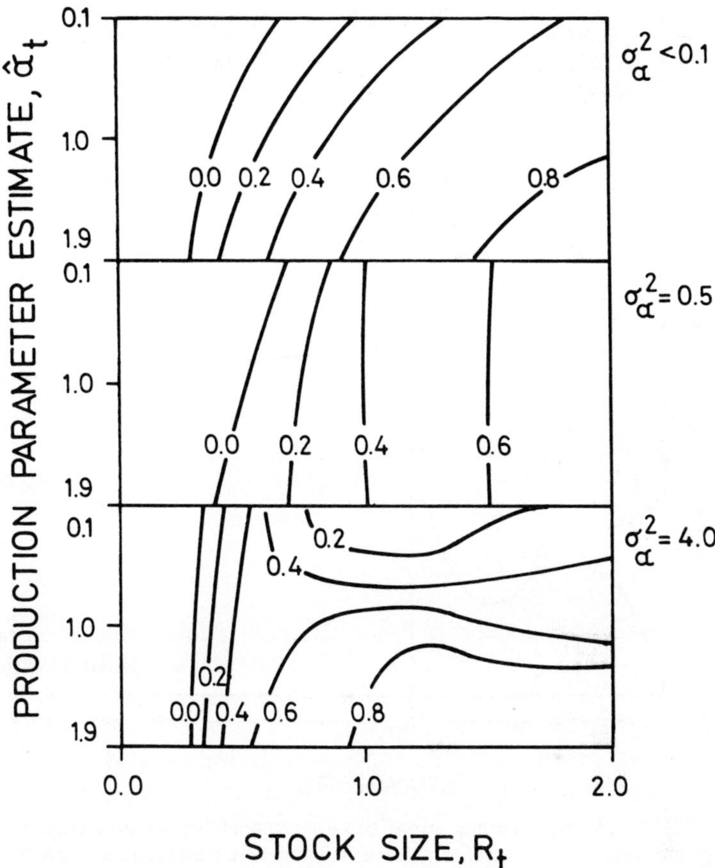

FIGURE 12.10 Isopleths of optimal exploitation rates for various stock sizes, production rate estimates ($\hat{a}_t$), and uncertainties about a ($\sigma_a{}^2$), assuming the Ricker model form is correct and equilibrium stock is known (case 1 of Figure 12.9). These results were obtained with environmental variance $\sigma^2 = 0.5$ and discount rate $\delta = 4\%$ per generation. After Walters and Hilborn (1976).

exploitation rates (Figure 12.12). Furthermore, variation in the environmental factors that affect salmon survival also alters the boundary location. If the historical distribution of environmental factors is measured, then it is possible to calculate the probability that a stock will cross the boundary into the lower domain, given the spawning population size and the exploitation rate (Figure 12.13). As will be mentioned later, another method for calculating boundary locations can be used when there are two or more stocks subject to the same predation and the same commercial fishery.

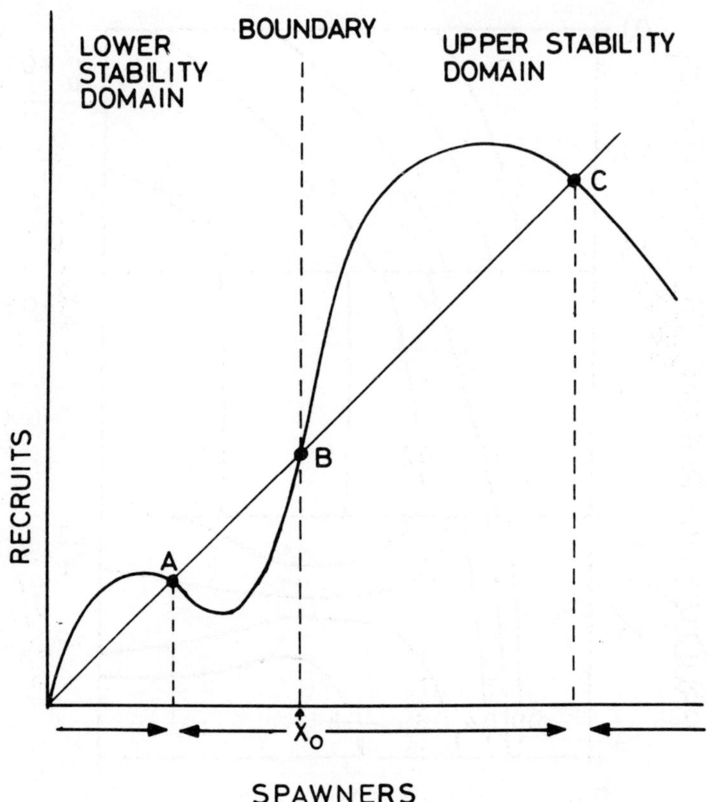

FIGURE 12.11 A recruitment curve showing the effect of predation mortality. The diagonal line is the replacement line, where recruits equal spawners. After Peterman (1977b).

The behavior of population models based on these multiple-equilibrium stock recruit relations is consistent with catastrophe models that have recently been applied to ecological problems (Chapters 6 and 11; Jones, 1975; Jones and Walters, 1976). Incremental changes in certain management actions or in biological parameters can drastically alter the fish population size. Catastrophe manifold representations have proved valuable in clarifying to managers, for instance, that maximum sustainable yield harvest rates are invariably dangerously close to overexploitation levels (Peterman, 1977b).

ADAPTIVE MANAGEMENT

Another way of dealing with some of the uncertainties mentioned above is through adaptive management, a concept based on the theories of adaptive control processes, a well-developed area of engineering (Bellman, 1961). The adaptive management

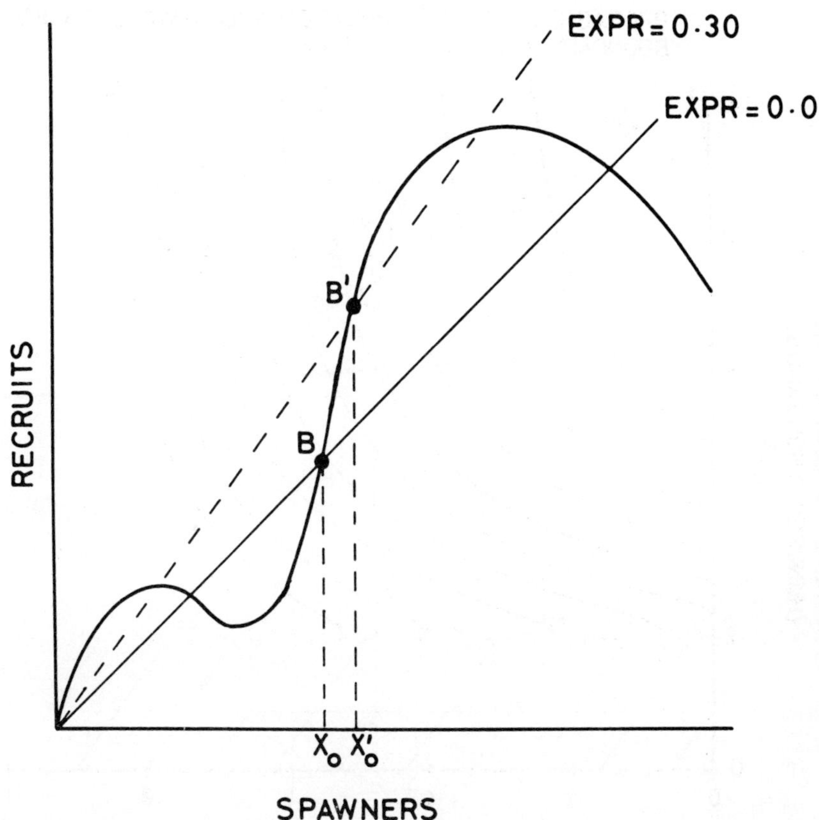

FIGURE 12.12 The slope of the replacement line changes when the exploitation rate (EXPR) is altered. The boundary population size then changes from X_0 to X'_0. After Peterman (1977b).

concept states that when uncertainties about system characteristics are large, there may be considerable value in designing the management perturbations so that information as well as other benefits (in this case catch) are obtained. This information would reduce the uncertainty about the underlying biological relations, and more precise management actions could be taken. In this way, the harvesting or enhancement policies would become research tools as well as management tools. Two examples illustrate the adaptive management concept in salmon fisheries management.

First, we have already mentioned the problem of Pacific salmon stocks that migrate into their home rivers at the same time and that are therefore subjected to the same exploitation rate. Some of these stocks are less productive than others and cannot sustain harvest regimes designed for optimal exploitation of the more productive stocks. One proposed management solution to this problem of overexploiting less productive stocks is to bring all the stock productivities on a given river

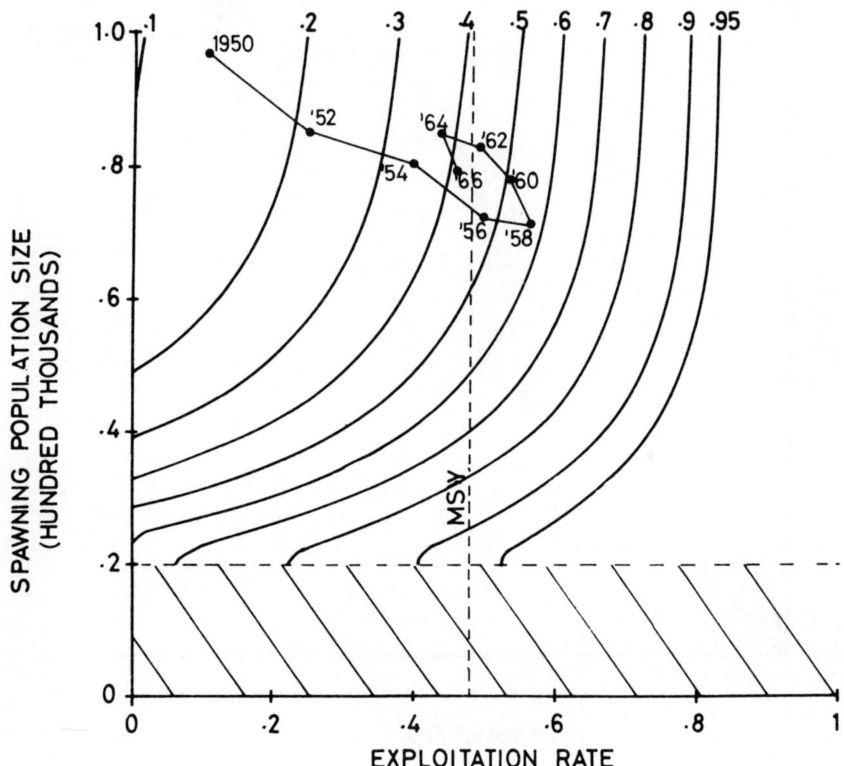

FIGURE 12.13 The contours give the probability that a stock will cross into the lower domain if a given exploitation rate is applied to its offspring. Superimposed on these contours is the time course of a hypothetical developing fishery. The maximum sustainable yield exploitation rate (MSY) is indicated by the vertical dotted line. Below the dashed line, there exists only a single domain of attraction – in this case, the lower domain. After Peterman (1977b).

system to the same level by means of enhancement – hatcheries, spawning channels, and the like (Ricker, 1975). While this approach may greatly reduce the probability of overexploiting the less productive stocks, it does nothing to prevent the increase of fishing effort until all stocks are overexploited simultaneously. In fact, this policy of making productivities equal removes the possibility of feedback or warning signals from the loss in catch when less productive stocks are overharvested. Such warning signals could help restrain the development of the fishery; without them, the equal productivities policy might just lead to bigger disasters more efficiently.

So what is the way out of this problem? Current practises, in seeking to greatly reduce the probability of failure, may increase the cost of failure when it does occur. Instead, we suggest that actions be considered that do not necessarily attempt to reduce the probability of disasters occurring, but that try to minimize the costs resulting from the inevitable disaster (Holling and Clark, 1975; Jones and Walters, 1976; Peterman, 1977b). This might be done most effectively by designing the management actions to create periodic disturbances, thereby selecting for maintenance of the response mechanisms in the natural (as well as the institutional) system. In the multiple-stock salmon enhancement example cited above, the "creative disturbance" management option would maintain stocks with a mix of different productivities that would provide feedback information when less productive stocks were overexploited; this could help prevent overharvest of the more productive fish by creating incentive to restrain the expansion of fishing capacity or fleet size (Peterman, 1977b).

Overharvesting of the less productive stocks could also provide information of a different sort: the stability boundaries of the more productive stocks could be calculated (Peterman, 1977b). Three conditions must be met to permit this calculation: (a) stocks must have a stock recruitment relation of the basic form shown in Figure 12.11; (b) stocks must share the same sources and magnitude of predation in early life (e.g., stocks reared in the same lake); (c) the exploitation rate at which the less productive stock collapses into its lower domain of stability must be known. These conditions are probably fulfilled more frequently than is commonly believed. Thus, managers should seriously consider the possibility that some stocks deliberately be made expendable in order to provide information about the total fishery complex. In this way, a "self-monitoring" system would be created, whereby money saved by not doing detailed studies of recruitment relations for each stock would be put into rehabilitation of the overharvested stock.

The second example of adaptive management comes from a case that is common in salmon management. Historical data occur over such a small range of stock sizes that it is not even possible to estimate the fundamental form of the underlying stock recruitment relation, let alone its parameter values. For the case shown in Figure 12.14, the question is whether the correct relationship is η_1, η_2, or something in between. If the present escapement goal of 1.0 million fish is maintained, then data points will likely be generated only down in the present range of values, which will not permit discrimination between the alternative models. Thus, some deliberate perturbation of escapements (and therefore of catch) may be necessary. Walters and Hilborn (1976) discuss the procedure involved in deciding what the best change in escapements would be in order to determine the correct underlying model. The elements of this procedure are (a) description of possible alternative underlying models, (b) assignment of probabilities of being "correct" to each of these alternative models, (c) identification of a series of harvest experiments that would alter escapements by different amounts and for different lengths of time, (d) calculation of expected long-term benefits for each combination of harvest

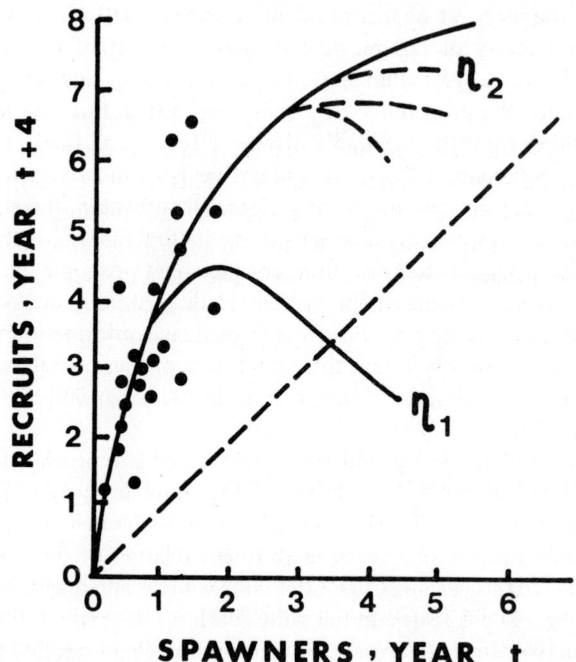

FIGURE 12.14 Alternative stock-recruitment models for Fraser River sockeye salmon, off-cycle years. Data shown are for 1939–1973, omitting every fourth or cycle year beginning in 1942. η_1, least-squares fit to Ricker model; η_2, visual fit to Beverton–Holt (1957) model. Graph axes in millions of fish. After Walters and Hilborn (1976).

experiment and underlying model, and (e) choice of experiment with highest benefits.

When this procedure was applied to the case shown in Figure 12.14, there was no circumstance in which the best escapement policy was the present 1.0 million fish. If a discount rate of 1 percent was used, then an escapement of 2.0 million fish for 5 years was optimal; if the discount rate was greater than 20 percent, then 1.5 million escapement for 15 years was best. Thus, the adaptive control procedure found that in all cases, some reduction in catch, and therefore increase in escapement, would be valuable in order to reduce the uncertainty associated with the underlying stock recruitment relation. The harvesting regime would thereby provide information as well as catch. The reduction in uncertainty results from increased escapements because data points are generated in the right-hand portion of the graph in Figure 12.14. As data points accumulate every year, it becomes easier to tell which of the hypothesized underlying models is correct, even with a great deal of environmental noise.

Simulation gaming has verified what is intuitively clear – that with large escapements less time is necessary to clarify which stock recruitment model is correct than with small escapements. However, for the sockeye population shown in Figure 12.14, which matures in 4 years, it was found that 10 to 15 years of large escapements was needed to enable a group of managers in a gaming session to guess with 80 percent accuracy what the correct model was. This result brings up a critical issue of adaptive management, and that is the value of information. How much catch should be sacrificed for how long in order to gain information that will in theory permit more precise management of the salmon? The value of that information should be quantified so that managers can include it in their objectives. In the following section we give a rather detailed example of how value of information might be calculated, but for a different situation from the one discussed above.

VALUE OF INFORMATION: HOW MUCH INVESTMENT IN ENHANCEMENT MONITORING IS JUSTIFIABLE?

Some salmon enhancement projects will almost certainly fail, at least in the sense of not resulting in increased returns or in damaging nearby natural populations. This statement is not a condemnation of the enhancement program as a whole; rather, it is simply a recognition that salmon biology is not completely understood and that mistakes will therefore be made. There are two approaches to situations where the possibility of failure exists but cannot be detected in advance by pilot-scale operations:

- Select only those projects whose probability of failure is, in prior judgment, considered to be acceptably small.
- Allow for investment in riskier alternatives, but monitor such projects so that failure can be rapidly detected and used as a guide to further actions.

When such alternative approaches are discussed, it is usually pointed out that monitoring (e.g., stock separation in catches, accurate escapement counts before and after disturbance, juvenile life stage estimates) can be very expensive, thus making the second approach economically unattractive (compare our previous comments on "self-monitoring" systems).

Our interest here is to present a simple formula for estimating the maximum monitoring cost that should be considered justifiable for any single project. When applied across the interrelated set of projects that make up an overall program, the formula provides a rough estimate of the monitoring costs necessary to make the second approach a reasonable alternative.

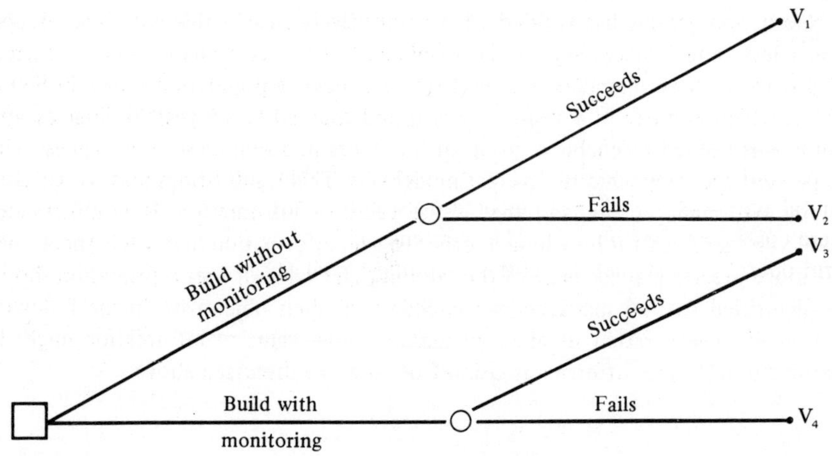

FIGURE 12.15 Decision tree for a fishery enhancement project.

The Basic Criterion

The formula is based on a very simple concept: the *expected* net benefit of a project is the probability that it will succeed times the net benefit if it does, plus the probability that it will fail times the net benefit (perhaps negative) if it does (Moore and Thomas, 1976; Raiffa, 1968). When many outcomes between complete success and complete failure are considered, the expectation becomes a more complex summation of probabilities times net benefits. To keep the discussion from becoming mathematically involved, we will pretend that only two outcomes are likely; this simplification will not change the basic conclusion, provided that "success" and "failure" are defined in a conservative manner. Tribus (1969) provides a readable account of the more realistic and complex case.

Consider a proposed fishery enhancement project that may either succeed, increasing future catches, or fail, damaging the natural stocks and decreasing future catches. Further, assume that it is possible to design a monitoring scheme that will detect failure, if it occurs, in time to terminate the project with no damage to the natural stocks. The problem is to determine how much we should be willing to pay for such a monitoring scheme. The "decision tree" of Figure 12.15 shows the two alternative decisions (build the facility without monitoring or build it with monitoring) and the two possible outcomes (project success or failure) for each.

Each path from left to right ends in a point to which it is simple to assign a value:

V_1 = net value if the project without monitoring is successful
V_2 = net value if the project without monitoring fails
V_3 = net value if the project with monitoring is successful
V_4 = net value if the project with monitoring fails

Suppose the probability of *failure* is P. Then the expected value of the "without monitoring" decision is $PV_2 + (1 - P)V_1$, and the expected value of the "with monitoring" decision is $PV_4 + (1 - P)V_3$. To decide which decision has the higher expected value, we must now define the net values more precisely in terms of cost and benefit components.

All outcomes will share the same nonrecoverable costs for development and capital outlay on the basic project; let us denote the discounted future total of these costs by the symbol C_f. The outcomes V_1, V_2, and V_3 will all involve long-term operating costs; let us call the discounted total of these costs C_0. Outcome V_4 will involve detection that the facility has failed, so that C_0 will be avoided; for simplicity, costs during the operating period before the failure is detected will be considered part of the development cost C_f. For V_3 and V_4, we must add a discounted total monitoring cost C_m. Finally, call B the net discounted value of the increase in catch that results from a successful project, and denote the net discounted value of the loss in natural stocks that results from an undetected failure as D.

Putting the costs and benefits as defined above together, we get

$$V_1 = B - C_f - C_0 \quad \text{(increased catch, no monitoring costs)}$$
$$V_2 = -C_f - C_0 - D \quad \text{(damaged catch, no monitoring costs)}$$
$$V_3 = B - C_f - C_0 - C_m \quad \text{(increased catch, monitoring costs)}$$
$$V_4 = -C_f - C_m \quad \text{(no change in catch, monitoring costs, no sustained operating cost)}$$

Recalling that P is the probability of failure, and calculating expected costs, we conclude that the "monitoring" decision is best only if

$$PV_2 + (1 - P)V_1 < PV_4 + (1 - P)V_3 \; .$$

When we put the more precise definition of the V's into this inequality and simplify, the final result is

$$C_m < P(C_0 + D) \; .$$

That is, we should invest in a monitoring system only if the total discounted monitoring costs are less than the probability of failure times the total discounted operating costs plus the natural stock damage costs. If we allow further branches in the decision tree to account for the possibility that a monitoring investment C_m might (with some probability) fail to detect the damages D or even the overall failure, then the value of monitoring will be somewhat decreased.

The startling feature of this decision rule is that it shows that investment in monitoring should *not* depend either on total expected benefits given success or on capital costs, except as these investment indicators might influence the probability of failure. We could complicate the analysis by including other variables, such as the time required to detect failures, differential probabilities for facility failure versus natural stock damages, and so on; none of these complications would affect the basic conclusion: monitoring has value precisely to the extent that it makes *some* costs avoidable.

Extensions to Multiproject Situations

Suppose now that by monitoring just one project we can determine whether an additional n similar projects will fail or succeed. If all n are built at the same time as the monitored project, the monitoring value criterion becomes

$$C_m < Pn(C_0 + D) \ .$$

That is, we should be willing to invest n times as much in monitoring the one project (this conclusion depends critically on the notion that the one project is *completely informative* about what the other n are doing).

Finally, suppose that by monitoring one project we can determine unequivocally whether an additional k similar projects will be successful, where these other projects will not be started until the first is fully evaluated. Then the decision criterion becomes complicated unless we ignore discounting over the evaluation period (see below). Making that simplification, we get

$$C_m < P[k \cdot C_f + (k+1) \cdot (C_0 + D)] \ .$$

Thus, in the sequential decision situation, monitoring may result in a saving in capital development costs (C_f), thereby increasing its value.

Effect of Discounting

Consider the situation where a single facility begun now can determine for certain whether an additional k facilities of similar cost–benefit structure will succeed, given that these facilities are not to be started in any case until τ years after the single facility. If we now discount the value of the additional projects out to the starting year τ, the criterion for permissible monitoring cost becomes

$$C_m < P\{k \cdot (1-\delta)^{\tau} \cdot C_f + [1 + k \cdot (1-\delta)^{\tau}] \cdot (C_0 + D)\} \ ,$$

where δ is the annual discount rate. This equation depends critically on the assumptions that (a) the investment C_m will be certain to detect damages or failure within τ years; and (b) the k later facilities would not be started for τ years whether or not the first facility is monitored.

Basically what the above inequality says is that

The value of monitoring increases with the size of the later investment as measured by k

Monitoring value *decreases* as either the discount rate δ or the evaluation period τ is *increased*

TABLE 12.1 Maximum Tolerable Monitoring Cost ($ millions)

Prior Probability of Failure P (First Facility)	Evaluation Period (τ) (yr)					
	3	5	7	9	11	13
0.1	0.8	0.7	0.6	0.5	0.4	0.3
0.2	1.6	1.4	1.1	1.0	0.8	0.7
0.3	2.5	2.1	1.7	1.4	1.2	1.0
0.4	3.3	2.8	2.3	1.9	1.6	1.4
0.5	4.1	3.5	2.9	2.4	2.0	1.8
0.6	5.0	4.1	3.5	2.9	2.5	2.2
0.7	5.8	4.8	4.0	3.4	2.9	2.6

To give some concrete interpretation of these conclusions, Table 12.1 gives maximum tolerable monitoring costs for the case in which capital cost (C_f) is $1 million, annual operating cost is $100,000, the damages ($D$) are negligible, the annual discount rate is $\delta = 10\%$, and there are $k = 5$ later projects that will not be funded if the first try is monitored and fails. These numbers suggest that, for reasonable failure probabilities ($P = 0.1$ to 0.5) and evaluation periods ($\tau = 9$–11 years), monitoring costs on the same order as the capital investment cost are justified for projects that will be informative about several (here, 5) future project possibilities. Even higher monitoring costs would be justified if a lower discount rate were used (Table 12.2). Note that the monitoring costs in tables 12.1 and 12.2 refer to the amount that could be spent while still maintaining a *better* benefit–cost ratio than expected for the no-monitoring alternative.

Difficulties

The main problem with using the criteria outlined above is in finding a reasonable *a priori* estimate of P, the probability of failure. The value of monitoring is directly proportional to this estimate. Decision theorists have proposed question-and-answer or gaming procedures for eliciting estimates of P from subject-matter specialists, but

TABLE 12.2 Effect of Different Discount Rates on Allowable Monitoring Costs[a]

Discount Rate	Allowable Monitoring Cost
.01	$2.0 million
.03	1.7
.05	1.4
.07	1.15
.09	1.0

[a] τ = 10 yr;
P = 0.2.

until many projects have been evaluated, all such estimates must be subjective.

Other problems relate to the much more complex decision tree hiding behind the yes–no representation used here. We should be looking at multiple outcomes, at time streams of benefits and costs, at partially informative monitoring procedures, at the degree to which any single project is informative about others, and at the whole question of how to measure costs and benefits when the decision makers are risk averse.

APPLICATION OF RESULTS

Many of the results of the systems analyses discussed above have been applied in the management and research activities of the Federal Fisheries and Marine Service and to a lesser extent in the British Columbia Fish and Wildlife Branch. We cannot overemphasize the role that short-term modeling and interactive gaming workshops, as described in Chapters 3 and 4, have played in the transferral of concepts, methods, and results to these clients. These workshops have been a much more efficient way to expose people to approaches, assumptions, and recommendations than any written document. Approaches to present fisheries management problems have a great deal of inertia, and, as a result, our results have had less impact in this area than in the relatively new area of large-scale salmon enhancement.

In areas of present management problems, our cooperative work with the fisheries people has pointed out critical areas where research is needed. In addition, managers have recognized the need to quantify objects, not only their own but also those of other interest groups such as sport fishermen, native Indians, and commercial fishermen. We are now engaged in further studies to attempt to measure utility functions of these groups.

We are presently involved in a project to develop new management regulations for sport and troll fishing in Georgia Strait, near Vancouver, British Columbia. Data have recently been collected that show that the sport catch of chinook and coho salmon may be twice as high as previously thought. This catch, in combination with commercial harvests, may seriously threaten the persistence of these species in this area. In conjunction with Federal Fisheries scientists, we are presently applying population dynamics models, fishing effort models, utility analysis, and optimization to explore the ramifications of various proposed management actions.

Additional results from our studies have been fed into the plans for the large-scale Canadian salmon enhancement program, as demonstrated by the various planning documents (e.g., MacLeod, 1976). An explicit criterion in the choice of alternative ways of enhancing populations is to minimize the technological risk: small, simple facilities are preferred to large-scale, complex facilities such as hatcheries. Also, only a small proportion of any stock will be used for enhancement, the rest remaining in the natural state. Furthermore, the concept of option

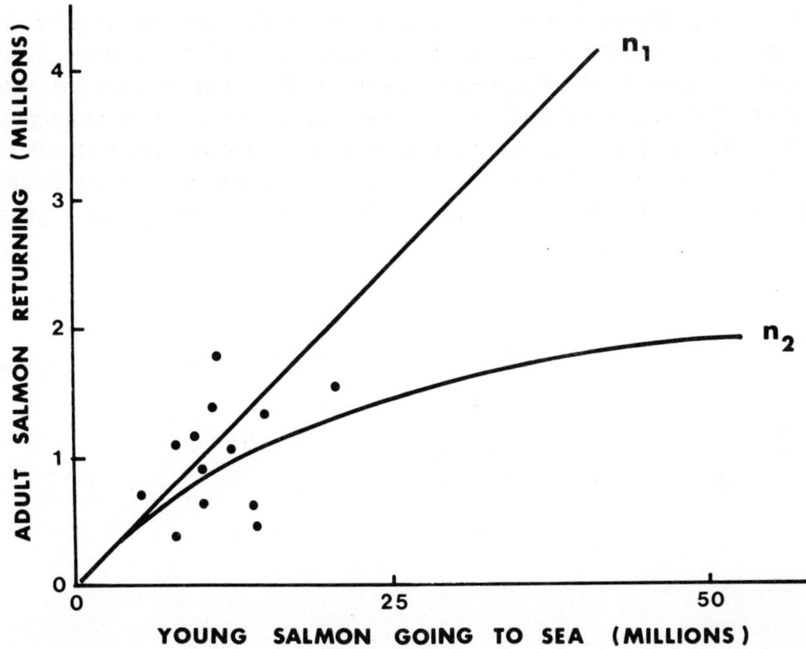

FIGURE 12.16 Historical abundances of juvenile salmon of this hypothetical stock have not produced data that permit us to distinguish between alternative models of ocean limitation (η_1 : no limitation; η_2 : a saturation level exists).

foreclosure mentioned in Chapters 1 and 10 is of prime importance in the planning process. Enhancement facilities that are very expensive to construct are less preferred even though they may have higher production per spawner, because if for some reason the facility does not produce as well as expected, there would be pressure to "fix" the expensive facility. Many future options would then be eliminated because of the large investment in correcting the first mistake.

Perhaps the most radical change in enhancement plans that has resulted from our systems studies is the recognition that the enhancement program needs to be viewed as a series of large-scale perturbation experiments. The gaps in data that have been discovered during model building have forced some salmon researchers as well as managers to realize that enhancement facilities should be set up to provide information as well as an increase in catch, perhaps even sacrificing some of the latter for the former. For instance, one large unknown is whether there is some maximum ocean capacity for salmon that will be reached when salmon fry production is doubled. In order to determine quickly which underlying relation exists for a particular stock (Figure 12.16), it might be best to do the riskier, large-scale perturbation of young salmon. In general, the adaptive management approach has become well-integrated into enhancement plans.

Finally, the fisheries management agencies have been stimulated to produce a large salmon production model that is being used to plan the complex phasing and siting elements of the enhancement program. The series of salmon modeling workshops that have been conducted over the past few years with salmon agency personnel have helped to create an awareness of systems analysis methods and implant some expertise in those methods within the agencies, thereby creating an environment in the agencies conducive to the carrying out of such systems studies.

13 Obergurgl: Development in High Mountain Regions of Austria

The Obergurgl case study describes a simulation model and policy analysis developed as a joint effort of the Austrian Man-and-the-Biosphere Program (MAB 6), the International Institute for Applied Systems Analysis (IIASA), and the Institute of Animal Resource Ecology, University of British Columbia. The effort focused on an intense 5-day workshop where a simulation model was developed to synthesize the research that had been conducted on the area and to provide some direction for further research and policy design. Participants included citizens of the village, representatives of the Tyrolean government, and scientists from the University of Innsbruck. The case study analysis is an example of a very rapid impact assessment in which a team of three spent a month on analysis. In addition, unlike the other examples in this volume, the public was involved from the beginning and throughout. After the workshop, considerable effort was devoted to communicating the results to the local residents, but these communication projects are not described here.

INTRODUCTION

The village of Obergurgl, in the Tyrolean Alps of Austria, faces problems similar to those in many areas of the world today. Beginning in about 1950, the village entered a period of economic growth driven by apparently unlimited demand for tourism in the area. This economic growth, expressed largely in terms of hotel construction, is beginning to have serious environmental consequences for the fragile alpine ecosystem and will soon be limited by availability of land, if nothing else. There is a key simplification in the system: land ownership is tightly controlled by a few families (originally farmers), and the economic development rate is limited by the rate of local human population growth, as this rate determines the number of people willing to invest in new hotels. Since hotels are easiest to build on valley bottomland, this productive land for agricultural grazing is rapidly being lost, and with it, a major economic option for the villagers. Thus, we see in Obergurgl a microcosm, with some elements missing and others exaggerated, of a major worldwide problem: population and economic growth in relation to diminishing resources. By study of such microcosms, we may be able to better identify ways to deal with larger problems.

Obergurgl is now receiving intensive study, mainly of ecological problems, as part of the Austrian Man-and-the-Biosphere Program. The International Institute for Applied Systems Analysis felt that it could contribute to this study by providing assistance with systems modeling. This chapter describes a preliminary dynamic model of Obergurgl that was developed during a 5-day workshop sponsored jointly by IIASA and MAB. The workshop (13–17 May 1974) was a truly interdisciplinary attempt to deal with the problem from a systems viewpoint; participants included hotel owners from Obergurgl, a representative of the Tyrolean government, ecologists from MAB projects in Austria and other European countries, a scattering of people from other sciences, and systems modelers from the University of British Columbia, Canada (representing IIASA).

The focus of the workshop was to develop a preliminary model of human impact on the alpine ecosystem. By combining the knowledge and insights of businessmen, government officials, and scientists, it was hoped that the modeling would help to identify better policy options for future development of the area. But, in a major sense, the model was not the primary "product" of the effort. In a 5-day period it is scarcely possible to develop and validate a rigorous descriptive model – nor to develop a convincing prescriptive analysis. Rather, the prime purpose was to use the model to identify the potential areas of conflict and the critical missing information, so that rational priorities could be set for further descriptive and prescriptive analyses.

The objectives of our modeling work therefore were three: (a) to promote communication among the various interest groups involved in Obergurgl studies, by using the simulation model to provide a common language and focus for attention; (b) to define, through data requirements for the model, critical research areas for the MAB 6 project; and (c) to provide tentative long-range (20–40 years) alternative forecasts for the people of Obergurgl concerning likely impacts of various development strategies that they consider practical. We did not expect before the workshop that the third objective could be fulfilled, considering the data and conceptual problems that usually arise in such modeling workshops. However, we were lucky, and it does appear that the model predictions can be taken seriously; we dwell on these predictions at some length in the final section of this chapter (p. 236).

For the casual reader, the model predictions can be summarized very simply:

1. The most likely natural limiting factor for Obergurgl's economic growth is safe land for building: on this basis, Obergurgl and the immediate surroundings

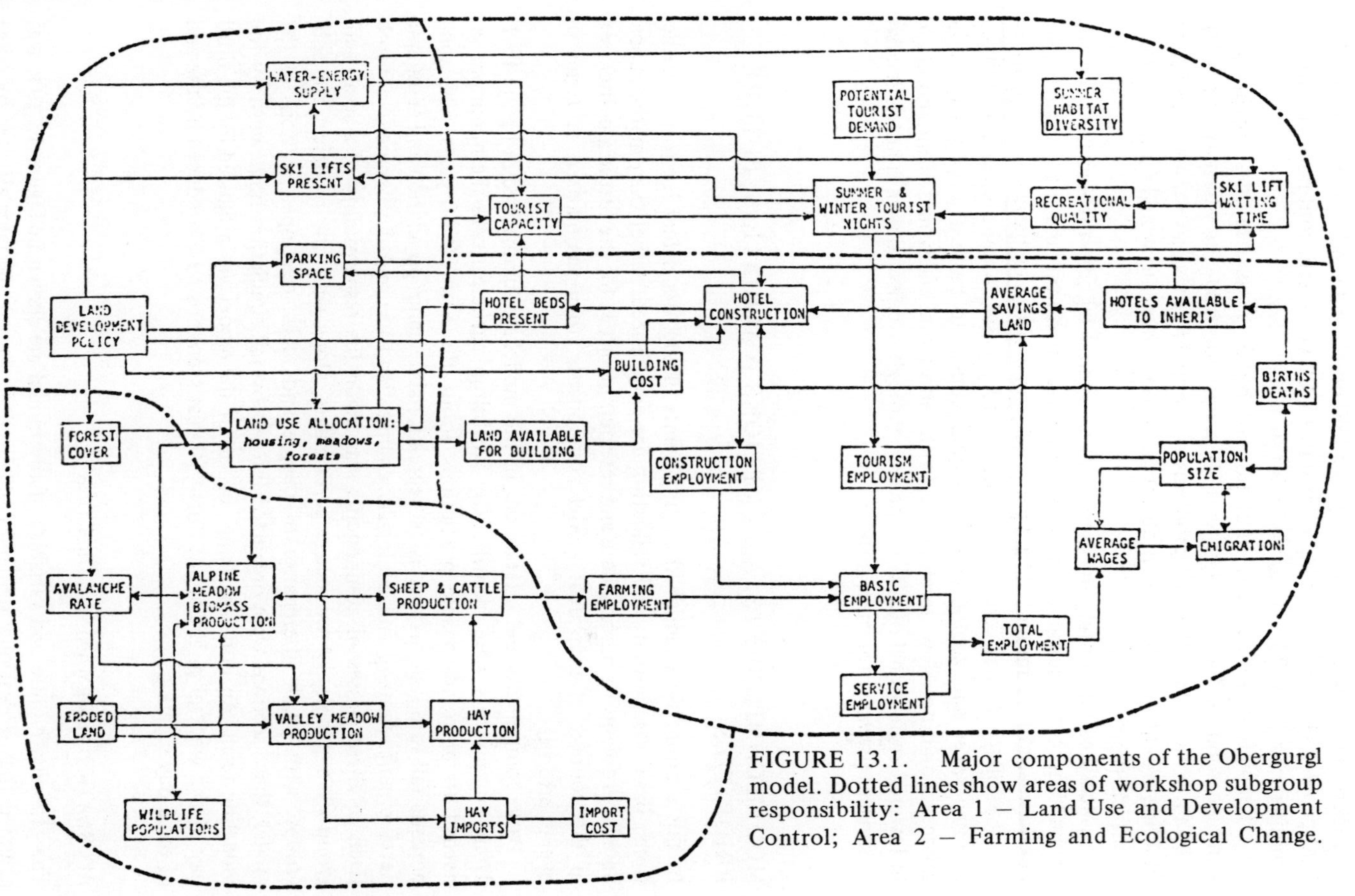

FIGURE 13.1. Major components of the Obergurgl model. Dotted lines show areas of workshop subgroup responsibility: Area 1 – Land Use and Development Control; Area 2 – Farming and Ecological Change.

together may reach a total size of around 90 hotels and a local population of 600–700 people. This limit could be reached in 15–20 years with continued government building subsidy, or 20–30 years without such subsidies.

2. Population growth and limitation of building opportunities are likely to combine soon to force a major wave of emigration from the village (perhaps 100 people), with attendant social problems. Government subsidies for continued hotel building would postpone this problem for a short time, but would ultimately make its effects more dramatic.

3. Measures for limiting the growth of Obergurgl fall into three classes: controls on building costs (subsidies or taxes), zoning controls on land made available for development or on amount of land per hotel, and controls on basic services provided for the village (water, energy, ski lifts, road access). Among these possibilities, building taxes and zoning controls would appear to be best. Controls on basic services would not slow development in the short run, and would ultimately result in lowered recreational quality of the area through overinvestment in hotels relative to services provided for these hotels.

MODEL COMPONENTS: ASSUMPTIONS, VALIDATION, FUTURE PRIORITIES

In this section, we examine the components of the model that led to the predictions. Basic assumptions and validation are emphasized, rather than mathematical details. Problems of missing data and research priorities for the future are discussed in the context of individual model components, then summarized in terms of overall priorities.

Basic components and interactions in the model are summarized in Figure 13.1. These components were identified by workshop participants as the minimum set needed to make reasonable predictions about the next 30–40 years. The components fall into four major classes: recreational demand; population and economic development; farming and ecological change; land use and development control. Each of these classes of components was made the responsibility of a small subgroup (3–5 people) of workshop participants, along with one modeler. The subgroups, with much interchange of people and ideas, developed sections of the model; these sections were organized into an overall simulation framework by the modeling team. An initial working version of the model was produced by the third day of the workshop, and about thirty 50-year scenarios were produced by the end of the 5-day meeting.

RECREATIONAL DEMAND PREDICTIONS

The general structure and variables of the model are shown in Figure 13.1. It was assumed that recreational demand (measured by tourist nights) is affected by three main factors: a general potential based on population and economic conditions outside the area; the tourist capacity of the village, which would normally be the number of beds available but which could be limited by other services provided for the village (water, energy, parking); and recreational quality of the area, as measured by a habitat diversity index for summer conditions and by ski-lift waiting time for winter conditions.

Little is known about potential recreational demand. Winter hotel occupancy rates have been very high since 1950, and the only hint of any demand limit was a 10–15% drop in occupancy during 1973–1974. This drop coincided with the energy crisis in Europe, and with a monetary crisis in Germany (Germany and England are major tourist sources for Obergurgl). According to hotel owners, this drop might have been 10–20% greater, except that the Italian Dolomites had poor snow conditions. Judging from the general growth in skiing throughout Europe, there is reason to assume that potential winter demand is essentially infinite. On the other hand, summer occupancy rates have averaged 30% over the past 10 years, though a slight decline has been evident. (The total number of tourist nights has remained essentially constant since 1965, and these nights are distributed over more and more hotels.) Thus, changes in environmental quality over the past few years may be having an impact on summer use, though it is possible that mountain areas may become more and more popular for summer tourism as other vacation areas across Europe become more crowded. On balance, it seems safest to assume that (a) summer demand has reached its potential limit considering the existing population of Europe, and (b) further changes in environmental quality would cause summer demand to decrease.

These observations and assumptions formed the basis for our very simple demand submodel. In each simulated year, potential summer and winter demands are calculated as geometrically growing (2% per year) from a 1950 base level. As ski lifts become more crowded, winter demand is reduced according to the functional relationship shown in Figure 13.2. As the proportion of meadowland used for housing increases and more alpine meadow is lost to erosion, habitat diversity is assumed to decrease and summer demand is assumed to drop off, as shown in Figure 13.3. Other measures of recreational quality, such as ski slope crowding or alpine meadow crowding in summer, were not included in the model. A simple series of tests in the simulation program is used to determine whether the recreational demand as computed from the potential demand and environmental quality can be accommodated with existing facilities (rooms, water, parking). If not, the demand is reduced according to which facility is limiting, using the following requirements:

	Annual Tourist Nights per Unit Facility Provided	
Facility	Summer	Winter
Hotel rooms	180/room	270/room
Water delivered to village	16,000/liter/sec delivered	
Parking area (hectares)	150,000/ha	224,910/ha

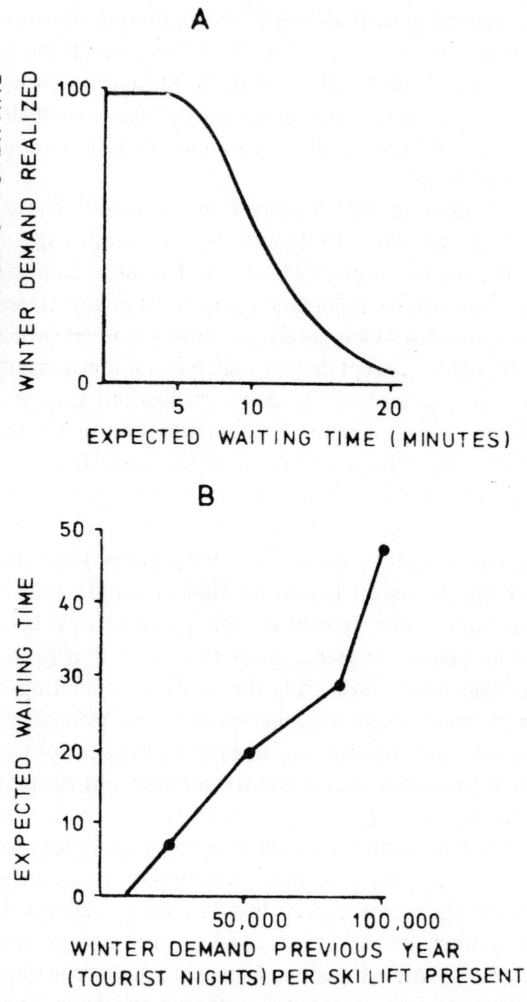

FIGURE 13.2 Winter recreational demand as a function of ski-lift waiting time (*A*), which is computed from the number of winter tourists and the number of lifts available (*B*).

These requirements were calculated from information supplied by the Obergurgl hotel owners. Note that no consideration is given to special requirements or crowding problems that might occur during short periods (peak weekends, for example) within any tourist season; only overall seasonal totals are used in the model.

Simulated and observed recreational demands for the period 1950–1973 are compared in Figure 13.4. The demand model easily mimics past changes, but this

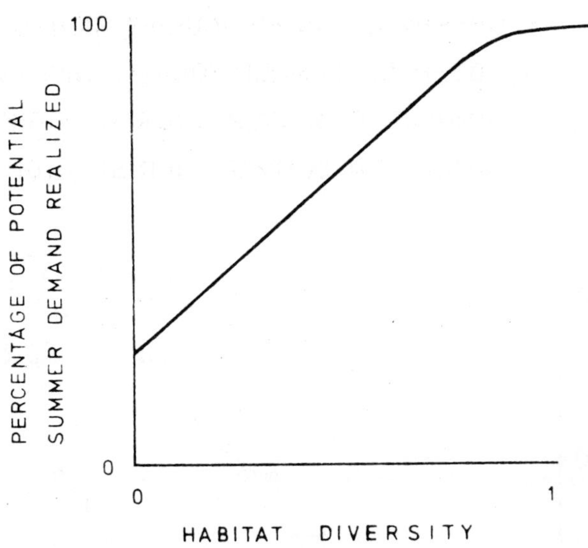

FIGURE 13.3 Summer demand as a function of habitat diversity, which is an index computed from the amount of valley and alpine meadow left untouched by building and erosion.

is not a good validation test because the past changes were used to construct the model in the first place. The simulated changes in winter tourist nights in Figure 13.4 are completely due to changes in the simulated number of hotel rooms available, since simulated occupancy remained very high (as did observed occupancy). Occupancy rates remained very high because ski lift waiting time remained low, in turn because the simulated number of lifts was increased (as observed) whenever waiting time exceeded 5 minutes. Simulated summer tourist nights closely follows observed levels simply because the simulated potential, which was estimated from the observed levels, was always met.

The key weakness in the recreation submodel is lack of data about likely responses of tourists to changed environmental quality. Also, the model does not represent the spatial distribution of quality relative to recreational use; low quality near the village may be important, even if the overall area is still in good condition. The people best able to acquire such data are the Obergurgl hotel owners themselves. We recommended that, as a first step, the hotel owners prepare a series of photographs of how the village might look after more development and present these scenarios to their guests. We consider this recommendation to have the highest priority of any developed in the workshop. Such a survey would at least indicate when the kind of people who now visit the area would stop coming. The photographic scenarios could be prepared very easily by drawing in additional hotels in the places where they are most likely to be built, and by inserting various

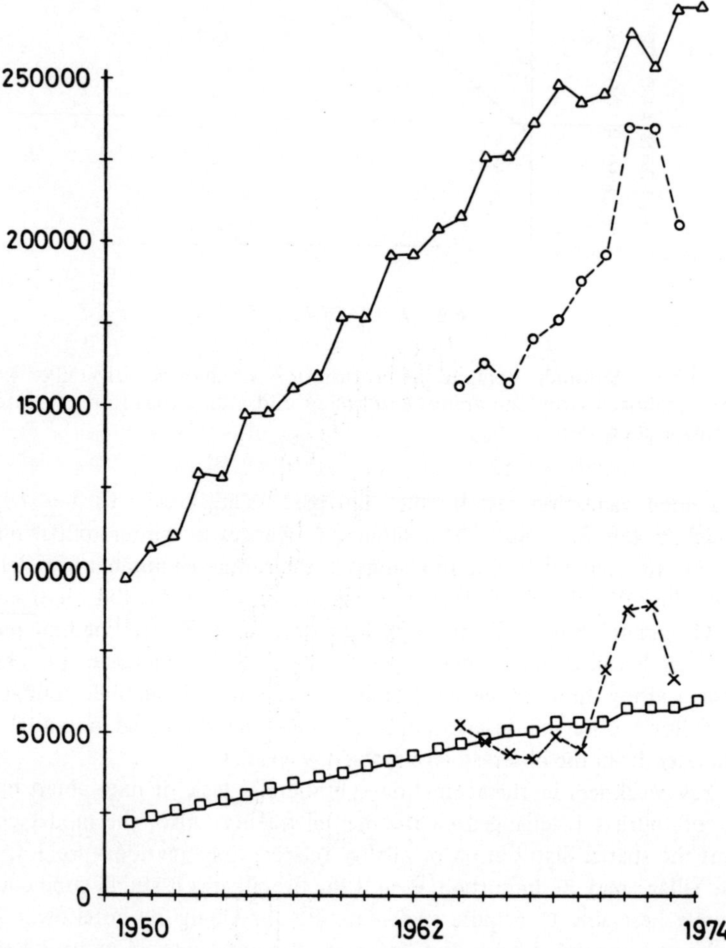

FIGURE 13.4a Simulated and observed summer and winter tourist nights.

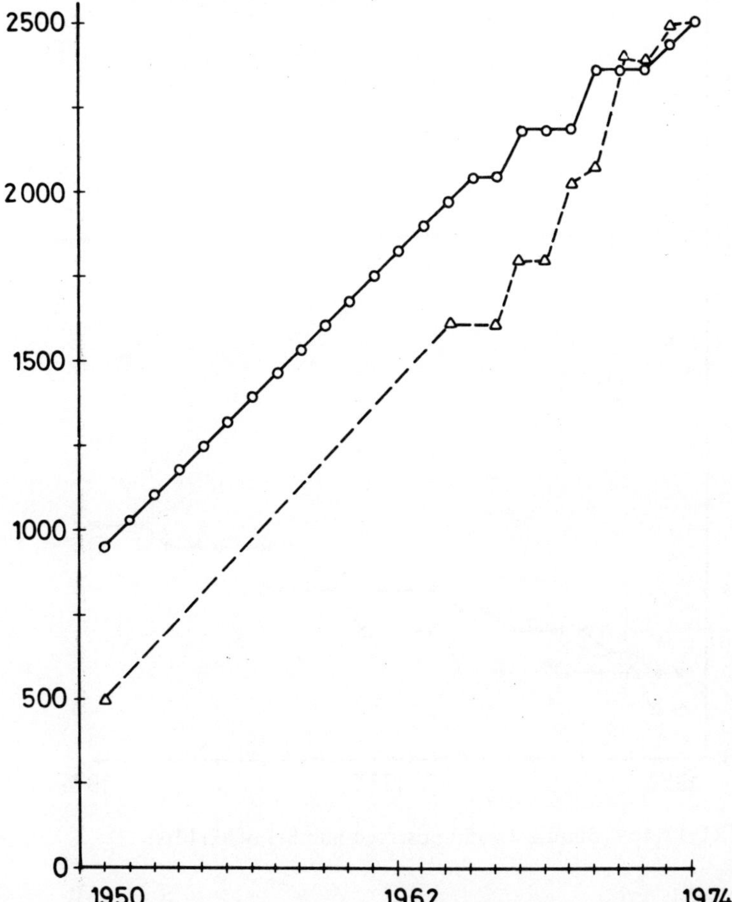

FIGURE 13.4b Simulated and observed hotel capacity (in beds) of Obergurgl.

kinds of environmental changes (e.g., eroded areas) in places where the MAB 6 ecologists think such changes are most likely to occur.

POPULATION GROWTH AND ECONOMIC DEVELOPMENT

As mentioned earlier, the key to economic growth in Obergurgl has been growth in its local population, since land ownership is tightly controlled. Thus, the population and economic components of the model are tightly interrelated, as shown

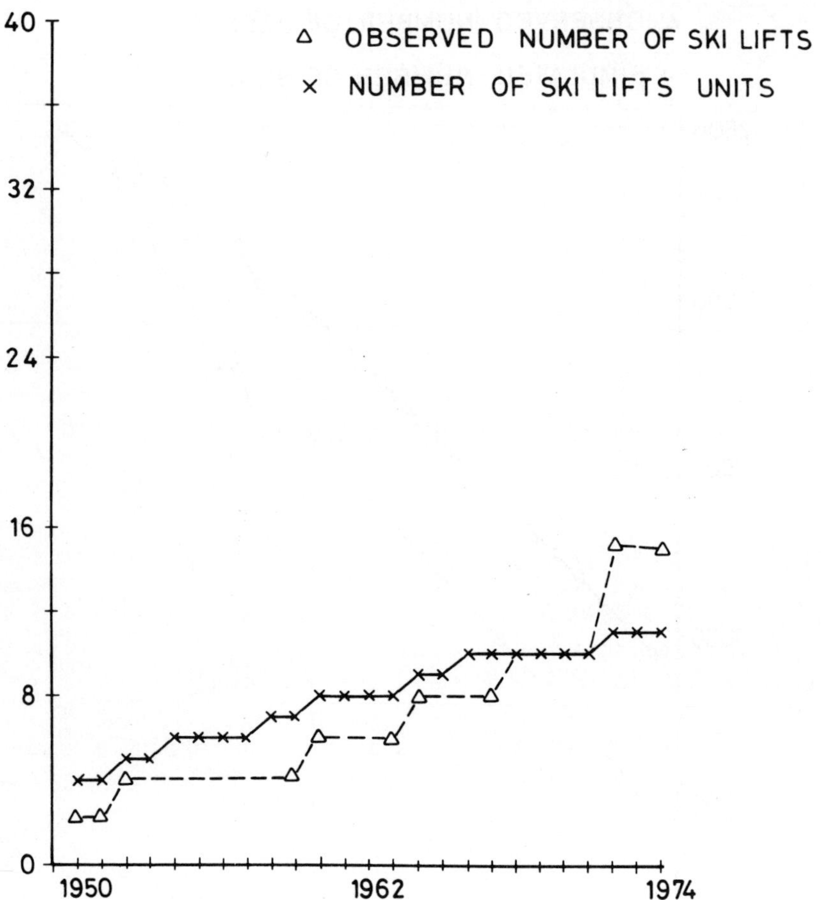

FIGURE 13.4c Simulated and observed number of ski lifts.

in Figure 13.1. Population growth is assumed to occur as a function of birth, death, immigration, and emigration rates; population structure at any time is represented in terms of four age classes (0–15, 15–30, 30–60, 60+) with different contributions to these rates. Economic development is represented in terms of hotel construction and four kinds of employment (tourism, farming, construction, service); it is not necessary to consider other kinds of capital development and building, since all buildings are used at least in part to house tourists.

Population change is simulated simply by adding or deleting proportions of the people in each age class each year. The annual proportional rates used for birth, death, and aging are shown in Table 13.1. Immigration rate is assumed to be negligible, since people from outside the village cannot purchase permanent housing

TABLE 13.1 Annual Proportional Rates for Birth, Death, and Aging

Age Class	Per Capita Birth Rate	Per Capita Death Rate	Per Capita Movement to Next Age Class	Initial Number (1950)
0–15	0	0	0.067	41
16–30	0	0	0.067	56
31–60	0.15 for house owners 0 for nonowners	0	0.033	40
61+	0	.005	0	9

and since few emigrants return to the village. Emigration rates for 15–30-year-olds are assumed to depend on employment opportunities in the village, according to the functional relationship shown in Figure 13.5; this relationship is pure guesswork, since employment has been good and there has been little emigration over the past 20 years. Emigration rates for 31–60-year-old people are assumed to depend on land ownership opportunities; people with hotels (either by inheritance or new building) are assumed never to emigrate, while 20 percent of the people over 30 who have not been able to build (see below) or inherit are assumed to leave each year.

This simple population model is able to mimic changes over the 1950–1974 period quite well, as shown in Table 13.2. The disparity in number of old people could be easily corrected, as could our underestimate of birth rate. However, predictions about the future depend most heavily on our assumptions concerning emigration rate changes, and we have no good empirical basis for those assumptions.

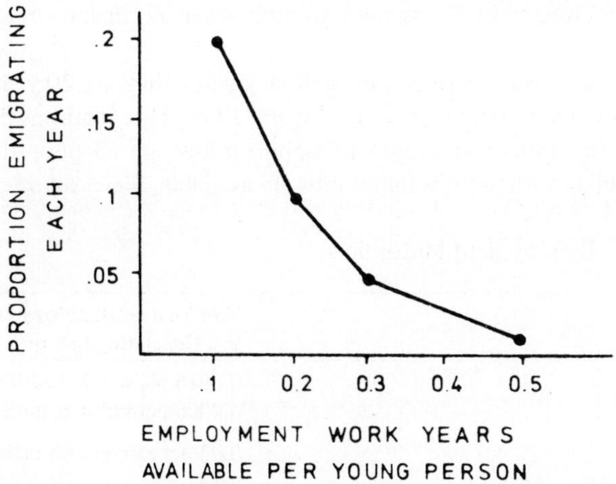

FIGURE 13.5 Assumed relationship between emigration rate of young people (16–30 years) and employment in the village.

TABLE 13.2 Observed and Simulated Population Changes, 1950–1974

Age Class	1974 Age Structure	
	Observed	Simulated from 1950 Base
0–15	107	90
16–30	49	61
31–60	86	76
61+	18	53
Total	260	280

In all economic calculations, employment man-years are used as a basic currency unit. Employment opportunities in the village each year are simulated with simple, empirical employment multipliers (Table 13.3). The number of animal units maintained by farmers is generated in the ecology submodel (see below), and tourism in the demand submodel (see above). Man-years of employment in excess of what village residents can take is assumed to go to seasonal nonresident workers. The supply of nonresident workers is assumed to be unlimited. The model predicted, starting from a 1950 base, that about 900 nonresident workers would be needed every winter by 1974; the actual number in the 1973–1974 winter was 800.

Perhaps the most critical variable in the population and economic development submodel is the hotel construction rate. This rate is assumed to depend on the number of resident men over 30 years of age who do not already have a hotel, the amount of savings these men could have accumulated, and building costs as a function of amount of land still available for development. Profitability of hotels already existing is also considered explicitly as a factor affecting investment, though savings accumulation should automatically take past profitability into account; hotel investment is assumed to stop when occupancy rates drop below 60%.

Young men are assumed to be saving money when they are 20 years old, according to the functional relationship in Figure 13.6. This relationship is modified downward when summer employment opportunities are so poor that no savings can be accumulated when no summer jobs are available. Since summer employment

TABLE 13.3 Employment Multipliers

Type of Work	Man-Years of Employment Generated and Generating Factor
Tourism	0.0016 per winter tourist night 0.0006 per summer tourist night
Farming	0.03 per animal unit maintained
Construction	13.4 per hotel built
Service	0.03 per man-year of other employment

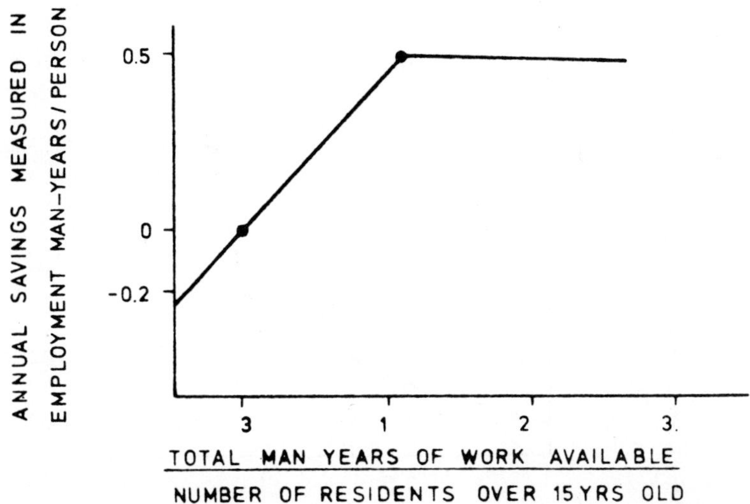

FIGURE 13.6 Rate of savings accumulation by prospective hotel owners as a function of employment in the village.

in the past few years has come in good part from hotel construction, the young villagers have become dependent on a growth economy: they cannot save enough money to build a hotel without summer employment, and this employment in turn depends on continued growth. We know that in the 1950s a young man could save enough in about 5 years to build his own hotel, but in recent years construction costs have risen (since poorer building sites must be used), and about 7 years of saving are required.

We incorporated this problem into the model with the functional relationship shown in Figure 13.7. To find the amount of land that could be developed each year based on building costs, the average savings level among non-house-owners over 30 years of age is fed into Figure 13.7, and the corresponding amount of land developed is compared to that already developed. The amount of land developed is the potential calculated in this way, provided the potential is not negative and does not exceed the number of young men wanting a hotel divided by the size (hectares) of each hotel plus its lot. Hotels in the past have required an average area of 0.13 hectares, though a policy is contemplated to raise this area to 0.24 hectares. An implicit assumption in all of the calculations about savings and building costs is that all inflationary changes will balance one another: the inflationary effect on building cost is assumed to be cancelled by inflation in wages.

Starting from 20 hotels in the 1950 base year, the model predicted, as observed, that about 60 hotels (2,500 beds) should be present by 1974 (Figure 13.4). Thus, it appears that we have captured very well in the model the basic processes that determine land development. The critical relationship for further study is the one shown in Figure 13.7: if the building costs rise more rapidly in the future than we

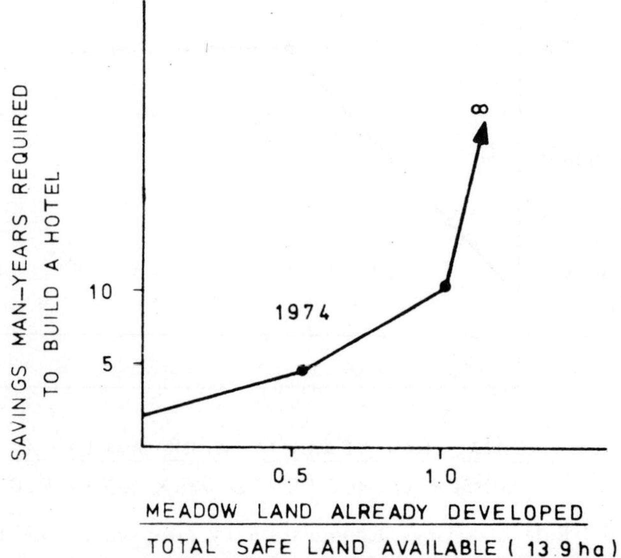

FIGURE 13.7 Assumed relationship between relative hotel construction cost and amount of land already developed. Relative cost is measured in terms of how long a young man must save money in order to afford to start building.

have assumed, growth of the village may be limited well before and below the levels we have predicted. As the development cost relationship is essentially an economic and engineering problem, we recommend that these disciplines be brought into the MAB 6 Obergurgl project.

FARMING AND ECOLOGICAL CHANGE

In keeping with the general objectives of MAB, the basic biological processes in the Obergurgl area have been treated as secondary factors. The intent of this approach was not to deny the importance of the biotic environment, but to concentrate the attention of the workshop participants on key economic and policy questions. Despite the secondary treatment of many natural processes, certain key areas of future research were outlined and are presented in the following discussion.

The "environmental" submodel treats three broad groups of phenomena. First, it determines the status of wild and domestic animal populations, including the forage necessary to support these animals. Second, it determines the status of the forest, allowing for growth, death, regeneration, and planting. Finally, it considers changes in land use due to the process of erosion, including several contributing factors.

Most of the ecological processes we considered have not been critically evaluated by field experimentation or documentation. Many interactions and parameter values required purely subjective estimation. There was not always agreement among the workshop participants as to what the estimated values should be, and hence the model was constructed to allow the option of using different hypotheses or estimates during simulation.

Animal Population Patterns

Three species of domestic animals and one wild species are considered in the model. The chamois is the only wildlife species considered; it is potentially important in model predictions because of its aesthetic value to tourists, recreational value to hunters, and possible role in damaging forest regeneration. Its population dynamics were simulated simply by postulating birth, death, and hunter kill rates in relation to basic habitat conditions (vegetation patterns). Model test runs indicated that population sizes are not likely to change dramatically in the next few decades, so the chamois can be treated as a constant component of environmental quality.

Cows, on the other hand, are directly important to the tourist industry of Obergurgl in at least two ways: provision of fresh dairy products and contribution to the picturesque nature of the landscape. The model sets initial stocking rates for cows as well as for horses, sheep, and sheep brought in from other portions of the Tyrol for summer grazing. Stocking rates for the Obergurgl animals are reduced if insufficient forage is available: horses are considered a luxury, and, when forage is limited, their numbers are reduced first, then sheep, and finally cows.

Forage available for the Obergurgl domestic stock is calculated in three steps. First, the production from the valley meadows and alpine hay meadows is computed. Then, forage requirements of the livestock are determined. Finally, the amount of hay that must be imported to meet these requirements is determined and when economically possible, this hay is imported.

Production estimates are computed simply: an average production figure per hectare (3,700 kg/ha/yr for valley bottom meadows and 1,750 kg/ha/yr for alpine hay meadows) is multiplied by the number of hectares of the appropriate meadow available. At present, there are 96 ha of valley bottom meadow producing 355,000 kg annually and 90 ha of alpine hay meadows producing 157,500 kg annually.

The model assumes that summer grazing of cows now occurs in areas that are not explicitly considered by the model (modified dwarf shrub zone). Thus, summer grazing requirements of cows are ignored. Sheep grazing effects are similarly considered inconsequential and are invoked only during the computation of one of the two formulations of their contribution to erosion. One formulation of the erosion process assumes that sheep contribute in a manner directly proportional to their grazing intensity and density. The grazing intensity is represented by a variable that approximates 1 as grazing requirements relative to the amount available become large, and tends to 0 as requirements become small relative to amounts of forage available. The grazing requirements of sheep are computed by summing the daily food demand per sheep for both resident and nonresident (e.g., Südtirol) sheep over the number of days each group is present in the alpine areas of Obergurgl.

Winter forage requirements for domestic livestock are typically met by local haying and import of other hay. The model computes total forage requirements by summing the needs of all livestock. Cattle and horses are assumed to require 3,600 kg of forage per animal over the winter, and sheep are assumed to require 730 kg/sheep/year.

Once the hay requirements have been computed, these are compared with hay production to determine whether hay must be imported. If the wage index is greater than or equals a specified parameter, all the required additional hay is imported; and if it is less than that parameter, no hay is imported. Furthermore, to account for inflation, the requisite wage index for import of all required hay grows at an annual rate. As already discussed, stock is reduced if insufficient fodder is available.

Forests

Forests are considered to modify the rates of avalanche and erosion. Thus, their growth and extent are simulated in the "ecological" submodel. The link from forest protection to tourism was left weaker than may be the case in reality; at present the model considers only a small effect on the amount of land eroded.

We included a policy variable for setting the number of hectares of forestable land which will be planted in a given year. For the first 2 years after planting, trees (*Pinus cembra*) are subject to a rather high mortality rate due to diseases and soil conditions. In addition, these young trees have a specified probability of being browsed by chamois or trampled by cows. Workshop discussions of the fate of recently planted trees were inconclusive, and workshop model runs allowed no browsing by chamois. Since establishment of forests protected from grazing would not only reduce erosion but would modify the protected area available for hotel building, the modeling exercise indicated that forest regeneration processes are potentially a matter of critical biological and economic concern and should therefore be the subject of further study.

Changes in the amounts of forested land are a result of growth into forest over many years, or losses due to erosion. Over the time span of the model the pine forests do not age sufficiently to decrease in extent, but they may be increased through reforestation practices.

Erosion

In some respects the transfers of land from one land-use category to another due to the processes of erosion may be the most important section of the environmental submodel, since the amount of land in each of the land-use categories influences many major processes. Erosion causes transfer of land from forestable land, alpine meadow, and alpine hay meadow to eroded land.

Alpine meadow suffers erosion due to sheep and tourists. Sheep erosion is calculated as proportional to overgrazing, as already discussed, or alternatively as a standard rate per sheep present (0.0003 ha/sheep/yr). Tourists "erode" according to the number of winter tourist days times a winter erosion rate (0.0000002 ha/tourist/day), plus the number of summer tourist days times a summer erosion rate (0.0000002 ha/tourist/day) plus an additional amount for the construction of each new ski lift unit (2 ha/lift unit).

Land suitable for forests is eroded according to an intrinsic rate subject to forest protection and the activity of cows. The model assumes that these lands are subject to an intrinsic rate of erosion (0.1 ha/yr), which can be decreased as more of the land becomes actually forested, according to the ratio

$$\text{ERVIV} = \frac{\text{forestable land}}{\text{forestable land} + \text{forested land}}.$$

The same forest protection ratio (ERVIV) is used to calculate the reduction in erosion rate per cow.

All erosion processes were assumed to be additive. The appropriate number of hectares is subtracted from the forestable, alpine, and alpine hay meadow areas, and added to the eroded land. Erosion recovery may be simulated as a natural rate or as a policy option by setting a parameter to correspond to a certain number of hectares per year transferred back from eroded to alpine meadow. All the erosion rate parameters were guesses, as no real data were available. There was again some disagreement about the magnitude (and even the existence) of the postulated effects. The parameter values mentioned above produced about 2 ha of eroded land not associated with ski-lift construction over the 25-year period, 1950–1974, when other model dynamics were realistic.

Model Dynamics

Initial model runs demonstrated that the ecological submodel was rather weakly linked to the socioeconomic sections. Trees and chamois grew at an intrinsic rate influenced only by set policies on hunting and reforestation. Cattle and sheep generated a slightly changing demand for imported hay. In some scenarios where wages decreased, we predicted that it might become necessary to reduce stocks considerably in about 10–20 years.

Just before the end of the workshop, the model was amended to produce a scenario in which the summer tourists would be very sensitive to the aesthetic quality of the landscape as measured by the percent of alpine meadow eroded. As erosion increased and summer tourism decreased, emigration was initiated somewhat earlier, hotel building stabilized, winter tourism stabilized, and the lower population in the area maintained a relatively steady wage level. Erosion rate also decreased as a result of less tourist activity. A natural stability was indicated. The critical question is to what extent tourists are sensitive to landscape aesthetics; and, if this sensitivity and resultant stabilization is to be expected, what quality of landscape will finally trigger the process. Stabilization due to an unaesthetic environment may not be in the best interests of the villagers.

A further interesting indication produced by the model was the time lag to be expected in a reforestation program. When reforestation was very high for the first 15 years ($\leqslant$15 ha/yr), no noticeable effect occurred in the model until about the thirtieth year of simulation. At that point, erosion rates significantly decreased because of a noticeable accumulation of young forest. In part, the lag is due to the slow growth rates of the forest. In part, it is due to the effects of forest on stabilizing adjacent hay meadow areas.

Implications

In summary, despite the rather simplistic nature of the ecological submodel, some key areas for further investigation were identified. These can be listed briefly:

- Forest regeneration processes and broad causes of failure – e.g., relative losses due to diseases, snow creep, trampling.
- Nature of environmental perception – e.g., how do tourists perceive and respond to changes in the environment?
- Processes that induce erosion and ameliorate or hasten recovery from erosion – e.g., what processes are critical in causing erosion, and how can recovery be hastened by fertilization, seeding, and so on?
- Grazing processes of wild and domestic stock – e.g., what is the spatial distribution and pattern of the grazing process?
- Successional patterns of present meadow areas – e.g., how are these influenced by grazing and erosion?

The five areas mentioned were all demonstrated to be important to the general predictions of the model. That is, their importance is not simply a matter of biological interest: they are significant for economic planning in the area. For example, it is impossible to answer hotel owners' questions concerning the use of domestic grazing stock to maintain "attractive" alpine meadows with the present model. The model framework is appropriate, but certain processes are not incorporated. Similarly, the model now suggests that protected areas suitable for hotel construction cannot be increased by forest planting practices alone, but would require some form of avalanche protection. While the suggestion is probably correct, more information on forest regeneration is necessary before potential economic advantages and disadvantages of such protection could be rigorously evaluated.

LAND USE AND DEVELOPMENT CONTROL

One subgroup of workshop participants was given the responsibility of identifying alternative schemes for controlling the growth of Obergurgl, and for ensuring that the submodels described above could accept such schemes. A necessary first step for this subgroup was to recognize that controllable variables are not necessarily the same as variables that measure the results of control; for example, hotel size may be controlled by zoning and may result in better environmental quality, but the environmental quality cannot be controlled directly. Thus, it was necessary to identify indicators for the results of control as well as the controllable factors.

Our work led to identification of possible control actions by the various institutions that have some influence on Obergurgl (Table 13.4). These control actions fall into three basic classes: land zoning, building rate modification, and provision of tourist services besides buildings. Obviously, many control actions are possible besides the ones listed above – for example, the formation of special nature protection areas; such controls were not considered because the model would not be sensitive to them because we had represented perception of environmental quality patterns too simplistically.

Land zoning and building rate controls are implemented in the model very simply by reducing the curve in Figure 13.7. Zoning controls change the total amount of land available, while subsidies and taxes lower or raise the building cost curve. Since the rate of land development never achieved very high values even in the absence of any controls, no scenarios were developed with explicit control on building rate.

In the absence of special input, the model adds basic services and recreational facilities according to demand alone. For example, the model "builds" a new ski lift whenever lift waiting time exceeds 5 minutes. To simulate control of services, we simply programmed an upper limit for development of each service and set this upper limit at very high values, except in scenarios designed to test the limit.

To provide an independent assessment of the likely impacts of various development policies, the workshop participants were asked to fill out a "presimulation expectations table" (Table 13.5). In this table they indicated what they thought

TABLE 13.4 Possible Land Use and Development Control Actions

Control Action	Institutional Responsibility
Regulation of room prices to control occupancy rates	Hotel owners
Total area zoned for building	Village, regional government
Hotel size (per building plus surrounding lot)	Village government
Hotels built per year	Village government
Hotel building subsidy or tax	Regional government
Reforestation and agricultural maintenance subsidy	Regional government
Provision of basic services to village (water, energy)	Village (water) or regional government (energy)
Provision of recreational facilities (ski lifts, trails)	Village (hotel-owner consortium)

TABLE 13.5 Pre-simulation Expectations Table (For each position in this table, participants indicated whether the control action would improve the condition in the column or make the condition worse relative to what would occur with no control. Numbers in each box indicate how many participants had each opinion.)

	Impact Variable								
	Population Impacts					Environmental Impacts			
Control Action and Agency Responsible	Final Number of Hotels	Occupancy Rate	Final Population	Social Dissatisfaction (Emigration Rate)	Wage Level (Employment)	Farming Potential	Environmental Quality (Diversity)	Ski Area Crowding	Final Meadow Area
Room prices	+(2)	+(0)	+(4)	+(3)	+(7)	+(5)	+(10)	+(1)	+(3)
(hotel owners)	—(5)	—(8)	—(4)	—(3)	—(2)	—(2)	—(0)	—(1)	—(2)
	0(3)	0(1)	0(2)	0(4)	0(1)	0(3)	0(0)	0(8)	0(5)
Total area	+(3)	+(6)	+(2)	+(10)	+(1)	+(5)	+(7)	+(3)	+(7)
for buildings	—(7)	—(3)	—(8)	—(0)	—(4)	—(3)	—(3)	—(7)	—(3)
(Region-town)	0(0)	0(1)	0(0)	0(0)	0(5)	0(2)	0(0)	0(0)	0(0)
Beds/hotel	+(0)	+(1)	+(4)	+(2)	+(8)	+(3)	+(0)	+(8)	+(1)
(town)	—(7)	—(6)	—(3)	—(5)	—(1)	—(3)	—(9)	—(0)	—(3)
	[illegible]	[illegible]	[illegible]	[illegible]	[illegible]	0(4)	0(1)	0(2)	0(6)

	[illegible]	[illegible]	[illegible]	—(2)	—(4)	—(6)	—(2)	—(6)	—(7)
	0(2)	0(1)	0(2)	0(2)	0(0)	0(2)	0(0)	0(2)	0(1)
Area for hotels	+(0)	+(7)	+(1)	+(8)	+(0)	+(2)	+(7)	+(0)	+(5)
each year	—(9)	—(2)	—(7)	—(1)	—(4)	—(0)	—(3)	—(9)	—(3)
(town)	0(1)	0(1)	0(2)	0(1)	0(6)	0(6)	0(0)	0(1)	0(1)
Building cost	+(1)	+(3)	+(1)	+(9)	+(2)	+(6)	+(9)	+(1)	+(7)
tax (region)	—(8)	—(4)	—(6)	—(0)	—(4)	—(2)	—(0)	—(7)	—(1)
	0(1)	0(2)	0(3)	0(1)	0(3)	0(2)	0(1)	0(2)	0(2)
Reforestation	+(4)	+(7)	+(5)	+(2)	+(6)	+(4)	+(9)	+(5)	+(1)
(region)	—(2)	—(0)	—(2)	—(2)	—(2)	—(5)	—(1)	—(2)	—(7)
	0(4)	0(3)	0(3)	0(6)	0(2)	0(1)	0(0)	0(3)	0(2)
Water and energy	+(2)	+(4)	+(3)	+(6)	+(3)	+(2)	+(7)	+(2)	+(3)
supply fixed	—(6)	—(3)	—(6)	—(4)	—(4)	—(7)	—(3)	—(6)	—(2)
(region)	0(1)	0(2)	0(1)	0(0)	0(3)	0(1)	0(0)	0(2)	0(4)

the qualitative effects (plus or minus) of a series of alternative controls would be on each of a series of "impact indicators." The impact indicators are simulation variables that measure quality of life in various ways. As Table 13.5 shows, there was little consensus among participants about most effects of most policies. For the environmental impact indicators, this is somewhat surprising, since most of the participants were ecologists with presumably the same general outlook. None of the presimulation expectations bear any clear relationship to the final predictions made by the model.

GENERAL PREDICTIONS

Though the model was developed to represent a rich variety of interactions and feedback mechanisms, its final predictions depend largely on a few key relationships. As shown in the "no-control" scenario of Figure 13.8, these relationships can be summarized very simply:

- In the face of essentially infinite potential demand, growth of the recreation industry has been limited by the rate of local population growth.
- The amount of safe land for development is disappearing rapidly, while the local demand for building sites is continuing to grow.
- As land is developed, prime agricultural land is lost and environmental quality decreases.
- Recreational demand may begin to decrease if environmental quality deteriorates further.

Thus, the village may soon be caught in a painful trap as its growing population and economy collide with declining resources and demand. This collision may be felt by the older, established hotel owners as well as the younger people, if more hotels are forced to share a declining number of tourists.

Figure 13.9 shows an alternative future, again without development control, but under the assumption that recreational demand will remain at 1973–1974 levels (e.g., continued energy and monetary crises in Europe). A key aspect of this prediction is that stabilization of demand will not stop the growth of Obergurgl immediately; there is no reason to suppose that investment in hotels will suddenly stop, since the recreation business is still profitable. Instead, overinvestment in hotels is likely to occur until no owners are doing very well. In addition, a continued slowing of demand should spread the inevitable emigration pulse over a longer period by initiating it earlier, so that widespread social dissatisfaction would not develop all at once.

The effects of a government subsidy to help young people build hotels are shown in Figure 13.10, where unlimited potential demand is assumed. Unlike the other scenarios, safe building land is exhausted much earlier, triggering emigration

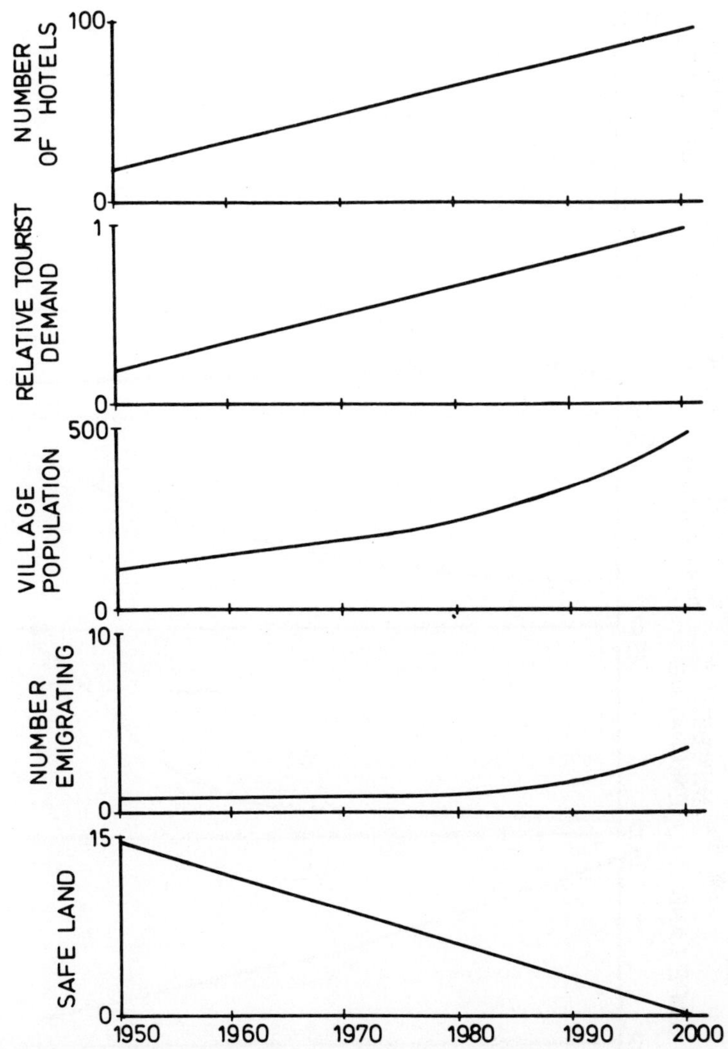

FIGURE 13.8 Simulated behavior of five selected variables without development controls.

of young people earlier. The subsidy should not have a great effect on rate of economic growth, but it should make conditions much worse when growth does stop. If the government does pursue a subsidization policy, a major planning focus for the village should be to begin educating young people immediately about the problems they will soon face, with a view to helping these young people find alternative ways of life.

At another extreme, Figure 13.11 shows a scenario involving government taxes

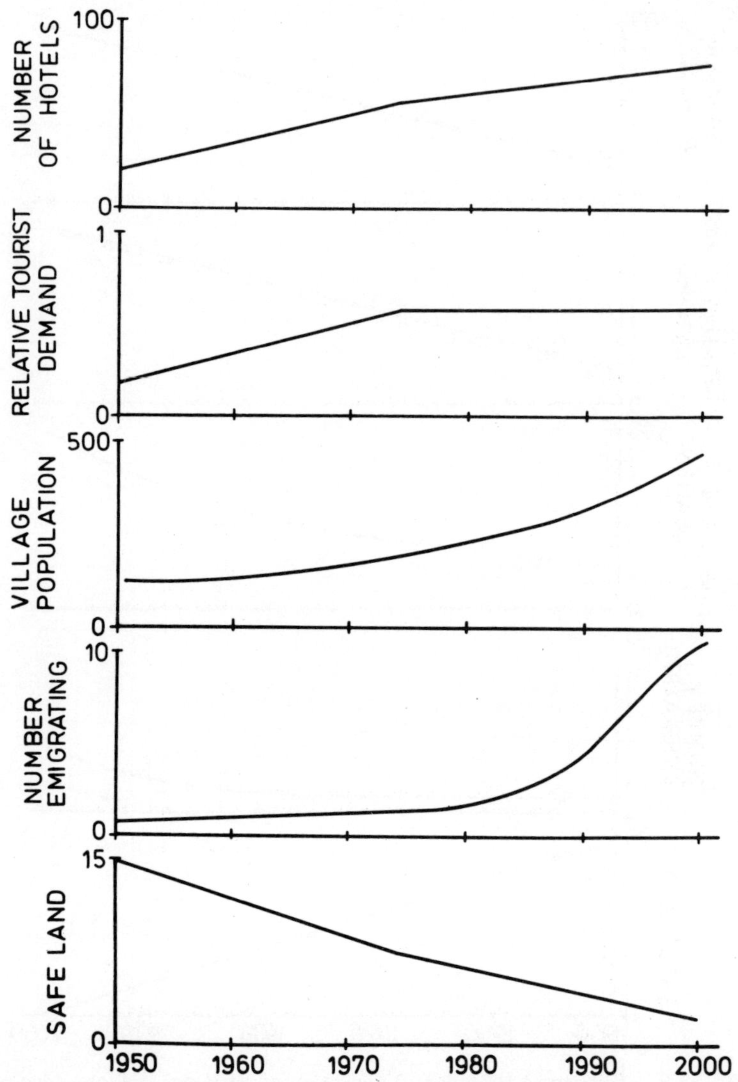

FIGURE 13.9 Simulated behavior of five selected variables without development controls but with recreational demand maintained after 1974 at the 1974 level.

to make new building more difficult. This policy would slow economic development and spread out the emigration pulse. Though attractive at first glance, this scenario is probably not politically feasible: no government that imposed a discriminatory tax on a large body of voters, the young people, would last very long.

In an effort to find more subtle controls, we looked at several scenarios involving limitation of services (e.g., ski lifts, water) provided for tourists. All of these

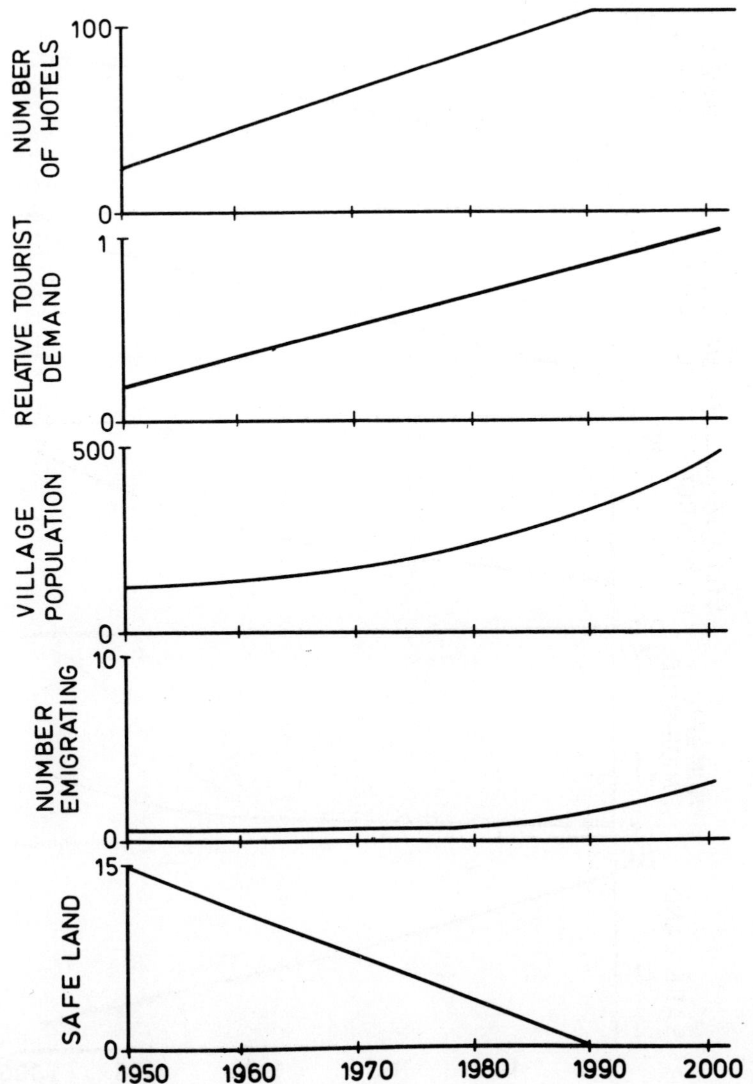

FIGURE 13.10 Simulated behavior of five selected variables with a government subsidy added to help young people build hotels.

scenarios involved limitation of recreational demand rather than village growth, just as in the demand crisis scenarios of Figure 13.9. The same problems of overcapitalization in hotels and extended emigration arose in all cases. In addition, the quality of the recreational experience for most tourists would decline, so everyone would lose in the long run. Thus, we strongly recommended against any control policies involving limitation of tourist services other than hotels.

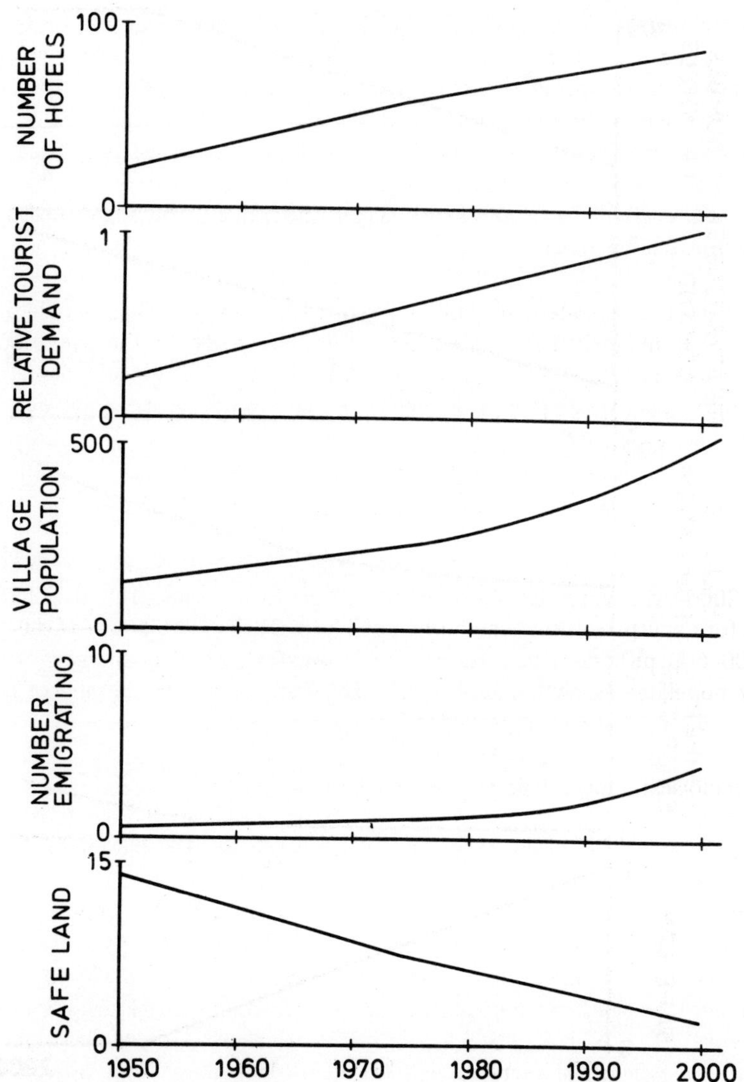

FIGURE 13.11 Simulated behavior of five selected variables with a government tax added to make new building more difficult.

A scenario was tried that called for land zoning to make each new hotel use a larger lot (buildings not larger, but more spread out). The effect of this policy would be to slow hotel building (since young people would be forced to use more expensive sites sooner) and to decrease the eventual maximum size of the village. However, the emigration problem would not be solved, in effect no meadowland would be saved, and the village might still look too large to many tourists. Before any development control of this kind is initiated, tourists should be presented, as recommended above, with alternative pictures of how the village would look with future hotels spread out, as compared to clustered together. Spreading hotels out might well do more harm than good.

We could continue on and on in discussion of alternative scenarios for controlling growth, but the short discussions above appear to cover the main feasible options. From the variety of scenarios tried, some most likely and some most extreme predictions can be drawn:

- Even if meadowland for building were not limited, the village would probably not grow to more than 150 hotels (double its present size) by the year 2000, based on the number of young people who are likely to reach the hotel-building age. The most likely prediction is 80–90 hotels when the village reaches its safe land limits in about 20 years.
- Hotel building will not significantly alter the amount of valley grazing meadow in the near future; only about 20 percent more of this land is ever likely to be developed.
- With no land limits, the local population could reach 700 persons by the year 2000, with a tourist use of about 600,000 nights/year. The most likely estimate for population is that equilibrium will be reached near the turn of the century, at 500–600 persons with a tourist use of about 350,000 nights/year. The most likely population growth rate for the next decade or two is 2.6 percent per year, considering the increases that are likely in emigration rates.

The ecological implications of these predictions were not made clear by the modeling work, since the ecological data base is still very poor. Present recreational use may already be more than the sensitive alpine meadows can tolerate; doubling of recreational use is not unlikely and may be disastrous.

A variety of recommendations for further research emerged from the workshop and modeling exercise; toward the end of the workshop, participants were asked to rank these recommended projects to give a clearer picture for the MAB 6 planners. After considerable discussion, consensus was reached on the following priorities:

1. Sociology of villagers in relation to attitudes about land ownership, emigration, and economic opportunities
2. Perception of environmental quality by villagers and by tourists, initially by means of photographic scenarios of future possibilities
3. Basic mapping of ecological conditions in the area, especially in relation to ski development and soil erosion
4. Determination of primary production of pastures and alpine meadows in relation to grazing by wild and domestic animals
5. Projection of potential recreational demand in relation to changing transportation systems and public attitudes across Europe

6. Continued "policy analysis" of alternative development schemes and research priorities, as done in this report

7. Experimental ecological studies involving manipulation of grazing patterns, trampling of meadows by people, and construction activities

8. Economic analysis of the village in terms of employment structure, savings patterns, and cost problems in hotel construction

In retrospect, it appears that the model described in this report can, after some relatively minor refinement, provide a solid basis for predictions about the human aspects of environmental change in Obergurgl. It remains for future modeling work to develop the ecological side of the story more fully, so a truly balanced picture of the whole system can emerge.

14 An Analysis of Regional Development in Venezuela

The Rio Orinoco basin, the second largest in South America after the Amazon, covers an area of almost 1,100,000 km^2, with an average annual flow of 1,400,000,000 m^3. Within this basin, south of the Orinoco River, is the Rio Caroni watershed (Figure 14.1), with an area of approximately 100,000 km^2. The population of this region is about 400,000, of which about 70 percent are found in Ciudad Bolivar, capital of the State of Bolivar, and Ciudad Guayana, a development and industrial center that is one of the most dynamic cities in the country. By the year 2000 Ciudad Guayana will probably have approximately 1,000,000 people and Ciudad Bolivar 350,000.

There seems to be no good quality agricultural land in the region, although it is expected that some land could be cultivated with adequate management.

North of the confluence of the Caroni and Paragua Rivers is the Raul Leoni Dam, also called the Guri Hydroelectric Project, which will be completed in two steps. The first step, with a total installed capacity of 2,650,000 kW, was inaugurated in November 1968 and was finished in 1977. The second step, expected to be completed in 1982, will take the level of the reservoir from its present level of 200 m to the height of 270 m and raise capacity to 9,000,000 kW.

Most of the hydroelectric production is consumed locally by the industries that have developed in the region. In 1974 a total of 33,576 metric tons (Tm) of aluminum was produced by ALCASA (Alumino del Caroni, S.A), and the Siderurgica del Orinoco (SIDOR) produced a total of 1,602,770 Tm of steel between January and October. Both these factories are very near the dam site. Also in 1974, between January and September, a total of 88,500 Tm of cement was produced in the area. These and other industries have plans for development and expansion in the coming years. Furthermore, there are plans to expand the fine steel, ferrosilicate, cement, motor, machinery, and other industries. Most of the organization, planning, and implementation of the development of the area is in the hands of the Corporacion

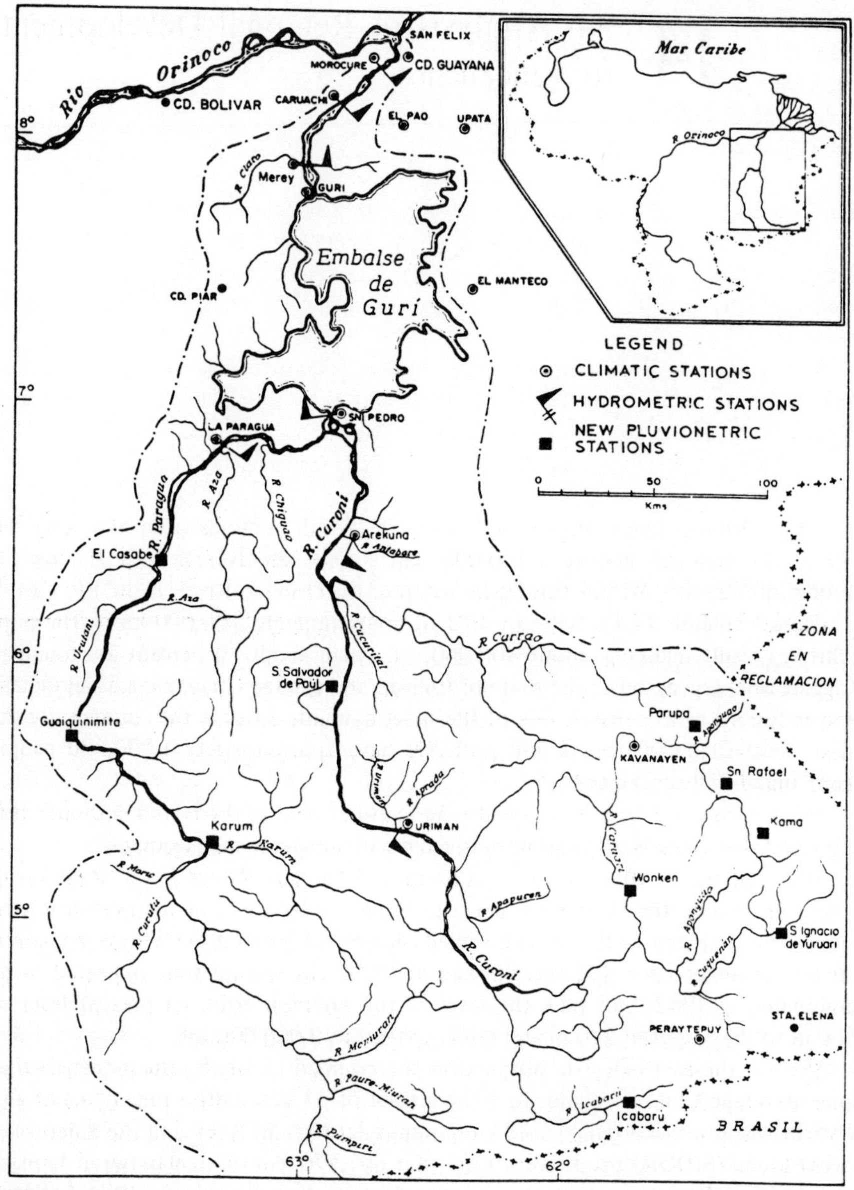

FIGURE 14.1 The Rio Caroni Basin, State of Bolivar, Venezuela (reproduced from CVG, 1974).

Venezolana de Guayana (CVG). This mixed (both government and private) corporation is autonomous with its own budget and reports directly to the President's office.

In terms of hydroelectric development, investment anticipated in the construction of the dam's final step by 1982 is of the order of 6 billion bolivars; the associated transmission system is expected to require an investment of about 2 billion bolivars (1 U.S. dollar = 4.3 bolivars).

At completion, the capital of the EDELCA company, the owner of the dam, will be 5 billion bolivars. It is estimated that employment will be generated for 8,000 people during the second-step peak of construction.

The markets for the energy generated are the region and its industrial complex itself, the east, the center including Caracas, and a few areas in the west of Venezuela. High-voltage transmission lines transmit the energy of the Caroni to these areas.

The Guayana region offers resources that lend themselves ideally to the location there of an important part of the industry needed by the country. The region contains high-quality iron ore, as well as other minerals; abundant and cheap hydroelectric energy; oil and natural gas in the nearby eastern region (including the oil shale strip near the Orinoco); and the most extensively forested regions of the country, with the navigable Orinoco as its main artery. The Guayana program has been conceived as an important contribution to the diversification of the Venezuelan economy and to create a development center.

More than half of the Rio Caroni watershed is covered by highly valuable forests. This has resulted in great pressure to exploit the more valuable woods. Fortunately, logging is being carried out in a very selective way. Due to the large population growth in the area, regional self-sufficiency in the production of food is becoming desirable. However, local soils are relatively poor, and agricultural production on land that had been covered by stable tropical forests is of short duration. Thus, sustained food production would imply a progressive advance toward the higher parts of the watershed, producing an important and increasing change in the vegetation cover of the area.

These vegetation changes could eventually jeopardize the hydroelectric production complex in two ways: first, a change in the hydrologic regime in the area can be expected, with significant increases in river flows in the rainy season, and reductions in the "dry" season; and second, if there is an important reduction in the vegetation cover, there will be a potentially dangerous increase in erosion, which, in a region like the Guayana with a relatively broken terrain, could reach one, two, and even three orders of magnitude. The first consequence might affect hydroelectric production, perhaps forcing changes in dam operation. The second consequence could cause silting in the reservoir to the level of intakes of some of the turbines, shortening the life of the dam or at least reducing its productive capacity.

The potential conflict between possible land uses in this tropical watershed cannot be analyzed *in situ* because of the size of the development programs already under way in the region. Mathematical models, particularly mathematical simulation models that operate with digital computers, allow a quantitative comparative analysis of different possible strategies of action. A simulation model was constructed at the Ecology Center of the Instituto Venezolano de Investigaciones Cientificas (IVIC) to describe quantitatively the rain–vegetation–soil–river relationship in the Rio Caroni watershed.

Given a certain precipitation in the watershed, the model simulates the river flow that feeds the Guri reservoir. Because of the potential conflict between land uses and hydroelectric production, the model was built in such a way as to facilitate the simulation of possible intervention strategies in the watershed in terms of changes produced in the vegetation cover. The model contemplates possible intervention strategies through actions at different intensity levels. For simplicity's sake, two kinds of possible environmental intervention were evaluated: the rate of logging over a period of 50 years, and the percentage of the area exploited for lumber that is turned into agricultural production.

Like any other model, the Guri model simplifies the real world. In the specific case of the model of the Caroni River, many important simplifying assumptions were made. The work was performed with an appreciable degree of aggregation, so that any prediction of the model can be considered only approximate. However, even with a very gross degree of approximation in forecasting, the results of the model seem to be clear enough to suggest what decisions should be made. It is not the intention of a model such as this to produce precise and reliable forecasts either in the magnitude of its variables or in the timing of different events.

DEFINITION OF THE SYSTEM

LOCATION

The Rio Caroni watershed is located on the south side of the Orinoco River in the State of Bolivar in the southeastern part of Venezuela known as Guayana. The State of Bolivar covers approximately 238,000 km^2 and is the largest political entity in Venezuela, accounting for 26.1% of the national territory.

GEOLOGY AND TOPOGRAPHY

The watershed is located in the Guayana Shield, one of the continent's oldest geological formations. This shield, relatively flat and slightly inclined towards the Orinoco, consisting of old rock, generally metamorphic and granitic, is in some places covered by quartzite and in others by intrusions of igneous rock (Vila, 1960). Over this relatively flat relief important materials of fluvial origin were deposited, producing the Roraima Formation, layers of sandstone and conglomerate.

From a panoramic point of view, the topography of Guayana impresses one as totally chaotic. Its mesas are cut like staircases, the tabular peaks slightly inclined. It is, in general, a vast mountainous block cut by river valleys and canyons, without any really defined orographic systems in the strict sense of the word. Actually, the whole shield is an immense rounded block fragmented into minor blocks, which in turn were tilted by tectonic pressure.

The rock composition of the Guayana Shield has a very low capacity for holding underground water. There are some fractured areas with structures favorable to the accumulation of local water, but only near the Roraima mountains and on the south side of the Orinoco River do we find extensive and continous aquifers of any importance. Because of the local intrusions of igneous material in the sedimentary rock of the large mesas, the sandstones are frequently fractured, especially in the upper part of the mesas where the circulation of superficial water has carved deep canyons following the diaclases. Although these offer good water access to the interior of the rock, the rock itself is very compact and does not accept major infiltration. However, these sandstones show some conic hollows formed by dissolution that locally can constitute a good source of underground water.

HYDROLOGY

The Orinoco River basin is Venezuela's most important watershed, with a mean annual discharge of 33,000 m^3/sec and with a length of 1,530 km to its confluence with the Caroni River. The Caroni River watershed spreads over an area of 93,500 km^2, carrying a volume of 129 billion m^3 of water, which represents an average discharge of 4,100 m^3/sec. This flow is the result of relatively high precipitation (2,600 mm over the whole watershed). Based on 25 years of accumulated information (1949–1973), the mean annual maximum discharge registered was 12,979 m^3/sec, giving a total annual average of 4,891 m^3/sec.

The Caroni River presents several particularities when compared with other rivers of the Guayana: it possesses a very large hydrographic area in its upper region that by itself represents more than half the basin. The watershed extends about 160 km in a north–south direction, and about 100 km in an east–west direction. At the height of San Pedro de las Bocas, the Caroni becomes an important river at its confluence with the Paragua River, which is the next largest river in terms of discharge within the basin. The Paragua River rises in the mountains on the border with Brazil.

CLIMATOLOGY

The climate in most parts of the area is characterized by high precipitation fairly well distributed throughout the year, a temperature with small annual seasonality. This climate is humid, and there are no months that are actually dry.

The mean annual temperature ranges from approximately 20°C in the Gran Sabana to approximately 28°C near the confluence of the Caroni with the Orinoco.

Precipitation, one of the main factors determining water dynamics in any watershed, increases from north to south: the average annual values are very low

(849 mm) west of Ciudad Bolivar and increase progressively to high values of 4,000 mm/year towards the border with Brazil; the area average is 2,600 mm/yr. In a climate like this, in which temperatures are relatively constant during the year and where relative humidity, evaporation, and radiation present very small seasonal variations, changes in precipitation are basically associated with orography and the prevailing wind, which is one of the main climatic elements.

The rainiest period lasts from May to November with a maximum in July and August. During these months the climate can be considered very humid or superhumid at almost every site in the area; the average monthly precipitation is above 200 mm; in some stations there are months with more than 500 mm (CTV, MAC, NPS, 1974). From December to April there is a slight decline in precipitation, although not enough to limit the vegetation growth. In general, the relative humidity of this area is high, with an average value around 75% and small annual variation that follows precipitation.

SOILS

The soil is one of the main unknowns in the resources of the Guayana. Soil studies in the region are extremely scarce and are based entirely on point samples taken for agrological purposes.

One of the areas in which the effort has been somewhat greater is the National Park La Gran Sabana, from which we will extrapolate to the rest of the watershed. However, even in this region most of the information about the nature of the soil was obtained from observations of present-day geological characteristics and from agricultural land yields. In general the soil is high in minerals, low in natural fertility, and highly susceptible to erosion. Furthermore, it does not show good physicochemical characteristics, such as texture, water retention, or acidity. This low fertility, which determines a low agricultural yield, does not conflict with the high vegetation biomass that we find in most parts of the Caroni River watershed under natural conditions. Most of the elements essential to this development of vegetation are added by permanent circulation that takes place at a high turnover rate. Very few elements remain permanently in the soil.

At any rate, based on geologic information, climatology, topography, and agricultural land use, the soils of the National Park La Gran Sabana have been classified into four dominant units, reflecting the main soil associations that result from the predominant physiographic and pedogenetic processes (CTV, MAC, NPS, 1974): Unit A, constituted by the Tepuis and neighboring areas; Unit B, constituted by the high and low savannas and the valleys; Unit C, constituted by the areas of igneous material; and Unit D, constituted by soils occurring on high slopes.

VEGETATION

Using information provided by Ewel and Madriz (1968), Hueck (1968), and the Torrence vegetation map, we prepared a map that condensed most of the characteristics used in these studies and was translated into the Beard System of Vegetation Types (Beard, 1953). From this condensation 12 different types of vegetation were recognized in the area studied:

1. Rain forest, from 0 to 800 masl (meters above sea level) with more than 2,500 mm of precipitation per year and 0–2 "dry" months
2. Intermediate rain forest, 600–1,500 masl with more than 1,000 mm and up to a maximum of 2,500 mm of precipitation
3. Evergreen summer forest, with the same characteristics as rain forest but with 3 dry months
4. Semideciduous summer forest, same as to rain forest but with 4 dry months
5. Cloud forest, at more than 1,500 masl and with 1,200–1,500 mm of precipitation
6. Deciduous summer forest, at 0–800 masl with more than 2,500 mm of precipitation and 5–6 dry months
7. Chaparral (forested savanna), at 0–800 masl in the flat areas and with clay soil
8. Mud savanna, near the rivers, at 0–800 masl with poor drainage
9. Mountain small forest, at heights above 1,500 masl with 1,200–1,500 mm of precipitation and good drainage
10. Gallery forests, at 0–800 masl near rivers and with more than 1,500 mm of precipitation
11. Rocky savanna, in the low parts (0–200 m) of the watersheds with rocky soils
12. Morichal, from 0–1,000 masl, near the rivers and replacing the gallery forests

THE GURI MODEL

THE HYDROLOGIC CYCLE

We will not describe the natural hydrologic cycle in detail; rather, we will point out those aspects that are most relevant to the rain–vegetation–soil–river relationship. The rain that falls on the forest is in part intercepted by the vegetation cover and in part reaches the soil. The intercepted water can be absorbed by the plants themselves, although most of it returns to the atmosphere through evaporation. The water reaches the ground, either directly or as runoff over the leaves and trunks of the trees. Once there, it either infiltrates or runs on the surface. The infiltrated water can either run laterally within the soil or percolate toward the deeper parts of the soil. It can also return to the atmosphere through the process of evapotranspiration. The superficial runoff, together with water that runs laterally within the soil, plus the water that eventually percolates to the deeper part of the rocks all add up to produce the springs and streams that feed the rivers.

The quantitative description of the dynamics of this process is very complex. Because of the high degree of aggregation in this model, inclusion of all factors was not justified; such factors as variations in the water table and the dynamics of the percolating water were left out, as were other aspects that affect the movement of water, such as conductivity of the soil. Below is a short description of the main elements that were considered and included in the model used for this simulation.

DESCRIPTION OF THE RAIN–VEGETATION–SOIL–RIVER MODEL

Rain Interception

The coefficients that represent the way vegetation intercepts precipitation are a function not only of the vegetation cover itself but also of the storm characteristics of the rain. Because of scarcity of information about the vegetation cover, it was decided to elaborate interception coefficients that would be functions of vegetation biomass, from which it was possible to quantify the vegetation information of the watershed. Because there was no information on the storm characteristics of the rain (climatic information in terms of precipitation was available only day by day, but the hourly distribution of rain during a day was not known), it was decided to ignore the effect of the hourly distribution of rain.

The combined effect of the amount of rainfall and the vegetation biomass was obtained from Rutter (1963) and Ovington (1965). The fit to these data produced the following forms of calculation:

$$A = -6.732642219 \times 10^{-3} + 7.957346446 \times 10^{-6}\,V - 9.707299074 \times 10^{-11}\,V^2$$
$$B = -8.434753042 \times 10^{-3} + 8.789413126 \times 10^{-6}\,V - 1.096428530 \times 10^{-10}\,V^2$$
$$C_i = A + BP;\ A_i = P\,C_i;\ P_e = P - A_i\,,$$

where

V = vegetation biomass, (grams of dry matter/m^2)
P = precipitation (cm)
C_i = coefficient of interception (with values between 0 and 1)
A_i = amount of water intercepted (cm)
P_e = effective precipitation; that is, the amount of rain that reaches the soil (cm)

Infiltration

Penetration of water into the soil (infiltration) may be the key process in the water dynamics in this model. The amount of effective rainfall that infiltrates will depend on the saturation deficit of the soil and the slope of the terrain. In view of this importance, let us consider in more detail the properties of soil saturation in the process of water penetration.

Because of the scarcity of soil data in general and in this watershed in particular, it was decided to use one of the simplest indicators of soil texture: the proportion of clay in the soil. Hildago (1971) gives us information that allows the calculation of the field capacity of a soil as well as its wilting point as a function of the proportion of clay. From this information the following two straight-line relationships were obtained:

$$CC = 4.11 + 52.51\,PA$$
$$PMP = 2.01 + 25.54\,PA,$$

where

CC = field capacity (cm)
PMP = wilting point (cm)
PA = proportion of clay in the soil (between 0 and 1)

Once the field capacity and the wilting point are known (the latter can be considered analogous to the volume of capillary pores), the maximum amount of water in the soil, that is, the saturation capacity, can be found if we know the volume of pores or percentage of noncapillary pores in the soil. Hardy (1970) gives us the saturation capacity of three types of soils (clay soils, loamy soils, and sandy soils). Based on this information, the following straight-line was obtained:

$$CS = 17.22 + 35.42\,PA,$$

where

CS = saturation capacity (cm).

Thus, the difference between saturation capacity of the soil and its field capacity would give us an index of the volume of noncapillary porosity, which is one of the factors most linked to the saturation deficit of the soil, which in turn is the most important factor that affects the penetration of soil by water.

Since it is known that the infiltration of water responds to the content of water in the soil in a sigmoid fashion (H. van Keulen, Agricultural University, Wageningen, the Netherlands, personal communication), the inverse tangent function was used to describe this process. As this function passes through the origin, the equation was divided by π and the value 0.5 was added. This produced an axis translation that transformed the function so that it was totally included in the upper right-hand quadrant of a system of Cartesian axes. The curve was calibrated to comply with two constraints: (a) when the soil contains an amount of water equal to the field capacity, the infiltration coefficient is 0.5; (b) when the soil has a minimum content of water, the coefficient of infiltration has an arbitrary value of 0.9.

In order that the inverse tangent curve, after the axis translation, comply with these constraints, the argument has been transformed in the following manner:

$$X = (DEF - CC)\,(3.07768354/CA)\,,$$

where DEF is the water deficit of the soil. The first factor forces constraint (a) and the second factor constraint (b). If the soil has a water deficit equal to its field capacity ($DEF = CC$),

$$X = (CC - CC)\,(3.07768354/CA) = 0;$$

$$INF = \frac{\tan^{-1} 0}{\pi} + 0.5 = 0.5$$

where INF is the coefficient of infiltration, or the proportion of water above the ground that will infiltrate during a 24-hr period. If the soil has a minimum amount of water ($DEF = CC = CA$),

$$X = (CC + CA - CC)\,\frac{3.07768354}{CA} = 3.07768354\ .$$

Thus,

$$INF = \frac{\tan^{-1} 3.07768354}{\pi} + 0.5 = 0.9\ .$$

After the coefficient of infiltration has been calculated as a function of the water deficit in the soil, a correction for slope is applied, which is given by

$$C_p = 1 - P_m/P_M\,,$$

where

C_p = slope correction
P_m = average slope of the region
P_M = maximum slope of the subregion

Thus the equation that determines the amount of water infiltrated has the following form:

$$I = \left\{P_n \frac{\tan^{-1}\left[(DEF - CC)\left\{\frac{3.07768354}{CA}\right\}\right]}{\pi} + \frac{1}{2}\right\}\left(1 - \frac{P_m}{P_M}\right)$$

where

I = amount of water infiltrated (in $cm/m^2/day$)
P_n = net precipitation

DEF = water deficit in the soil
CA = water in the soil at a given moment

Percolation

This process consists of the flow of water from the surface toward the deepest part of the soil when water content of the soil is equal to its field capacity. Under these conditions, because the water tension is equal to or less than one atmosphere, water is in a state of free gravitation.

Considering that percolation increases rapidly when the water content of the soil increases, we calculate percolation (cm) by the following equation:

$$Per = \frac{CA.(CA - CC)}{CS} .$$

If the amount of water in the soil equals the field capacity,

$$Per = \frac{CC\,(CC - CC)}{CS} = 0$$

If the amount of water in the soil equals the saturation point at any instant, then

$$Per = CS - CC .$$

Evapotranspiration

The process of evapotranspiration, that is, the loss of soil water due to both the direct action of evaporation and the transpiration from the leaves, is of great importance in the hydrologic cycle. Among the most important factors that affect evapotranspiration are the water content of the soil in the root zone, the degree of insolation, the wind, the type of vegetation, and the total plant biomass (although the leaf area index is more related to evapotranspiration). As there is little quantitative information to relate these factors to evapotranspiration and considering that the aggregation of the model did not justify the incorporation of all these factors, we decided to look for relationships in which evapotranspiration would depend exclusively upon the plant biomass.

From Ogawa *et al.* (1965) the relation between plant biomass and leaf area index was determined for the vegetation of the tropics. Although these authors did not establish the regression between these two variables, their tabulated data were used to try three types of data fitting: exponential, power, and logarithmic. It was concluded, using the chi-square test, that the most satisfactory fit was produced by a power relationship. The result of such a regression was:

$$IAF = 0.078770\,(BV)^{0.842191} .$$

Where

IAF = foliage (or leaf) area index
BV = plant biomass

No data were found in the literature for conversions from leaf area index into evapotranspiration, but personal information from Carl Jordan (Institute of Ecology, University of Georgia), based on his experience in the measurement of leaf area index and evapotranspiration in both tropical and temperate forests, allowed the establishment of a linear relationship. Information provided by Dr. Jordan was based upon forests in Puerto Rico, with actual evapotranspiration of 0.36 cm/day and with a leaf area index of 6.61, and upon similar measurements in a temperate forest in the United States (Illinois), with 0.49 cm/day of actual evapotranspiration and a leaf area index of 8. Also, the maximum value of evapotranspiration was known, and the evapotranspiration value had to be zero for no plant biomass. With these four points, a straight line was fitted, giving the following relationship:

$$y = 0.015773 + 0.053612x, \quad \begin{array}{l} \text{if } y < E_0, \text{ then } y = E_0 \\ \text{if } y \geqslant E_0, \text{ then } y = y \end{array}$$

where

y = evapotranspiration
x = leaf area index

Erosion

Erosion as a consequence of superficial runoff was calculated as a function of three factors: plant biomass, superficial runoff, and soil texture. The equation that relates these factors is

$$E = 0.00168 \exp(-0.00102\, V) R\, S,$$

where

0.00168 = the maximum erosion rate in cm/m²/day, calculated from the results of experiments carried out in the United States. The value corresponds to a plowed soil that is cultivated periodically but without sowing.

0.00102 = factor of erosion K, considering the vegetation after the formula $E(V) = E(0) \exp(-KV)$

$E(V)$ = erosion for a given vegetation, in this case that corresponding to maize, cm/m^2/day (0.000799)

$E(0)$ = erosion in plowed and cultivated soil, free of vegetation, in cm/m^2/day (0.00168)

K = factor to be calculated
V = plant biomass in grams of dry matter/m^2
R = factor that affects erosion as a function of runoff in the following form: $R = 20$ (RUNOF $- 0.03$), where 20 corresponds to 20% clay and RUNOF is the superficial runoff (cm/day).
S = factor that takes into account the effect of texture upon the erosion after the following relationship: S = clay fraction $\times$ 5.0

Figure 14.2 shows the different functions used in the point model in the rain–vegetation–soil relationship.

IMPLEMENTATION OF THE MODEL IN SPACE

The model described above, which establishes the relationships of the dynamics of the water from the time it enters the system as rain until it appears in the form of runoff, consists only of a point version of the rain–vegetation–soil–river model. We were interested in representing the hydrological dynamics in terms of the real space of the watershed. There were two basic ways of doing this. One of them was by subdividing the watershed into elementary subwatersheds, each of which could be integrated spatially. The other alternative was to subdivide the whole region into a series of unit areas by superimposing a grid over the watershed and to calculate water dynamics for each of these units, integrating them in space. For practical reasons, the latter was the one we used.

A series of maps was compiled, with all the information gathered and calculated represented in cells of 55.5 $\times$ 55.5 km. The distance of 55.5 km, although arbitrary, was selected because it represented one-half of one degree longitude. Each of these cells was numbered sequentially, and each of them was provided with climatological, hydrological, topographical, and vegetation information.

A FORTRAN program was prepared, and the point model was processed cell by cell and day by day, to be integrated later for the entire watershed. The spatial integration of the hydrologic dynamics was affected by many factors that intervened in different parts of the process, but for simplicity, only a phenomenological approach was used; that is, we looked for the data that provided the most representative time lags of the system. The discharge and rain integrated over all the watershed were compared by a cross-correlation program with the rain measured during 1972 at the San Pedro de las Bocas station. As a result, three to four maxima were obtained: the most important peak takes place with a lag of 4 days, the second one with a lag of 25 days, the third at 37 days, and the last at 50 days of delay. These results would suggest that superficial runoff, which is known to travel most rapidly, would have an average delay in the whole watershed on the order of 4 days. The infiltrated water that moves laterally within the soil could be identified with a lag of 25 days; and the percolated water, which probably travels most slowly, would take about 37 days on the average. The fourth peak of 50 days,

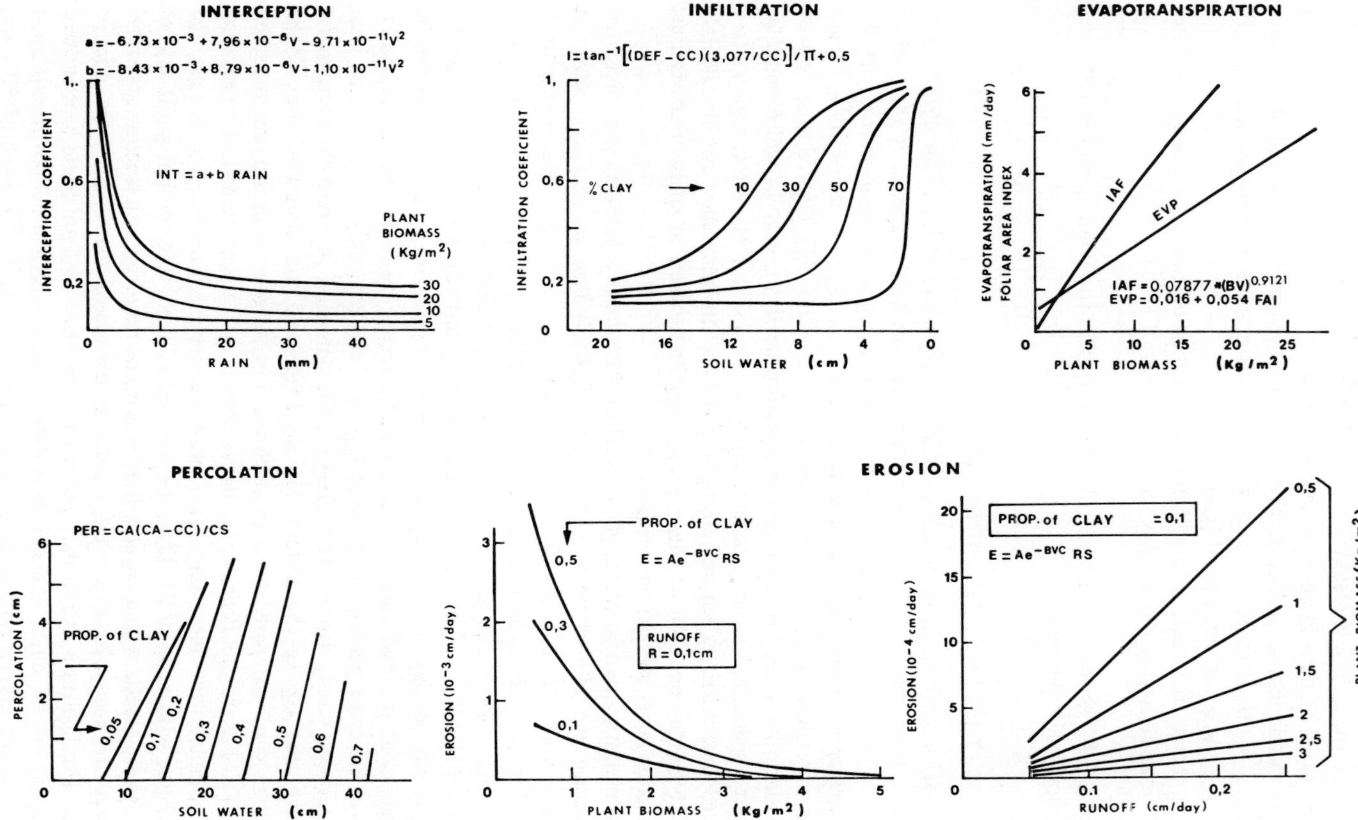

FIGURE 14.2 Main functional relationships of the point model rain–vegetation–soil.

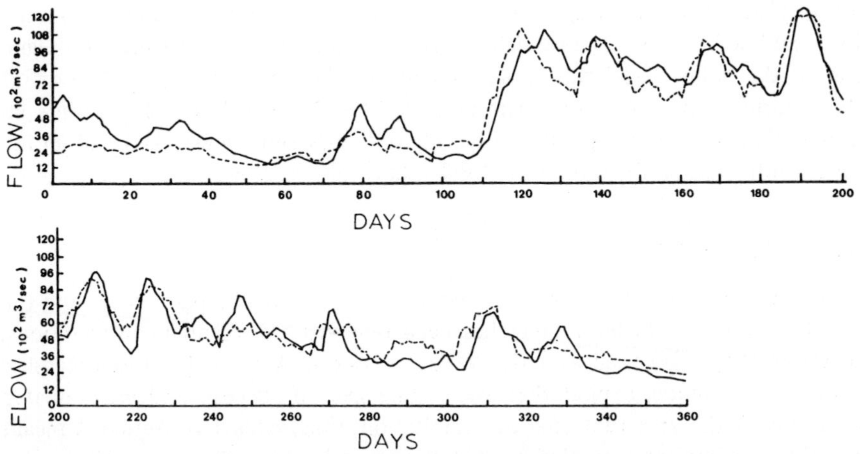

FIGURE 14.3 Comparison of actual and simulated river flows for year 1972. Solid line: field data; broken line: simulated results.

which is the weakest one in the cross-correlation analysis, is probably a symmetric reflection of the 25-day infiltrated-water lag.

After introducing the lags in the spatial integration of the point model, we obtained simulated daily values that were quite acceptable when compared with field information, as shown in Figure 14.3. Although there are still some discrepancies, the simulated results show a good correlation with the field data in periodicity and and average level of discharge.

SENSITIVITY OF THE MODEL

Sensitivity experiments to see how the model responds to different parameter values and coefficients were performed at the level of the point model, as well as with the integration of the point model in space and time under the conditions of the Caroni River watershed.

In relation to the point model, seven variables or parameters were selected that were considered fundamental to the process of the water dynamics: (a) the amount of water in the soil (cm); (b) the maximum slope of the terrain (degrees); (c) the local slope (degrees); (d) plant biomass (g/m^2 dry weight); (e) soil texture, expressed as proportion of clay; (f) precipitation in terms of amount of rainfall per day (cm); and (g) soil depth (m). There was a problem when the sensitivity experiments were designed. Even if only three different values were assigned to each of the seven variables or parameters, all possible combinations produced a total of 2,187 simulation runs. Due to the difficulty, in terms of both computer time and analysis and transcription of results, it was decided to carry out a sensitivity study of selected numerical values. The sensitivity of the model to selected values showed that it was not very sensitive with respect to many parameters with the exception of rain, slope, and soil texture. The sensitivity analysis with respect to the spatial integration of the point model was applied mainly to the lags and to partial losses of water during travel from one part of the watershed to another. The results indicated that the numerical values of both time lags and water losses had an important influence on the regime and total volume of river flow.

SIMULATION DESIGN

From the point of view of decision making, alteration of the plant cover and the use of land after valuable lumber has been removed are essential considerations. Therefore they were used as action variables. Action A was defined as a measure of the rate of lumber exploitation over a time span of 50 years and was evaluated by means of the area subjected to exploitation; thus, value 1 of Action A means that the area subjected to timber exploitation is kept constant at its 1975 value during the 50 years of simulation, value 2 of Action A implies that the area is doubled in the course of 50 years, and so on to value 5. Action B was defined as the percentage of the logged area that is used for agriculture; 5 levels were used for action B: 0, 20, 40, 60 and 80.

Five levels of intensity for Action A and five levels of intensity for Action B produce a total of 25 combinations that we can recognize as strategies of intervention. As a result, the model can be evaluated for each of the 25 strategies during each of the 50 years of simulation in terms of river discharges, erosion, volume of lumber produced, volume of agricultural products, and net benefit accumulated for all these activities during the simulation.

After having performed all the hydrologic and economic calculations, the simulation program was coupled by subroutine with a progam that generated energy use as input to the average monthly discharge. This program evaluates monthly energy production for every simulation year, depending upon river flow and the level of the reservoir. Figure 14.4 shows a flow diagram of the simulation design used for this study.

ECONOMIC ASPECTS

As can be seen from the flow diagram of Figure 14.4, all the economic calculations were carried out in separate subroutines. Within the cycle of the monthly simulation there are calls to subroutines MODIF and TALAR to calculate the area that would be subjected to timber exploitation in each month of the year. We used a monthly time unit to calculate this area because heavy rains prevent logging 5 months of the year. After a complete year is simulated, and once all the ecological calculations of the model have been carried out (runoff, erosion, discharges), the economic subroutines that calculate forest exploitation and agriculture are called.

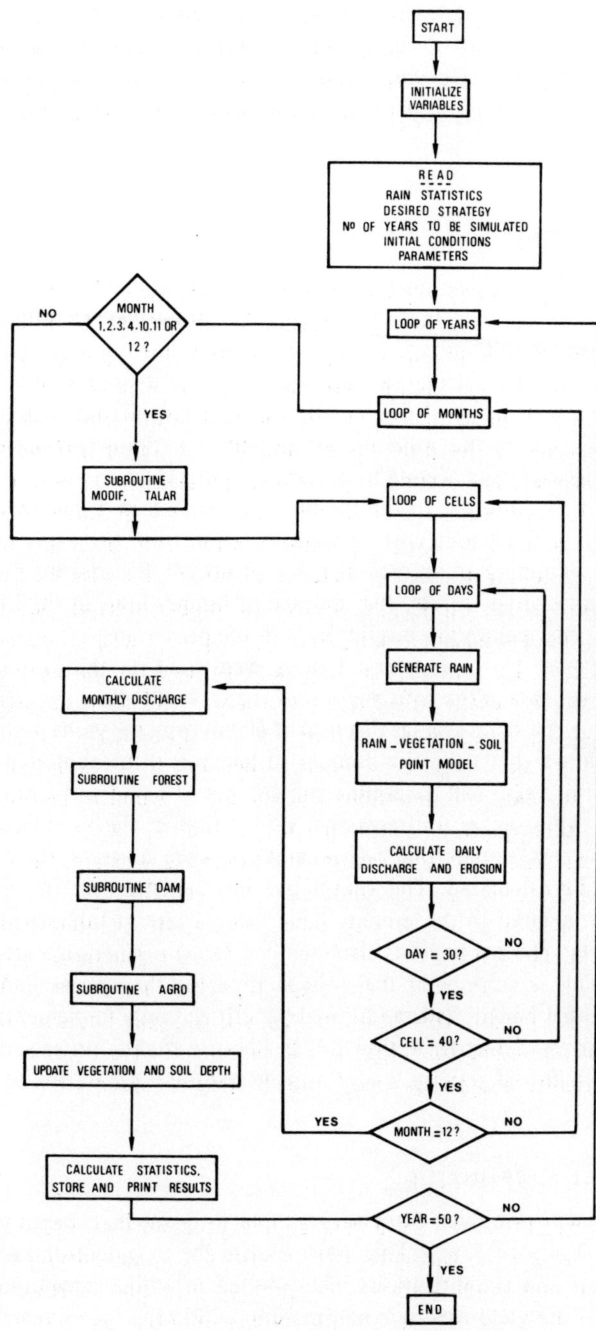

FIGURE 14.4 Flow diagram of the overall simulated model.

These subroutines are based upon the area subjected to exploitation, which in turn depends upon the year of simulation and the intervention strategy used in each case. The following is a very brief description of the main characteristics of the economic subroutines and the assumptions used to calculate hydroelectric benefits.

TIMBER SUBROUTINE

The timber subroutine carries out the calculations of costs and benefits of timber activities in more detail than the other economic subroutines. Despite this, many simplifications had to be imposed, among which the following two were the most important. First, all the calculations are based on the exploitation of only one tree species, for which most of the benefit and cost information was obtained in the field. The species is the moreillo or mureillo or dujun (*Erisma uncinatum* Warm.) (Vochysiaceae). The second important simplification relates to the distance from the sites of exploitation to the lumber mill centers. In Table 14.1 it can be seen that there is a fixed unit cost of transportation from the yards to the mills (1.5 Bs/m^3/km), assuming an average distance of 60 km. Because the Caroni River watershed is almost virgin forest, the absence of lumber mills in the high part of the basin makes this assumption invalid, both in the price transport constant and in the average distance. However, these figures were used on the assumption that government investments in the construction of roads would allow the establishment of lumber mills at the same average distance of 60 km from the yards to the deposits.

Table 14.1 shows that once the number of hectares to be exploited in a given year is known, this value will determine the volume of wood to be obtained, and as all costs are expressed as unit costs per m^3 of timber, the total cost for every year can be known. Assuming that salaries and prices are constant, the total annual net benefit can be calculated. The cumulative net benefits over the 50 years of simulation were updated to the present value using a rate of interest of 8%, common in Venezuela. The net benefits also included forest regeneration after 30 years of simulation. This is considered the average time for the species under analysis to reach commercial height. This additional benefit was only implemented through the strategies corresponding to Action B = 0, because for the other actions it was assumed that agricultural activity would impede natural regeneration of the forest.

AGRICULTURAL SUBROUTINE

This subroutine was processed by a very simple program that, based upon information given in Table 14.2, calculates net benefits due to agricultural activity. The main assumptions and simplifications incorporated into this subroutine are (a) a drastic decline in the yield of maize and manioc within the first 3 years of activity (particularly with manioc); (b) constant cost per hectare. Because of these factors, there is no net benefit from the cultivation of manioc after the first year.

TABLE 14.1 Yields and Unit Costs Used in the Economics of Timber Subroutine

Item	Value[a]
Tree density	1.25 trees/ha
Mean height of trees	12.30 m
Mean circumference of trees	3.10 m
Tree volume	−6.1776 + 0.367614 × height × circumference
Total volume timbered	tree volume × density × number of ha
Volume loss due to cutting	0.60
Volume loss due to sawmill	1.10
Cost of exploration and marking	20.00 Bs/m^3
Cost of construction of roads of penetration	20.00 Bs/m^3
Cost of piling	35.00 Bs/m^3
Cost of cutting	15.00 Bs/m^3
Cost of moving to trucks	10.00 Bs/m^3
Cost of transportation from the site of exploitation to the yard	2.00 Bs/m^3/km
Cost of transportation from the yard to the lumber mill	1.50 Bs/m^3/km
Mean salary of workers during exploitation	5000.00 Bs/mo
Mean salary of sawmill employees	2000.00 Bs/mo
Yield of the workers in wood exploitation	625.00 m^3/worker
Yield of workers in wood exploitation	1250.00 m^3/employee
No. of workers required in sawmill	25.9993 + 0.003942 sawmilled volume
Taxes	25.00 Bs/m^3
Selling price	390.00 Bs/m^3
Regeneration time of the moreillo (commercial height)	30.00 yr
Mean distance from exploitation site to yard	40.00 km
Mean distance from yard to sawmill	60.00 km

SOURCE: Raul Pietrantoni, Manager, Aserradero Upata (personal communication). Data are from an area about 50 km from the study area and vegetation, soil, climate and topography are almost identical

[a] 1 U.S.$ = 4.30 Bs(bolivars)

TABLE 14.2 Costs and Unit Benefits Used in the Agricultural Subroutine

	Maize			Manioc			
	Yr 1	Yr 2	Yr 3	Yr 1	Yr 2	Yr 3	Cattle
Yield (Kg/ha)	1,000	700	650	8,000	4,000	2,000	1 (head/50 ha)
Price (Bs/kg)	0.75	0.75	0.75	0.275	0.275	0.275	1,350 (Bs/head)
Gross benefit (Bs/ha)	750	525	510	2,200	1,100	550	27
Costs (Bs/ha)	500	500	500	2,000	2,000	2,000	17
Net benefit (Bs/ha)	250	25	10	200	0	0	10

SOURCE: *Anuario Estadistico Agropecuario,* Ministerio de Agricultura y Cria, Caracas, 1974; Juan Guevara, Oficina Tecnica "Caura," Caracas (personal communication)

The fundamental assumption upon which this reduction in productivity per hectare in corn and manioc is based is the delicate balance of tropical forests. Since the nutrients of the plant biomass are in a permanent state of circulation, they are mostly lost when the forest is burned over. The land gained is only good for a few years of agricultural exploitation, with ever-diminishing yields.

As was done with timber benefits, the results of agricultural activities that are computed year by year are accumulated as updated net benefit at the interest rate of 8%.

ECONOMIC ASPECTS OF HYDROELECTRIC PRODUCTION

The hydroelectric sector requires the simplest estimation of the total annual net benefit. As the simulation model gave us the total annual amount of energy generated, this value was multiplied by the local selling price (0.035 Bs/kWh). The transformation from gross benefit to net benefit was carried out using a coefficient provided by the electric company that operates the dam. This coefficient is increased throughout the simulation period, largely because of the reduction in the payment of interest and progressive depreciations. In year 1 of the simulation this coefficient was 0.45; it was increased annually in a linear fashion at the rate of 0.005, reaching a maximum of 0.7 for year 50 of the simulation. Also, as with the agricultural and timber subroutines, annual net benefits were accumulated during the simulation period at the rate of interest of 8%.

RESULTS

RESULTS OF THE PHYSICAL ASPECTS OF THE MODEL

Figure 14.3 allows us to compare the results obtained from the simulation of the Caroni River at San Pedro de Las Bocas using the rains of 1972, and the measured field discharges of that same year. The comparison is made day by day, and, taking into account the aggregation level of the model and the fairly large size of each cell of the grid, the result can be considered relatively satisfactory.

The changes in the river's discharge during the 50 years of simulation under different intervention strategies show the well-known effect of "storms," that when discharges are estimated by means of monthly averages, they show increases of the river flow in the rainy season and reductions in the dry season. In Figure 14.5 we can observe the changes, evaluating them through two of their main components: the water that runs off superficially, and the subsuperficial runoff, or water that runs laterally within the soil after having infiltrated. It is clear that there is a larger increase in the infiltrated water than in the superficial runoff, although both components show an increase in the rainy season. In any case, the total annual volume of water, particularly during the first years of intervention, is progressively larger as simulation is made under conditions of more severe interventions with the plant

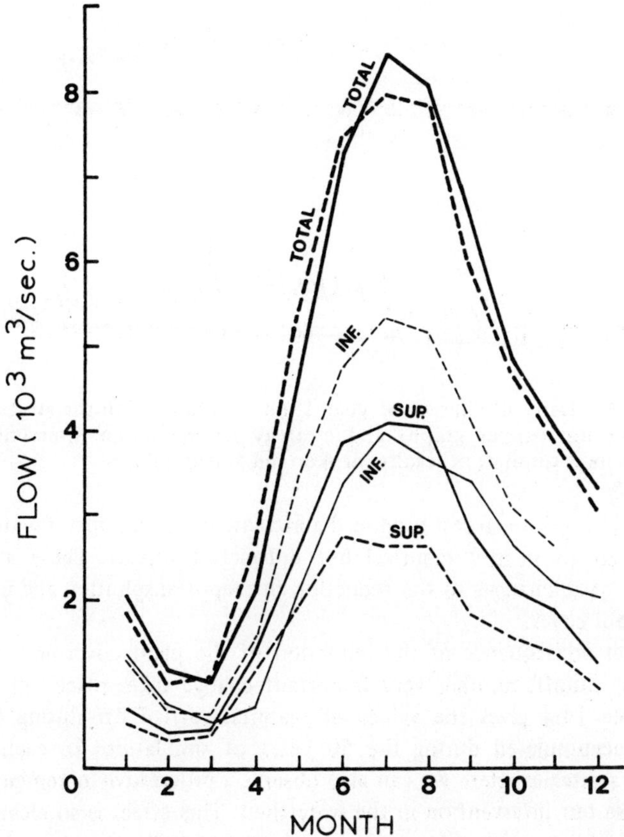

FIGURE 14.5 Total and component discharges of simulation year 50 for strategy 1 (solid line) and strategy 25 (broken line).

cover. This reduction in the plant cover is the factor that, through the changes in interception and evapotranspiration, produces the most important effects observed in Figure 14.5. Figure 14.6 shows the main differences in hydrologic discharge regime of the river, using the rains of 1964, under conditions of no change in vegetation and under conditions of maximum strategy of intervention at year 50 of simulation. The most noticeable change is the stormy character of the daily discharges, which reflects almost instantly the daily precipitation.

Table 14.3 shows the progressive increment in the average monthly discharge at year 50 of simulation for the 25 different strategies of intervention. The results are in agreement with previous knowledge of the dynamics of water in the forests and also with experimental field studies done in other countries. Thus, for example, Hornbeck *et al.* (1970) showed that experimental deforestation in the Hubbard

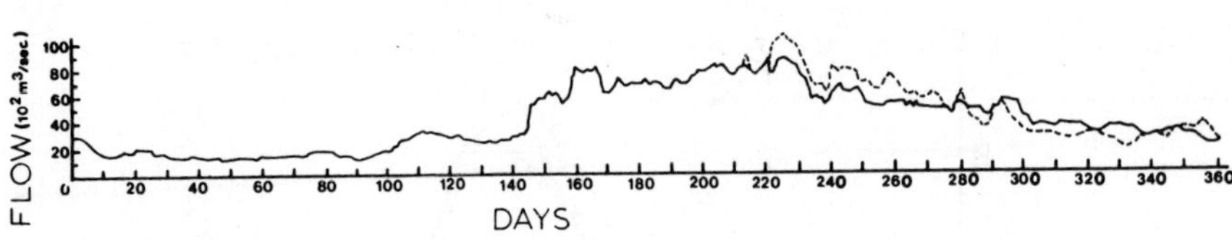

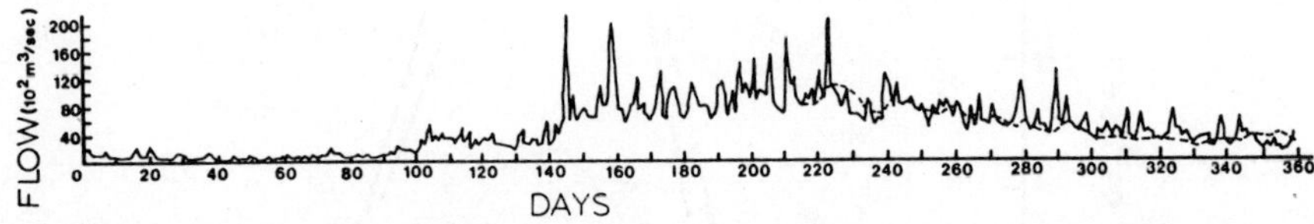

FIGURE 14.6 Daily discharges of year 1964 simulated with the strategy of minimum intervention (upper graph) and strategy of maximum intervention (lower graph). Solid line: simulation results; broken line: field data.

Brook, New Hampshire, forest produced a increase in the volume of water of about 40% compared to nearby identical but untouched forests. These authors also attribute the basic changes to the reduction in evapotranspiration and interception of rain by plant cover.

As a direct consequence of the reduction of the plant cover and the increase in superficial runoff, another very important change takes place: an increase in erosion. Table 14.4 gives the values of material carried off during the process of erosion, accumulated during the 50 years of simulation for each of the 25 intervention strategies. Here we can also observe a progressive increment in erosion as we increase our intervention in the watershed. This effect is so clear and direct that it was decided to use this erosion variable as an indicator of the degree of environmental degradation. This was done using intervention strategy 25 as the maximum value (100%) of environmental degradation. Thus we can express the other intervention strategies in terms of erosion as a given percentage of this maximum intervention strategy (Table 14.5).

The increase in erosion as we increase the degree of intervention in the vegetation of the watershed is of an impressive magnitude: the river carries 12.8 million m^3 of silt under conditions of no intervention. Erosion increases silt depo-

TABLE 14.3 Mean Monthly Flows (m^3/sec) at Year 50 of Simulation

	Action A				
Action B	1	2	3	4	5
1	4,964	4,984	4,989	4,989	4,989
2	5,110	5,223	5,250	5,250	5,250
3	5,356	5,529	5,675	5,675	5,675
4	5,677	6,096	6,224	6,224	6,224
5	6,073	6,701	6,905	6,905	6,905

TABLE 14.4 Total Erosion Material Accumulated in 50 Years (10^6 m^3)

Action B	Action A 1	2	3	4	5
1	1,001	1,204	1,365	1,466	1,534
2	2,610	3,718	4,596	5,145	5,519
3	4,679	6,920	8,701	9,814	10,573
4	6,830	10,220	12,921	14,610	15,761
5	9,068	13,624	17,261	19,536	21,086

sition to 743 million m^3 for year 50 of simulation for strategy 25. Thus a 58-fold increase should not be unexpected when important changes in the plant cover take place in tropical forests. Nye and Greenland (1965) inform us that in an African tropical forest with a slope of 12–15% and rainfall of approximately 2,160 mm per year, erosion of 0.000032947 tons/m^2/year was observed, while under similar conditions in a nearby place with a slope of 7–8%, but kept fallow, erosion was 0.011120 tons/m^2/year; this represents a 340-fold increase.

The magnitude of the increase of erosion with the degree of intervention in the watershed is such that the progressive accumulation of silt in the bottom of the reservoir is many times larger than any forecast made during the construction of the dam. A report made to the electric company (Salazar, 1962), based on 12 years of measurements of silt carried by the Caroni River, gave an average of 13.5 x 106 m^3/year. Considering the very large dimensions of the reservoir and its height–volume relationship, estimates of the average life of the reservoir before construction of the dam ran to about 300 years. However, these estimates were made under the assumption that there would be no important changes in the vegetation of the Caroni River watershed. Under the different conditions of simulation, the lifetime of the dam was evaluated in terms of erosion increases. Knowing the height of the intakes of the turbines (181 m for turbines 1–10, 200 m for turbines 11–14, and 217 m for turbines 15–20), it was possible to calculate the dead volume determined by such heights in order to determine the volume of silt that would be necessary to block some of the turbines.

TABLE 14.5 Indicator of Environmental Deterioration (%) Based on Total Erosion Accumulated in 50 Years

Action B	Action A 1	2	3	4	5
1	4.7	5.7	6.5	6.9	7.3
2	12.4	17.6	21.8	24.4	26.2
3	22.2	32.8	41.3	46.5	50.1
4	32.4	48.5	61.3	69.3	74.7
5	43.0	64.6	81.9	92.6	100.0

TABLE 14.6 Simulated Year in Which the Number of Operational Turbines is Reduced to 10 or to 6, for the Intervention Strategies[a]

		Reduction to 10					Reduction to 6				
		Action A					Action A				
		1	2	3	4	5	1	2	3	4	5
	1	–	–	–	–	–	–	–	–	–	–
	2	–	44	40	37	35	–	–	–	–	–
Action	3	40	35	32	30	29	–	–	48	45	43
B	4	35	31	28	27	25	–	46	42	39	37
	5	31	28	26	24	23	48	41	38	35	33

[a] The dash means that for year 50 of simulation the number of active turbines was not yet reduced to the specified number. For year 50 of simulation the number of active turbines is reduced to zero for strategy 25 (A = 5, B = 5).

Table 14.6 shows the tremendous impact of erosion on the operation of the dam through the number of turbines that remain operational. As the degree of deterioration of the watershed increases, there is a progressive reduction in the number of active turbines for a given year. The extreme case of strategy 25 (which has the maximum rate of erosion of $21{,}085.6 \times 10^6$ m^3 of silt in 50 years) shows that in year 50 of simulation the amount of silt carried by the river would reach the height of 217 m, blocking the last six turbines, which were active up to that year.

The results of the physical changes that take place in the simulation of the watershed under different strategies of intervention can also be expressed in terms of hydroelectric production. Figure 14.7 shows the isoclines for hydroelectric production, as GWh for year 50 of simulation for each of the 25 intervention strategies. It can be clearly observed that the curves show a reduction of hydroelectric production toward the highest levels of intensity of both Actions A and B. The peculiar shape of some of the isoclines is related to the silting up of the reservoir, where from one year to the next several turbines have to stop operation. The shape of some of the isoclines can be also explained by the saturation process that occurs in the exploitation of the watershed for the highest level of Action A. When Action A reaches level 3, the watershed has been completely saturated by year 43 of simulation; when Action A reaches level 4, the saturation is reached by simulation year 37; and for Action A at level 5, the whole watershed has been saturated by simulation year 35.

In terms of hydroelectric production, the following important assumption was made: if silting reaches the intake of a given turbine, the turbine will be taken out of operation and no attempt to clean the reservoir will be made.

RESULTS OF THE ECONOMIC ASPECTS OF THE MODEL

The results for net benefits for 50 years of simulation, for the agricultural and timber activities as well as for hydroelectric production, are shown in Figures 14.8

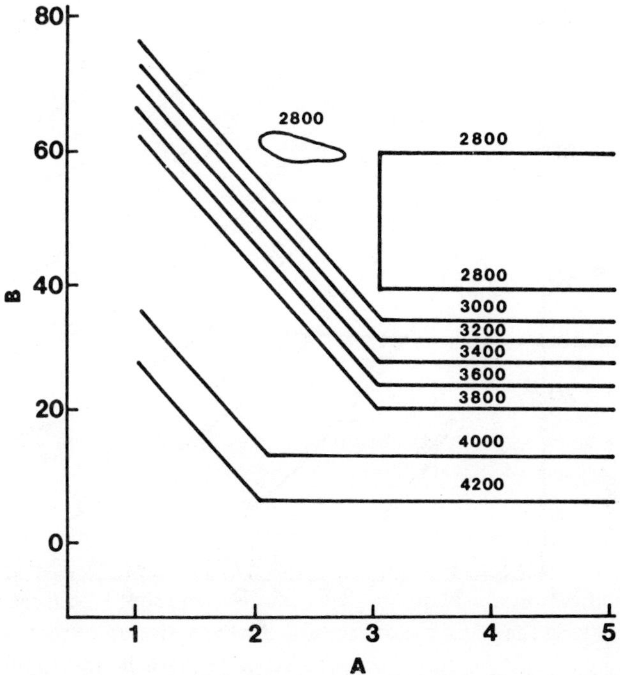

FIGURE 14.7 Hydroelectric energy production (GWh) in year 50 of simulation for the 25 intervention strategies. *A* is timber exploitation increase factor; *B* is percentage of logged area used for agriculture.

and 14.9, using the isoclines for the 25 intervention strategies. A progressive increase can be observed in the benefits of pooled agriculture and timber activities as we go toward strategies of maximum intervention. In relation to net benefit produced by hydroelectric production, there is an opposing tendency in the sense of diminishing net benefits with strategies of maximum interventions. Exceptions to this are levels 4 and 5 of Action B (percentage of exploited timber area that is turned into agriculture), where the lines become almost vertical. This implies that when we go from a 60% to an 80% intensity of agriculture, there is no appreciable increase in net benefit at any of the levels of Action A. On the other hand, that there is a relatively flat area in the lower left-hand corner of the graph shows that there is very little difference in the net benefits to be obtained by any of the different combinations of Actions A and B represented in that area of the graph.

Figure 14.10 shows the same results summarized for all benefits to be obtained during the simulation. Here we observe that the isoclines become more irregular, showing the effect of interaction between opposing trends of agriculture and timber benefits on the one hand and hydroelectric benefits on the other. A small crest towards the central diagonal of the graph represents a nonabsolute maximum, but smaller than the maximum that can be obtained in the upper left part of the

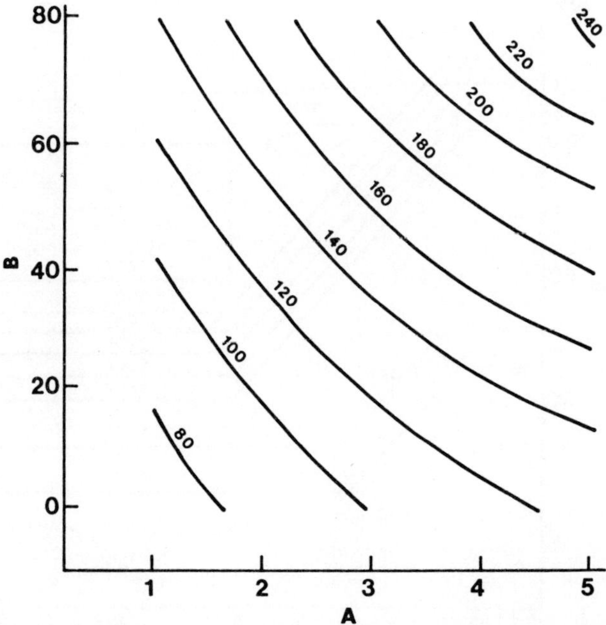

FIGURE 14.8 Net agricultural and timber benefits (millions of Bs) in year 50 of simulation, corresponding to the 25 intervention strategies.

graph. This is where the maximum accumulated net benefits for all possible intervention strategies can be obtained; that is, under the conditions of minimum timber exploitation and maximum agricultural exploitation.

USE OF THE MODEL FOR DECISION MAKING

IMPORTANCE OF THE TIME HORIZON

Figure 14.11 shows the net benefits accumulated at an 8% interest rate as a function of the degree of ecological deterioration for different time horizons. The curves drawn through the simulated points for every time horizon represent a second-degree polynomial that proved to be the best fit as measured by analysis of variance. Being a second degree polynomial, an analytical formulation that allows us to express total net benefits as function of the degree of environmental deterioration, it made possible the analysis of the importance of the time horizon in long-range decision making for the management of natural renewable resources. The first derivative with regard to environmental deterioration gives us the point

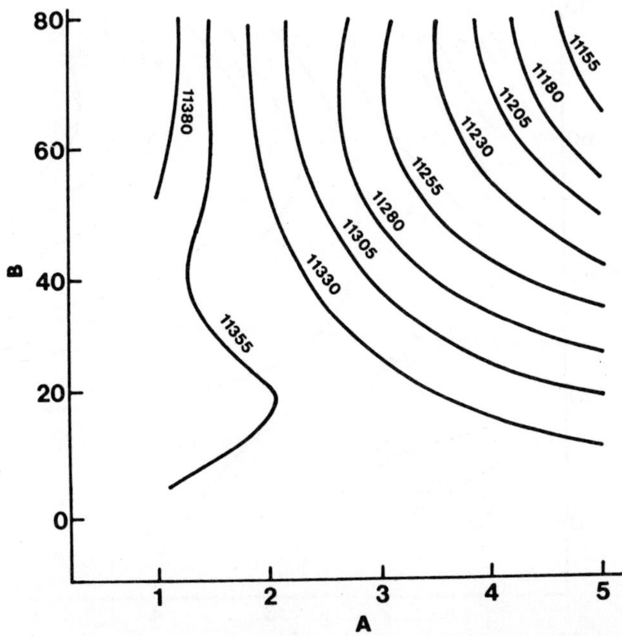

FIGURE 14.9 Net benefits produced by the hydroelectric activity (millions of Bs) in year 50 of simulation corresponding to the 25 intervention strategies.

at which net total benefits will reach their maximum. This analysis gave the following table:

Time Horizon (yr)	Degree of Ecological Degradation (%) That Produces the Maximum Total Net Benefits
50	40.8
45	54.1
40	70.5
35	92.5

This shows that if our time horizon had been relatively short, on the order of 35 years, a decision about possible alternative uses of land based exclusively on the criterion of a cost–benefit relationship would have resulted in maximum utilization of the watershed, leading to the highest ecological deterioration. As our time horizon increases, reaching 50 years, we will still be obtaining maximum net benefits, but at a lower degree of environmental degradation.

ENVIRONMENTAL COST OF ALTERNATIVE INTERVENTIONS

Figure 14.12 shows the net benefits that will be obtained for every cubic meter of soil loss as the ecological degradation increases with different intervention

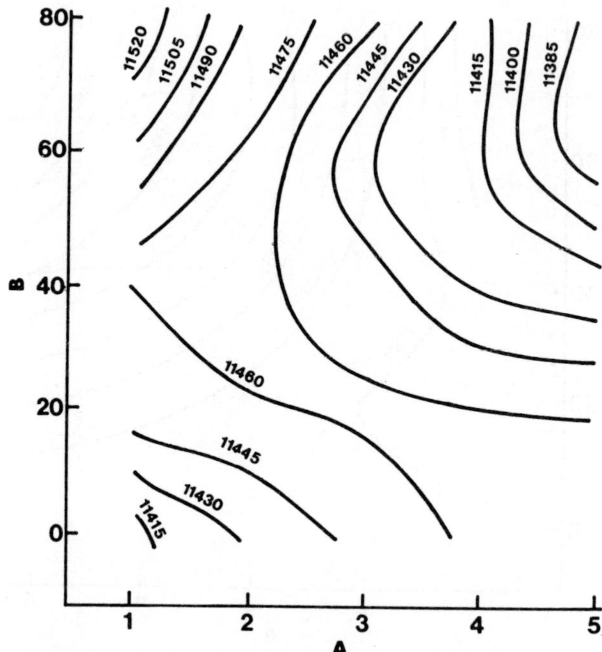

FIGURE 14.10 Total net benefits (millions of Bs) in year 50 of simulation corresponding to the 25 intervention strategies.

strategies. The results have been satisfactorily fitted to a power curve and show a very drastic fall of benefits for every cubic meter of soil loss after the initial exploitation of the watershed. In other words, after an environmental degradation of about 10% has been reached, the additional net benefit obtained for every cubic meter of soil loss become small and almost constant, leading to the conclusion that we will be paying an extremely high ecological price for a very small net additional benefit. In terms of this type of analysis, it would be advisable to select any of the five initial intervention strategies – that is, to carry out small or large timber activity, but no agricultural activity.

Of course, this analysis, and the one of the previous section relating to time horizon, are all based on results from a cost–benefit analysis, which for long-range planning probably is not the best basis for decision making.

OPTIMIZATION AND DECISION MAKING

The decision maker often would like to make optimal decisions based upon some criterion that is subjected to local constraints. Although many possible criteria can be applied to such an example as we have been developing, and many different real-world constraints will probably impose restrictions upon the decision maker,

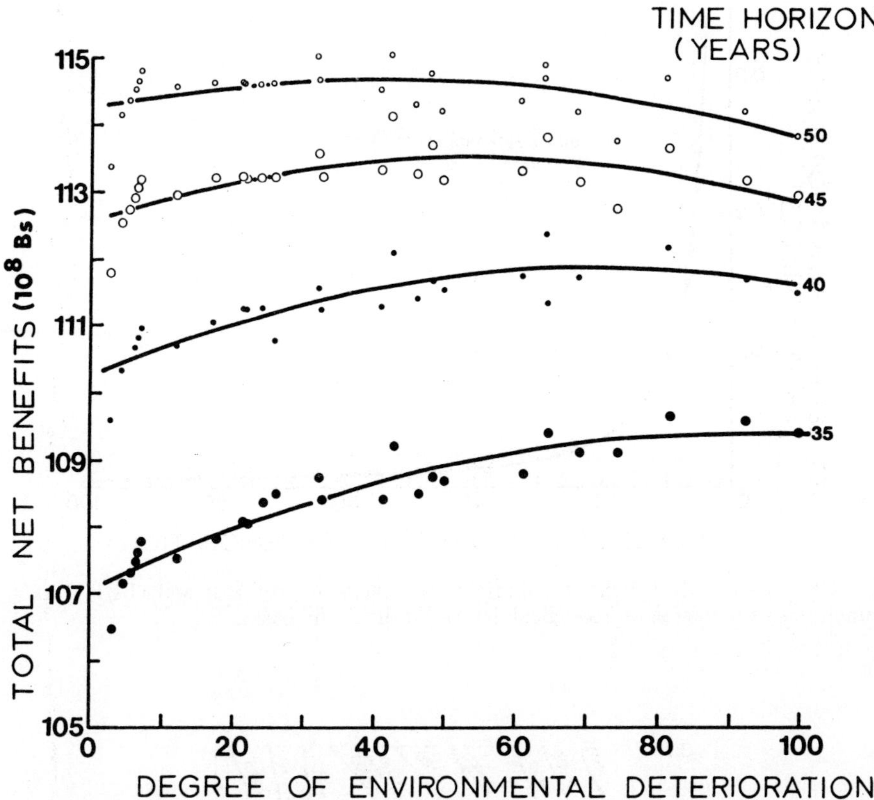

FIGURE 14.11 Total net benefit as a function of the degree of ecological deterioration of the basin, evaluated at 4 time horizons (35, 40, 45, and 50 years).

just for the sake of simplicity we can show how the results of this simulation can be applied to long-range environmental impact analysis and natural resources planning.

As most of the output of the simulation model has been expressed in terms of the 25 intervention strategies, and as these have been plotted as isoclines on the same scale, the possibility of using a very simple and graphically appealing method was raised. A method proposed by Peterman (1975), called the desk-top optimizer, was implemented in the following fashion. The variable to be maximized was the total net benefit accumulated over 50 years (in millions of bolivars) at a rate of interest of 8%. Two kinds of constraints were imposed upon the decision of maximizing such a variable: the goal of the electric company of keeping an average monthly energy production of 3750 GWh, and a given percentage of environmental degradation.

Figures 14.13, 14.14, 14.15, 14.16, and 14.17 show the results of maximizing the net total benefit under above-mentioned constraints. Figure 14.13 shows that

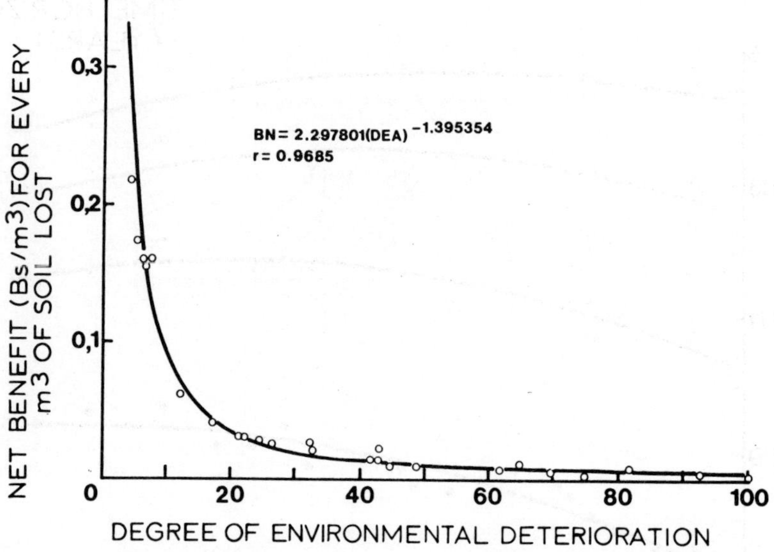

FIGURE 14.12 Net benefits obtained for every m³ of lost soil (Bs/m³) as a function of the degree of ecological deterioration of the basin.

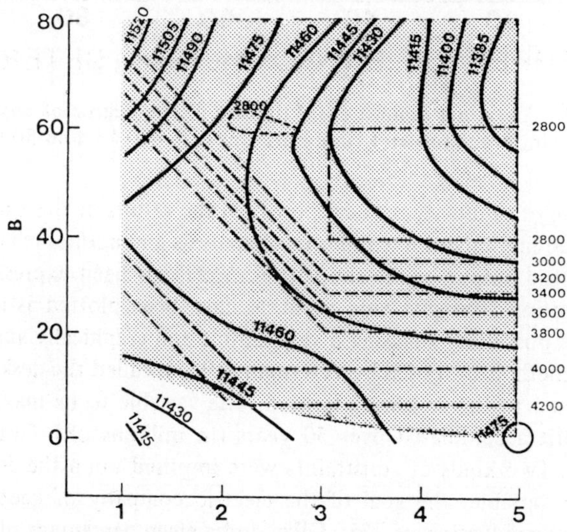

FIGURE 14.13 Optimum solution (circle) for maximizing total net benefits under a 50-year time horizon, constrained by an average hydroelectric production of 3,750 GWh and an ecological deterioration equal to or less then 10% (shaded area covers the non-possible solutions).

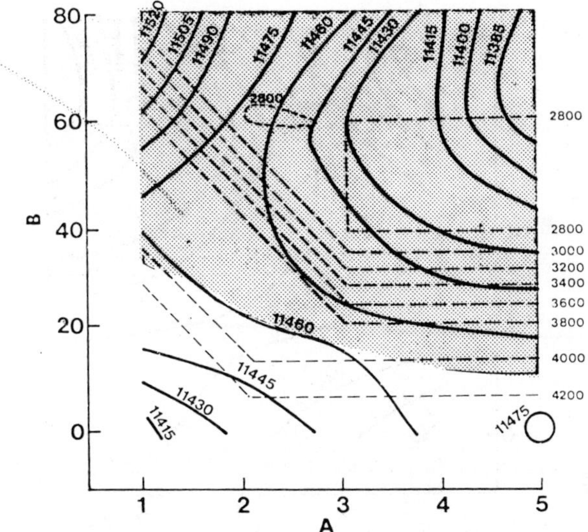

FIGURE 14.14 Optimum solution (circle) for maximizing total net benefits under a 50-year time horizon, constrained by an average hydroelectric production of 3,750 GWh and an ecological deterioration equal to or less than 20% (shaded area covers the non-possible solutions).

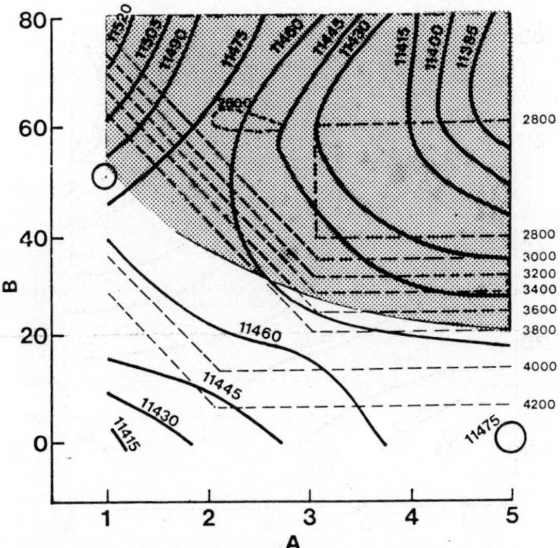

FIGURE 14.15 Optimum solutions (circles) for maximizing total net benefits under a 50-year time horizon, constrained by an average hydroelectric production of 3,750 GWh and an ecological deterioration equal to or less then 30% (shaded area covers the non-possible solutions).

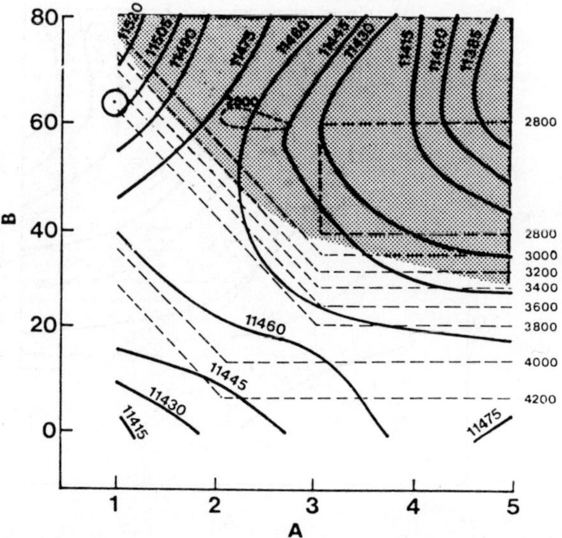

FIGURE 14.16 Optimum solution (circle) for maximizing total net benefits under a 50-year time horizon, constrained by an average hydroelectric production of 3,750 GWh and an ecological deterioration equal to or less than 40% (shaded area covers the non-possible solutions).

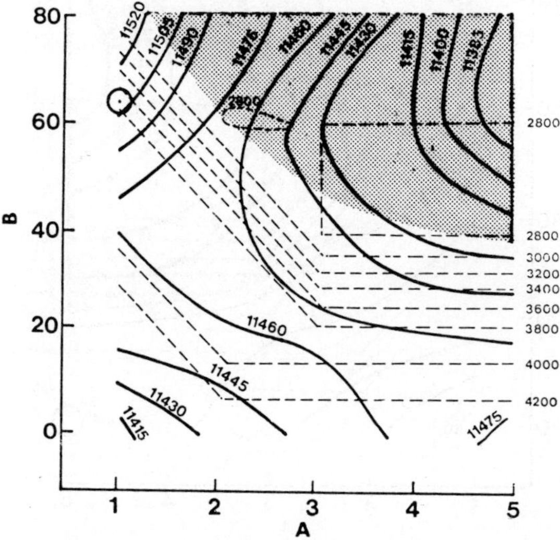

FIGURE 14.17 Optimum solution (circle) for maximizing total net benefits under a 50-year time horizon, constrained by an average hydroelectric production of 3,750 GWh and an ecological deterioration equal to or less than 50% (shaded area covers the non-possible solutions).

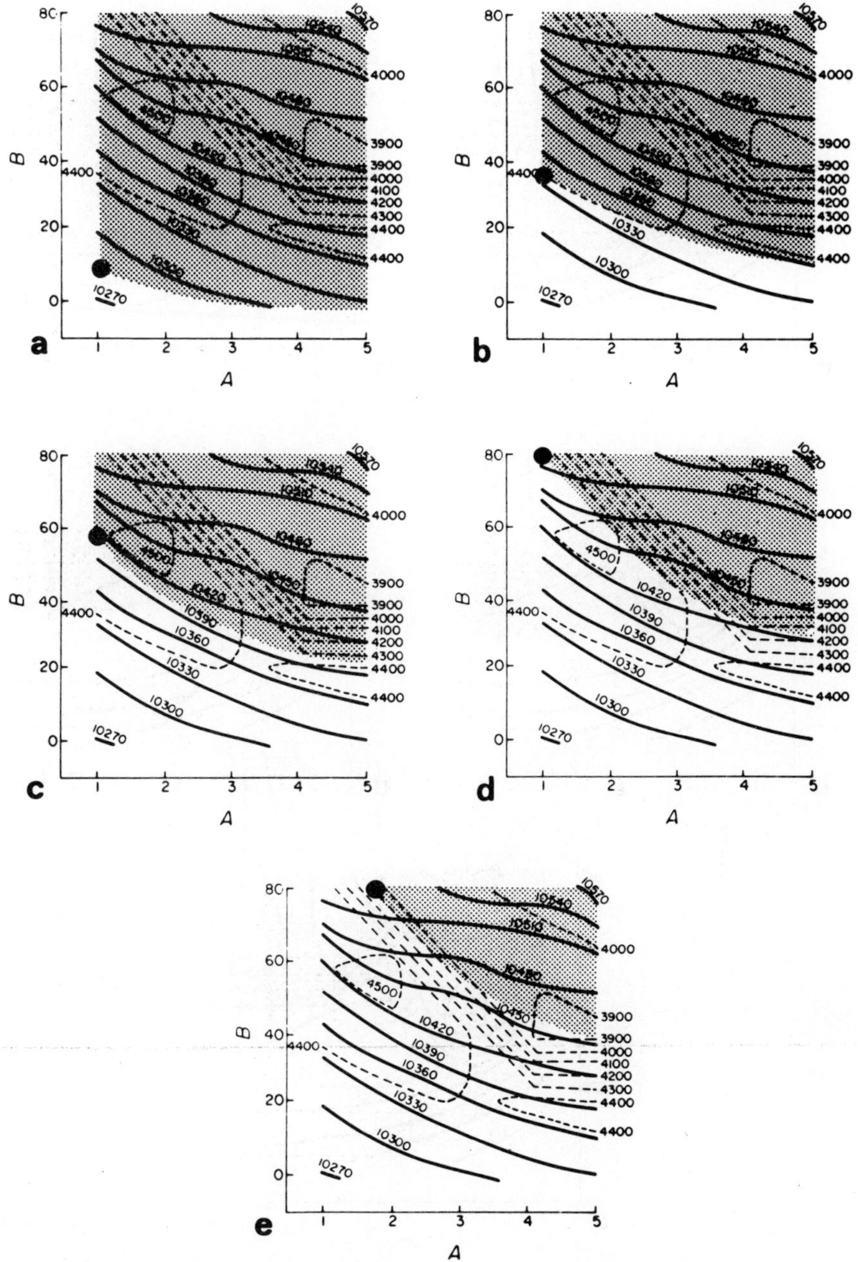

FIGURE 14.18 Sequence of optimum decisions similar to Figures 13–17 but for a 30-year time horizon.

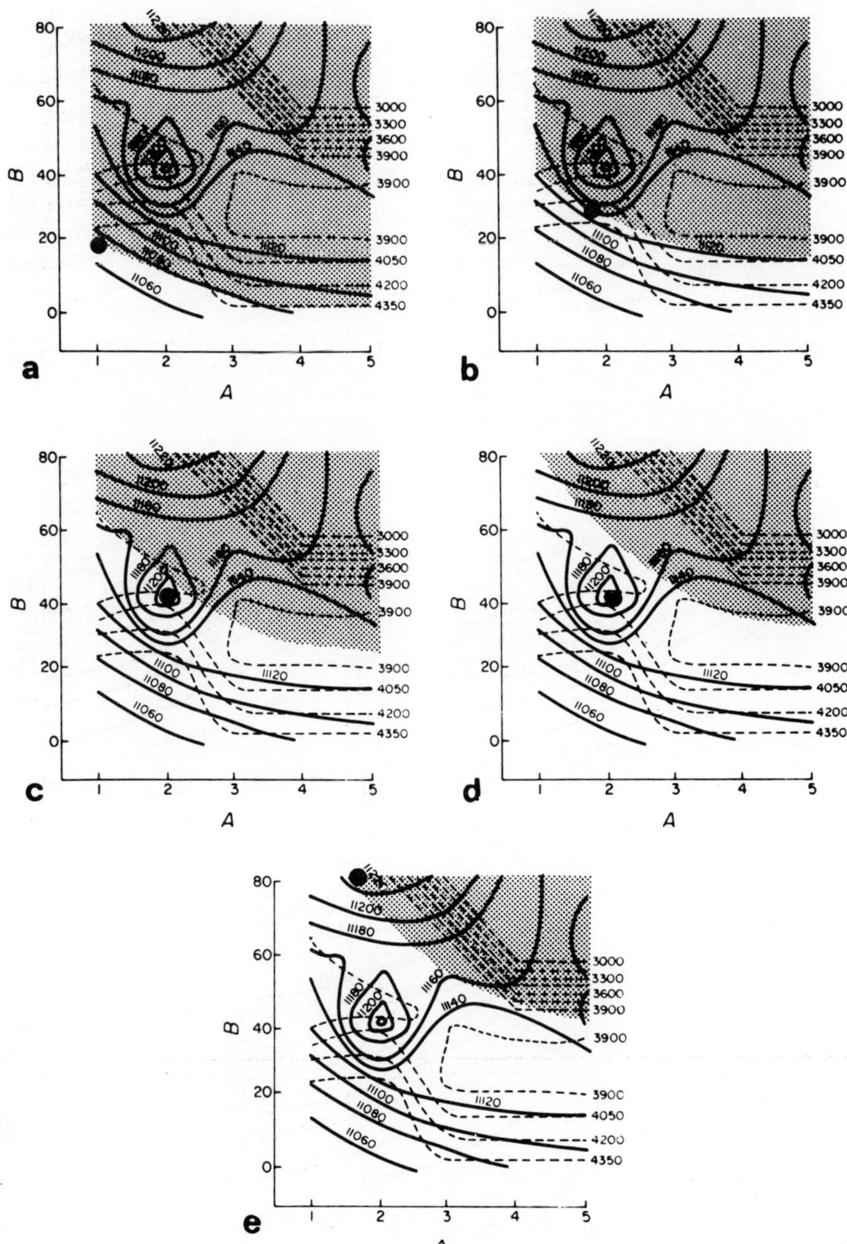

FIGURE 14.19 Sequence of optimum decisions similar to Figures 13–17, but for a 40-year time horizon.

TABLE 14.7 Optimal decision, Resulting from the Application of the Desk-Top Optimizer for Maximizing Total Net Benefits with Ecological and Monthly Hydroelectric Production Constraints (3750 GWh), for Three Time Horizons

Ecological Deterioration	Time Horizon (yr)[a] 30		40		50	
	A	B	A	B	A	B
10	1	9	1	17	5	0
20	1	35	1.8	30	5	0
30	1	59	2	43	5 (1)	0 (52)
40	1	80	2	43	1	64
50	1.8	80	1.7	80	1	64

[a] A and B correspond to the two action strategies used in the simulation.

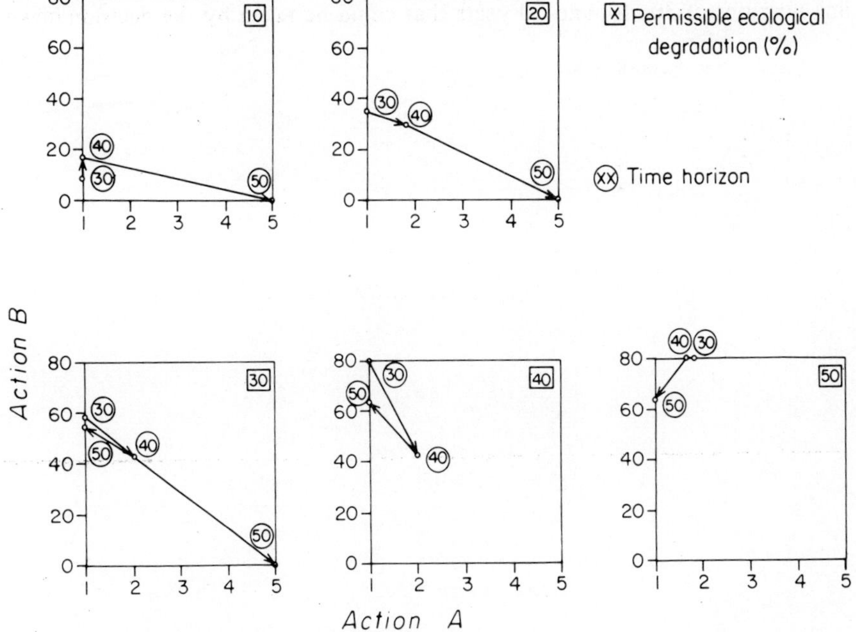

FIGURE 14.20 Three time horizon optimum decision trajectories for five different ecological deterioration constraints that maximize total net benefits with an average monthly hydroelectric production of 3,750 GWh.

the decision would be at Action A level 5, and Action B level 0. Figure 14.14 shows that when environmental degradation constraints go up to 20%, the decision would still be the same: level 5 of Action A, and level 0 of action B. When the environmental degradation constraints go up to 30%, there are two equally satisfactory solutions for maximizing the total benefit and also keeping the constraint of 3750 GWh; the solutions are either level 5 of Action A and level 0 of Action B or level 1 of Action A and level 52% of Action B (Figure 14.15). When the environmental degradation constraint is increased to 40%, there is again only one optimal solution, represented by level 1 of Action A and 64% of Action B (Figure 14.16). The same solution is obtained for any other constraints on ecological deterioration larger than 40%, as is shown in Figure 14.17 for 50%.

A similar analysis can be performed for total net benefits accumulated over a different time horizon, as we can see from Figures 14.18 and 14.19, where the graphs show the same type of results as shown for Figures 14.13–14.17. In all cases, the small circle shows the optimal decision for different time horizons under conditions of increasing ecological degradation constraints.

Table 14.7 shows which optimal solutions can be obtained for five increasing ecological degradation constraints for time horizons of 30, 40, and 50 years. These results are shown in Figure 14.20 as the possible optimal solution trajectories for time horizons of 30, 40, and 50 years that could be taken by the decision maker.

15 A Wildlife Impact Information System

This chapter describes a wildlife impact information system (WIIS) that is intended to facilitate more effective husbandry of wildlife resources that are affected by mining activities. The system is essentially an extension and partial redirection of the traditional environmental impact assessment process, with special adaptations to alleviate analysis problems that are peculiar to animal resources.WIIS was developed in Fort Collins, Colorado, by the Office of Biological Services, U.S. Fish and Wildlife Service. Development began in 1975 and is expected to continue for about 5 years.

WIIS is applicable to several levels of impact assessment problems. The basic application is at the level of site-specific impact for a particular mining disturbance. The next higher level of application is the analysis of an assemblage of site-specific impacts for a particular mine with the intent of producing alternative operating plans. The final level of application is the assembling of a set of impacts for a group of mines with the intent of recommending development sequencing.

A host of secondary benefits can be realized through the use of WIIS, of which four will suffice for an introduction. First, the system can lead to a reduction in the variety and quantity of biological data that must be collected and interpreted to produce rational assessments. Second, the system helps to create a meaningful association between the accumulation of baseline data, the prediction of impact, the monitoring of actual impacts, and the planning of corrective measures. Third, the system provides the capacity for rapid analysis and review of information. Fourth, the system provides a rational evaluation framework for the inevitable adversary atmosphere that develops around the assessment process.

DEVELOPMENT RATIONALE

CRITERIA FOR RELEVANCE

In an attempt to avoid many of the pitfalls normally encountered in designing computerized information management systems, the Tract C-a oil shale mine in northwestern Colorado was selected to serve as the basis for a real-world impact assessment program. Assessment information for the Tract C-a program was obtained from the tract's Detailed Development Plan (Gulf Oil Corporation and Standard Oil Company of Indiana, 1976) (DDP – somewhat equivalent to an in-depth environmental impact analysis) and numerous reports and evaluations pertaining to the area's biological and physical phenomena.

The Tract C-a program provided state-of-the-art scenarios for the evaluation of four major ingredients of the impact assessment process: (a) the capacity of ecological methodology to supply data relevant to assessment goals; (b) contemporary approaches to information processing and analysis; (c) the management agencies' capability to convert information into meaningful impact assessments; and (d) administrators' expectations and concerns for utilization of the assessment.

These four factors were adopted as the framework for developing WIIS. Thus, in addition to incorporating the appropriate roles of each real-world ingredient in the structure and function of WIIS, we had to integrate the four ingredients in such a manner as to carry the assessment process smoothly through all mining development phases.

Conversion of the Tract C-a individual activities into WIIS was accomplished through the development of in-depth scenarios of the intent and content of the activities and the elimination of unsound features from these scenarios according to a series of guidelines developed from various impact assessment and ecological concepts independent of the Tract C-a development. Apparent shortcomings in the Tract C-a activity scenarios were replaced with features more in conformity with established guidelines. In several cases, described in the following sections, the replacements represented major changes in the assessment process.

CRITERIA FOR APPLICATION

Among the most critical shortcomings in the Tract C-a assessment are features that have been grouped under the general heading of application deficiencies. These application deficiencies are design or analysis processes that lead to distorted or nonsensical assessments because the assessment processes are not tuned to elucidate some innate characteristics of the impact scenario. The following five criteria are perceived as being essential to the enhancement of the application potential of WIIS; they also indicate the major shortcomings of the Tract C-a assessment.

1. The system should have the capability to discern impact over areas of several hundred to several thousand square miles.

2. The system should be uniformly applicable to a reasonable representation of animal species in the geographic area of interest.

3. The system should allow for the analysis of influence of vegetation and habitat types in the geographic area of interest.

4. The system should be able to distinguish between ecological changes caused by the mining disturbance and ecological changes caused by natural phenomena.

5. The system should be able to distinguish between ecological changes caused by specific physical disturbances (i.e., land, air, and water).

STRATEGY FOR INFORMATION SYNTHESIS

A more subtle deficiency in the Tract C-a assessment was the information content and the relationships among the following basic information components that comprise the impact information scenario:

1. When is the impact likely to occur?
2. Where is the impact likely to occur?
3. Who (what fish and wildlife resources) is likely to be affected?
4. What level is the impact likely to reach?

A lack of information in one or more of the four components and an unclear relationship among the components precluded a well-rounded assessment, and management plans based on such an assessment are likely to be ill-conceived.

Much of the interpretation difficulty was caused by the failure of the Tract C-a assessment to follow the logical ordering of the components as they are shown. One must presumably know *when* and *where* impacts are likely to occur before defining *what* wildlife resources are likely to be affected. Likewise, *who* will be affected must be known before one attempts to determine *what* level the impact will reach.

There are two important implications for impact assessment in the content and arrangement of the components. The immediate implication is that the assessment information can be synthesized in an incremental fashion. This incremental approach is useful because the success of the assessment does not depend entirely on answering the fourth question. Although this is the implied and desired goal of every impact assessment project, it is seldom attained, leading to assessments that leave the manager at a loss for management guidance. But if impact information is developed in the proposed incremental fashion, each compartment can provide information that is useful to the administrator even without completion of the entire sequence. Since usable information is more readily assembled for the first than for latter compartments, at least a degree of rational assessment is highly probable for most assessment projects.

A less apparent implication of the four-component information synthesis strategy is the utility of using spatial discrimination as a common denominator throughout the assessment process. Spatiality was a more or less built-in fundamental quality in the *when* and *where* information for the Tract C-a assessment, but it became tenuous to nonexistent in the information for the *who* and *what* components. The loss of spatial discrimination in the *who* and *what* components practically negated the capacity of the Tract C-a assessment to achieve the degree of application desired for WIIS.

Thus, it was considered essential that the information synthesis process for WIIS follow the *when, where, who,* and *what* sequence, and that spatial discrimination function as a common basis for assessment through the four components.

MEASURES OF IMPACT

The capacity to measure the status and changes in status of the animal resource is an elementary requirement for the production of meaningful impact assessments. The Tract C-a assessment attempted to achieve this capability through the traditional approaches of measuring population densities and collecting an assortment of demographic, life history, and welfare characteristics for animal species.

Four general observations are sufficient to evaluate the Tract C-a approach: (a) much of the collected data provided no clear contribution to the assessment conclusions; (b) the data acquisition, synthesis, and interpretation failed to reach a sufficient level of comprehension to establish scientific or administrative credibility for the assessment conclusions; (c) the assessment conclusions considered only a few arbitrarily selected animal species from the several hundred known to inhabit the development area; and (d) the assessment conclusions involved such broad quantitative estimates that administrative interpretation was confused rather than clarified. Most of these difficulties cannot be divorced from problems created by using population density as a measure of impact.

In addition to the foregoing indictment of population density as an impact measure, a further evaluation was made in terms of the conceptual relationships among the physical disturbance, the resulting consequences for animal resources, and the direct measurement of those consequences (herein called monitoring) and the actions taken to correct deleterious consequences (herein called mitigation). The key point of inquiry is a set of demographic and life history features, called impact indicators in Table 15.1. The first decisive question involves the inferred versus the actual role played by traditional impact indicators in the mining and assessment process.

Mitigation targets are the animals' life requirements that are directly disturbed by the physical mining activities. These life requirements are thus the biological features that are of direct concern in maintaining the animal's welfare. But the current level of ecological knowledge and the state of ecological technology are so inadequate that the condition of these life requirements cannot be readily measured. For this reason, efforts to measure effects of the mining activity on

TABLE 15.1 Content and Organization of Basic Development Activity Phases Making up the Mining–Wildlife Husbandry Scenario

---

Disturbance Features (physical actions that cause ecological changes)
- Mine pits
- Spoil piles
- Water pollution
- Etc.

Mitigation targets (primary ecological components that are disturbed by physical actions)
- Nutrition
- Living space
- Social stimuli
- Etc.

Impact Indicators (secondary ecological components that are changed by physical actions)
- Population size
- Population distribution
  - Species richness
  - Species retention
  - Vegetation complement
  - Vegetation persistence
  - Etc.
- Population composition

Mitigation plans (physical actions that correct disturbed mitigation targets)
- Habitat enhancement
- Habitat replacement
- Habitat substitution
- Disturbance feature alteration

---

animals are shifted to the more tangible features, such as demography and life history. The information from these surrogate features is intended to suffice not only to measure change in the status of life requirements, but also to diagnose the nature of the impact to guide the designing of corrective actions.

Population density is the feature used universally as an indicator of the status of the animal's life requirements. An important reason for the failure of population density to play its expected role in the asssessment process is readily apparent when one considers the variety of life requirements that influence population density, as illustrated in a much simplified representation in Figure 15.1. The essence of Figure 15.1 is the relationship among a multitude of life requirements converging to determine population density, a relationship in which population density may be changed by one, several, or all of the life requirements.

The consequences for impact assessment of so many life requirements acting on population density become apparent if one considers the reverse situation – attempting to deduce the nature of changes in the life requirements by observing a change in a population's density. It is probably impossible to make such diagnostic

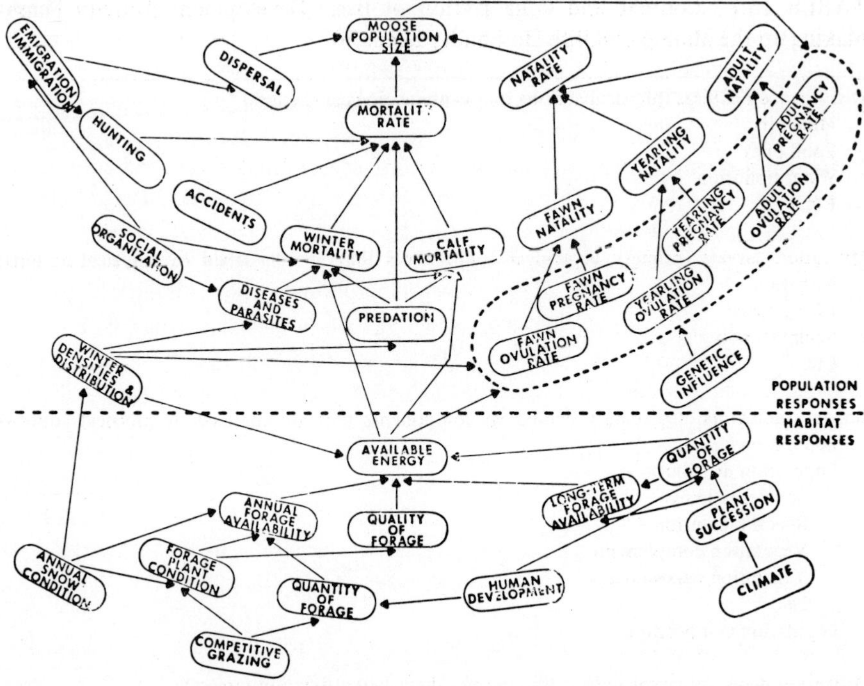

FIGURE 15.1 Simplified network of population and habitat features that combine to control a population's density (in this case, a moose population).

deductions without additional information on the status and functional relationships among the life requirements. The inclusion of extensive but essentially meaningless bits and pieces of biological data in the typical impact assessment is testimony to the futility of the approach. The approach is the primary cause of the syndrome of measuring everything for which a budget can be generated.

Population density as an impact assessment measure has a second major drawback: population density is difficult if not impossible to determine for most species that should be included in the assessment. The chronic problem is that attempts to determine population densities produce such wide statistical confidence limits that the values have little meaning for impact assessment. The usual corrective action is larger sampling programs to obtain larger sample sizes to reduce the confidence limits.

This characteristic of population density sampling becomes intolerable (for available time, manpower, and money) when viewed in terms of the five criteria of application previously discussed as essential features for WIIS. At best, the statistical confidence problems have been overcome only for species with the highest densities. Normally, such species comprise only a small percentage of all the species that should be considered in an impact assessment. For WIIS, an impact assessment based on studies of the five most abundant or dense populations was not an acceptable approach. It is reasonable to assume that those species whose densities are lowest may be the species most susceptible to the adverse effects of mining activities.

The third and final argument against population density as a focal point for impact assessment is that for the majority of species that should be considered, population density levels have nothing but arbitrary meaning. Unless the population density estimates involve an endangered species or a species of economic consequence where numbers can be easily converted to economics, population density *per se* has no meaning except the currently fashionable but ultimately senseless view that any decrease from an observed pre-impact level is damaging to the species and is thus intolerable.

Despite these population density difficulties, the assumption remains that measures of disturbance of animal populations should be based on some demographic or life-history feature of the populations. Thus, population phenomena other than density (e.g., distribution, yield, turnover, age composition, sex composition) were evaluated as potential impact indicators. For a number of reasons (such as practically no information in the Tract C-a DDP and the traditional difficulty of measurement), all population phenomena except population distribution were eliminated from consideration.

Using population distribution information as a measure of impact is feasible and practical for three reasons: (a) The only data required are whether or not a species occurs at the point of area of interest; thus, much time, manpower, and money is saved by eliminating the sustained sampling effort normally necessary to determine population densities. (b) Measurement of species distribution is apparently within the capability of contemporary ecological methodology. (c) Species distribution data can satisfy the five criteria of application previously discussed.

The inherent pitfalls of calculating a species' distribution are at least partially recognized by the WIIS project. For example, will changes in population size caused by physical disturbances be accompanied by changes in population distribution that can be measured? Will the impossibility of actually proving the absence of a species be such a bias that population distribution information will be as difficult to obtain as population size and density information? The answers to these questions will only be known after the approach has undergone field testing.

Population distribution data are only an intermediate step in developing the impact assessment, since they are converted into an assessment measure called species density. This conversion is achieved with the system's Biological Information Processor and is described in a later section.

STRATEGY FOR ASSESSMENT

It is the viewpoint of this analysis that the Tract C-a assessment fell far short of anticipated levels of prediction of the consequences of the Tract C-a disturbance for wildlife resources. The primary difficulty is the state of predictive ecology. Furthermore, there is little hope that an adequate level of ecological technology can be developed in the near future that will allow the level of prediction that is currently expected at the predevelopment stage of activity. Since predictive impact assessment is unlikely to be achievable within a reasonable time, the best course of action seems to be a system for monitoring the development and its associated consequences for wildlife resources in a manner that will produce assessment information that is useful to administrators as quickly as possible. This approach is referred to here as adaptive monitoring.

The key feature in the adaptive monitoring approach is a spatial monitoring scheme that can be adjusted to fit changes in spatial patterns of impact that occur during the course of the development. The simplest monitoring scheme is to encircle the physical disturbance area with two rings of sampling points, one ring at a best-guess distance from the disturbance where little or no impact is likely to occur but as close to the disturbance as possible (hereafter called the baseline ring), and one as near the center of disturbance as possible where impact is highly likely to occur (hereafter called the monitoring ring). The selection of appropriate locations for both rings, but particularly for the monitoring ring, is facilitated by the spatial analyses of physical disturbances that are produced by the Physical Information Processor (this is described in a later section).

The baseline ring of sampling points is intended to supply baseline-type data throughout the time span of the development, and, if properly located, it should not require repositioning during the development. The monitoring ring is intended to supply data on the location and magnitude of the impact. This ring is intended to be enlarged in whole or in part in response to its detection of impact. As impact is detected, the ring is expanded in small arbitrary increments until impact is no longer detected. In this manner, the *where* of the impact is reasonably defined. Each time the monitoring ring is enlarged, a small number of sampling points are maintained in the original positions for continued monitoring during the time span of the development. This set of sampling points provides data on what species are affected and on the overall magnitude of the impact.

SYSTEM DESCRIPTION

GENERAL PROCESSING FORMAT

The WIIS described in the following sections is the result of an attempt to incorporate into one system the desired features of relevance, application, assessment, and synthesis. In its simplest form, the system's operation is based on the assembling and manipulating of two modules of spatially related data, one module treating a geographic area's biological resources and the other module treating the same

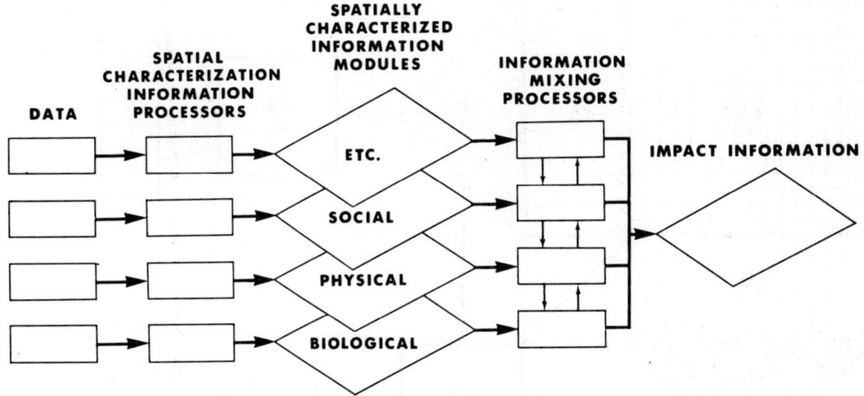

FIGURE 15.2 General processing format of WIIS, illustrating the system's dependence on spatial discrimination of impacts, the division of information into modules, and the combining of the information into a final spatial definition of impact.

geographic area's nonbiological resources and conditions (Figure 15.2).

The biological module contains information on plant and animal resources. The nonbiological module includes all influences that act directly on a wildlife resource, as well as influences that act on wildlife resources indirectly through land, air, and water disturbances. The nonbiological information may be divided into several modules to facilitate the assessment.

FUNCTIONAL COMPONENTS

A flow chart outlining the system's main features and their sequence of processing is illustrated in Figure 15.3. Each main feature of the WIIS is designated by a numbered compartment, with the numbers indicating the sequence during processing. Figure 15.3 illustrates three streams of information processing and storage: a physical information stream that includes compartments 1, 2, 3, and 4; a biological information stream that includes compartments 5, 6, 7, and 8; and a physical–biological information stream that includes compartments 9, 10, 4, and 8.

Compartments 1 and 5 are the system's data input facilities for the physical and biological information streams, respectively. The data input facilities are somewhat analogous to entering data into a computer with punch cards. Compartments 2, 6, and 9 are the system's computational facilities for processing information. They are computer models that handle the behavior of the physical, biological, and physical–biological components.

Compartments 3, 7, and 10 are the system's information storage facilities. These libraries contain all input data plus all new information generated by the physical, biological, and physical–biological information processors.

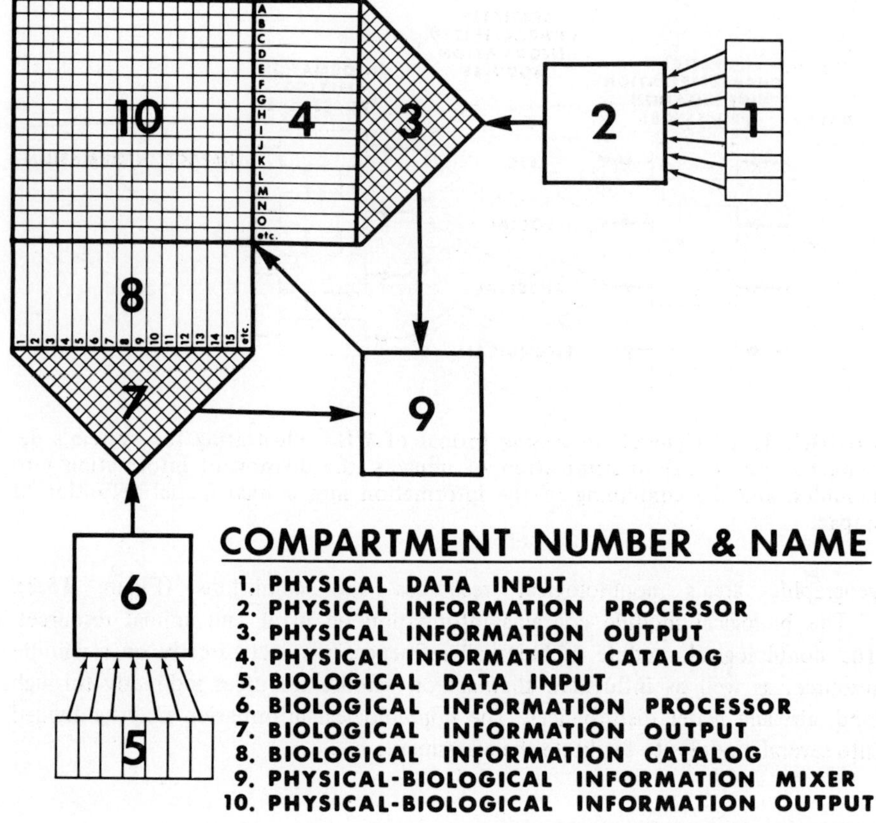

FIGURE 15.3 Contents and functional relationships of WIIS, illustrating computation sequences.

Compartments 4 and 8 are the system's catalogs to information contained in the libraries. The catalog names and the catalog operating program are the system's facilities for access to the libraries.

PHYSICAL INFORMATION PROCESSOR

The system's nonbiological information set is at this writing represented by only one component, the Physical Information Processor. Future additions will include a Social Information Processor and an Economic Information Processor. The Physical Information Processor (PIP) is component of the system that generates information on land, air, and water disturbances that occur as a result of mining activities. The PIP defines the *when* and *where* of the assessment process.

The basic rationale in the PIP's design was that the most meaningful evaluation of a mining development's impact on wildlife resources required the simultaneous expression of land, air, and water disturbances. Thus, the individual models that calculate such disturbances had to be integrated into one simulation system that would handle all effects simultaneously. Available models were too large (too many variables or too much complex calculating) to be combined into the required single system, so they were either reduced in size and complexity to fit the system's needs, or replaced with complete or partial models written by the WIIS project staff. As a result, PIP's individual land, air, and water models are considerably smaller and less complicated than most other models that do the same sorts of things. PIP thus gained two major advantages over the larger, more complex models.

First, the three physical models (land, air, and water) can be simulated simultaneously over a period of time. Such capability provides the desired comprehensive perspective of all disturbances created by the mining activities. Also, the simultaneous simulations are necessary for establishing realistic linkages among the individual models. Such linkages are critical for simulating the most realistic mining and disturbance scenarios.

Second, the reduced number of parameters required to execute PIP's models permits the models to be used with data that are readily available in typical impact assessments, detailed development plans, or other survey projects. Since PIP's models do not require elaborate data banks or data-collecting programs, they are sufficiently general and flexible to be applicable to a variety of mining situations (e.g., coal, phosphate, copper).

It should be clearly understood that PIP's physical models are intended to supply land, air, and water disturbance information at levels of detail commensurate with levels of detail useful in the evaluation of wildlife impact and mitigation. Thus, they are not intended to serve the more detailed purposes of the more sophisticated models.

Land Model

The land model is basically a bookkeeping system that monitors, through time and space, the volumes of topsoil, overburden, and ore that are removed from the mine pit, processed, and deposited in storage or disposal areas. The user-selected disposal sites may be designated for any combination of topsoil, overburden, and ore. Parameters provided in the model for controlling the spatial dynamics of land disturbance include location (in relation to a reference map) and shape of the mine pit, location and shape of disposal areas, and path of mine-pit migration. These parameters for controlling spatial dynamics are augmented by parameters that specify physical characteristics, such as stratigraphy of the pit area, characteristics of the ore, and capacities of the disposal sites.

Parameters provided to control the temporal dynamics of land disturbance include the development schedule and production rate (e.g., barrels of oil produced per day), the latter being PIP's main driving variable. In addition, numerous parameters that control the timing and sequencing of activities are automatically calculated by the model. For example, the timing of retort operations is determined by the accumulation of a sufficient quantity of ore. Likewise, water used for revegetation (a linkage with the water submodel) is keyed to the amount of material accumulated in the disposal areas.

Water Model

The basic structure of the water model is similar to the land model in that the model keeps track of water volumes according to origin, flows through the spatial system as affected by the mining activity, and final deposition. The bookkeeping system is based on watershed subunits, their sequential linkages, and man-made impoundments within the subunits.

Water origin for surface hydrology simulations is controlled by three parameters: precipitation, water imported from outside the simulated environmental system, and water pumped to the surface as a result of mine de-watering. Water flow through the environmental system is controlled by parameters that represent natural characteristics such as size and arrangement of watershed subunits, evaporation, interception, percolation, soil moisture content, and snowmelt. Water flow through the system is also controlled by parameters representing a variety of uses, including dust suppression, revegetation, leaching, and spent-shale moisturizing, associated with mining and processing. Final deposition of water is controlled by parameters that designate the uses, locations, capacities, surface-to-volume ratios, and bypass rates for impoundments and storage tanks. Water pollutant concentrations from origin, to flow-through, to final deposition are also monitored within the hydrologic model.

Air Model

The air model uses available meteorological data (chiefly wind direction, wind velocity, and air turbulence), stack characteristics (such as emission temperature, emission components, velocity, height, and emission concentrations), and topographic data (elevation of surrounding terrain relative to stack elevations) to compute ground-level concentrations for airborne stack-emitted pollutants. Concentrations generated may represent instantaneous, worst-case conditions or mean levels for longer averaging times.

BIOLOGICAL INFORMATION PROCESSOR

The primary role of the Biological Information Processor (BIP) in the WIIS is to convert species distribution maps or other data into species density values and thence into a set of impact measures. Impact measures are properties of the wildlife resource whose values provide the *who* and *what* information in the incremental assessment approach. The operating format of the BIP is to convert information on wildlife resources into a spatial scheme that can be integrated with the spatial scheme of mining disturbances generated by the PIP.

Spatial discrimination of biological information is developed according to two formats, one keyed to the activity phase typically referred to as predevelopment assessment and the other keyed to the activity phase typically referred to as impact monitoring. The predevelopment format for computing spatial discrimination, referred to as area discrimination in the WIIS, produces a continuum of information across a geographic area. Area discrimination information is intended to move the assessment stage to the *who* level – i.e., what fish and wildlife resources are likely to be affected by the physical disturbances. As discussed earlier in the section on prediction capabilities, the *who* level of assessment is probably all that can be achieved at the predevelopment activity phase.

The monitoring format for computing spatial discrimination, referred to as point discrimination in the WIIS, produces information at one or more point locations across a geographic area. The point discrimination approach provides the facility for spatial assessment based on data from field monitoring stations. Point discrimination information is intended to move the assessment stage to the *what* level – i.e., what the level of effect is likely to be.

Area Discrimination

The continuum of species density values for a geographic area is calculated by scanning a series of individual species distribution maps and counting the number of maps (i.e., species) that are encountered at each point in a set of points. Although the distribution of points can follow any pattern, a rectangular grid produces the most broadly applicable continuum of species density values. Individual species distribution maps are entered into the BIP through standard map digitization procedures. The grid of species density values is subdivided into zones of vegetative types or associations (predevelopment part of Figure 15.4). The impact measures are then computed from combinations of species density and vegetative types. The four assessment measures thus far developed are described in Table 15.2.

Species richness (and its time-lapse counterpart, species retention) is the principal baseline assessment measure for establishing a quantitative level for wildlife resources in a geographic area over a period of time. The rationale for this approach (i.e., species density extrapolated over space) for quantifying wildlife resources was explained in detail in an earlier section. Vegetation complement (and its time-lapse counterpart, vegetation persistence) is a secondary baseline assessment measure, but it is more qualitative than species richness because it essentially reflects the comparative diversity of habitat a species or group occupies.

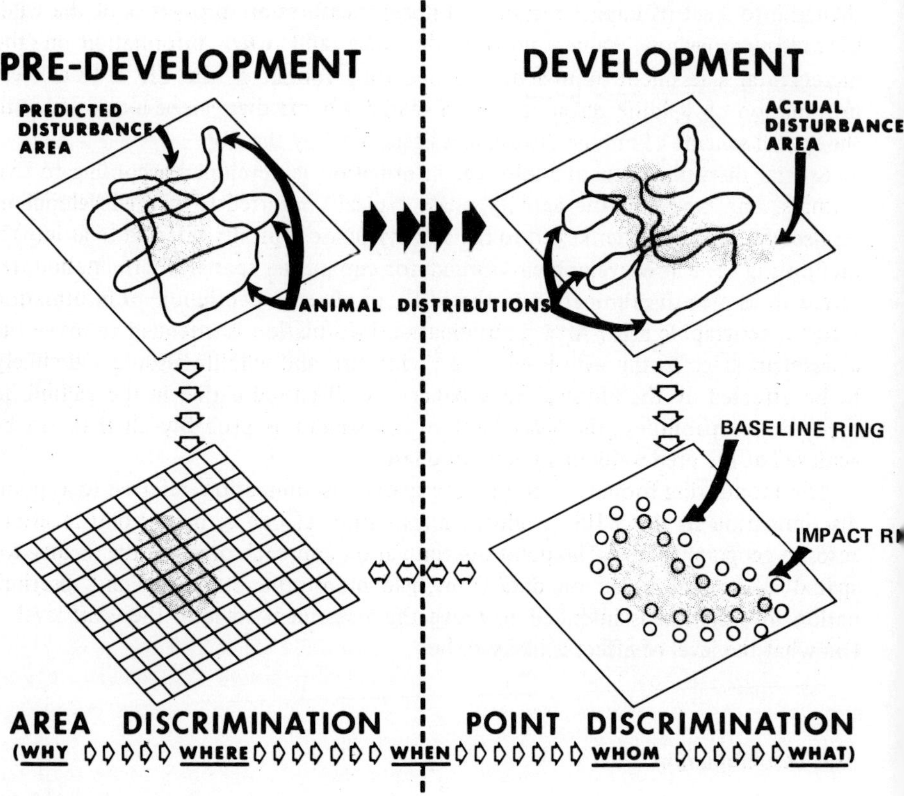

FIGURE 15.4 General representation of the system's treatment of impact information for a mining development's main phases.

Point Discrimination

Point discrimination of species density values are intended to be derived primarily from field studies in which species densities are measured directly. The switch from area discrimination to point discrimination for the monitoring approach was necessary because point measurements are necessary to adequate determination of the extent of impact. The rationale for the adaptive monitoring approach was explained in an earlier section, but, in review, the point discrimination approach provides the basic data for separating areas of impact from areas of nonimpact (development part of Figure 15.4).

Other than the methodology of obtaining species density information, the process of converting species densities to impact measures is the same for point discrimination as explained for area discrimination. But the point discrimination process carries the assessment into (a) the stages of defining more precisely the

TABLE 15.2 Assessment Measures Calculated from Species Densities and Vegetation Types

Measure	Description
Species richness	The number of animal species supported for a given area of vegetation type
Species retention	The number of animal species that occupied the area before development that remain in the area after development for a given area of vegetation type
Vegetation complement	The number of vegetation types or associations occupied by an animal species or group
Vegetation persistence	The number of vegetation types or associations occupied by an animal species or group before development that are still occupied after development (either inside or outside the disturbance area)

expected *where* and *who* that were tentatively derived from, respectively, the Physical Information Processor and the area discrimination phase of the Biological Information Processor and (b) the stages of defining the *what* of assessment in terms of the impact measures that have been established for the WIIS.

The ability of the point discrimination system to describe the *what* of assessment is based on the system's separation of biological changes that occur as a result of natural processes from biological changes that occur as a result of the mining activity. Natural changes are distinguished by time-course analysis of the impact measures obtained from the baseline ring of sample points (Figure 15.4). Mining-related changes are distinguished by time-course analysis of impact measures obtained from the impact ring of sample points (Figure 15.4).

Impact Index Calculation

There are four values available for each impact measure (Figure 15.4): (1) the value outside the impact area before the development started, as provided by the area discrimination process; (2) the value inside the potential impact area before the development started, as provided by the area discrimination process; (3) the value outside the impact area after the development started, as provided by the point-discrimination process; and (4) the value inside the impact area after the development started, as provided by the point-discrimination process.

The rationale for calculating impact indices from these four impact measures is as follows. The difference between values 2 and 4 is the change that occurred on the development site, and thus provides an apparent level of impact. But one must consider the possibility of natural changes in the biological resource that occurred at the same time as the changes apparently caused by the mining. The difference between values 3 and 4 would tentatively provide this clarification. But the possibilities then arise that (a) values 3 and 4 may not have been affected by the same influences over time; or (b) if they were, they may have started from different predevelopment levels. Thus, value 1 must be compared with value 3 to clear up possibility (a), and value 1 must be compared with value 2 to clear up possibility (b). The overall results (called an impact index) of these comparisons would then indicate whether the observed difference between values 2 and 4 represented a true impact caused by the mining activities.

Calculating the impact indices involves the graphical analysis of four ratio values calculated from the four impact measures. The ratios are Before-Out/Total-Out; After-In/Total-After; After-In/Total-In; and Before-Out/Total-Before. Before-Out is the value before the impact occurs and outside the impact area. Total-Out is the sum of values before and after the impact outside the impact area. After-In is the value after impact within the impact area. Total-After is the sum of values inside and outside the impact area after impact. Total-In is the sum of values before and after impact within the impact area. Total-Before is the sum of the values inside and outside the impact area before impact. These ratios are plotted on a graph as indicated in Figure 15.5. The ratio values are connected with straight lines, left to right and top to bottom, and the lower right quadrant angle created by the two crossed lines is measured. If the angle is less than 90°, the physical disturbance has had a negative effect on the impact measure, thus indicating a deleterious impact. If the angle is greater than 90°, the implication is that the impact was positive. A 90° angle indicates no effect by the disturbance.

PHYSICAL–BIOLOGICAL INFORMATION MIXER

The principal role of the Physical–Biological Information Mixer (PBIM) is to transfer the disturbed and nondisturbed areas from the PIP to the BIP. This mixing of information from the biological and nonbiological spatial information modules is required before any of the impact measures can be calculated.

INFORMATION MANAGER

All information contained in the WIIS is controlled with the systems Information Manager (IM). The IM consists of two primary information repositories, one called the Biological Library (BL) and one called the Physical Library (PL). The BL contains all information pertaining to plants and animals, and the PL contains all nonbiological information. Each library is arranged in the form of a catalog of subject-matter names, each name acting as a reference and call variable for information stored in the system.

The library catalogs may be used in two ways. First, the individual catalog names may be used to retrieve information pertaining only to the name's subject matter. Second, the IM supports libraries of cross-referenced information that are stored

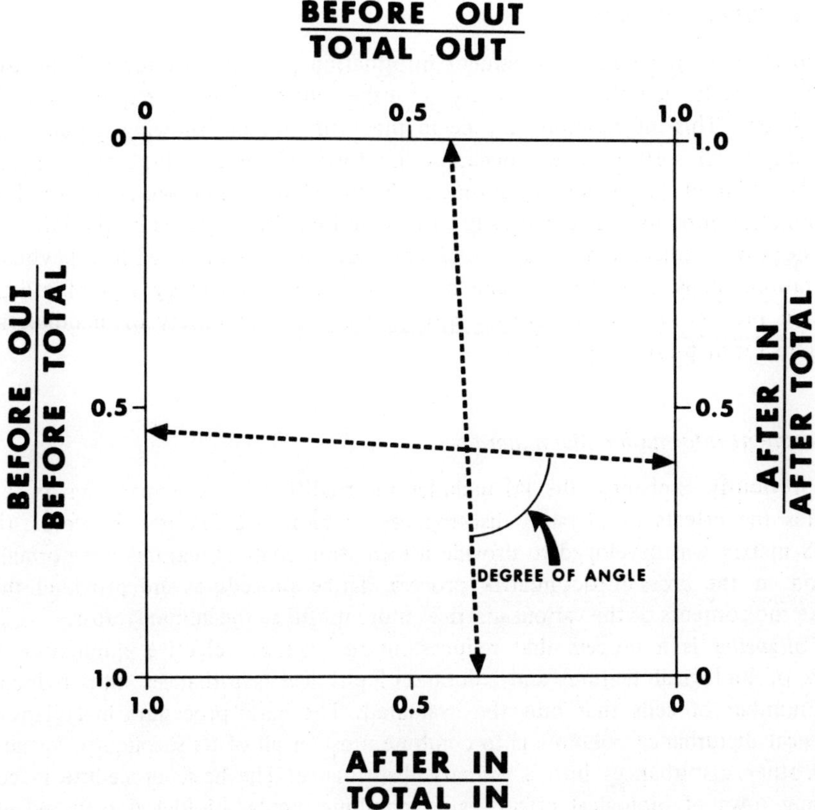

FIGURE 15.5 Graphic process for computing impact indices from impact measures.

under any combination of two names from the library catalogs. Thus, in addition to the typical cross-referenced information between mining disturbance and biological features, mining disturbance can be cross-referenced with mining disturbance, and biological feature can be cross-referenced with biological feature. An extension of the cross-referencing feature is the capability to store multiple linkages of cross-referenced information.

The IM provides the system with four basic functions: (a) an automatic repository for impact indices and other information generated in the PIP and BIP; (b) manual information input capabilities for storing maps, graphic displays, tabular data, and narrative information; (c) manipulation of impact assessment information to reduce complexity or to simplify evaluation in terms of selected criteria; and (d) output capabilities sufficient to meet a broad range of display demands. Each of the last three functions is discussed in the following sections.

Manual Information Input

In addition to the impact assessment information generated by the PIP and BIP, a considerable quantity and variety of other information is required for the assessment. This information may be in the form of maps showing spatial distributions of all sorts of phenomena, in the form of narrative-type explanations, in the form of tables and equations, or in the form of line sketches. All these information formats can be manually entered and readily displayed by the IM.

Narrative explanations, tables, and equations are typed in with a keyboard operation. Maps, line sketches and pictographs are drawn in by a graphic digitization process. The latter process also provides a wide variety of manipulative options for map-type information.

Assessment Information Manipulation

As previously explained, the IM includes the traditional cross-impact matrix that relates the effects of physical disturbances to biological features. However, the WIIS matrix was developed to provide information analysis features not normally found in the cross-impact matrix process. Three procedures are provided that make the contents of the various matrices more useful to the administrator.

Collapsing is a process that reduces matrix size by selective elimination of rows of biological features and columns of physical disturbances, thus reducing the number of cells that must be evaluated. The basic procedure in collapsing physical disturbance columns is to combine most or all of its secondary, tertiary, and other disturbances into a primary disturbance. The basic procedure in collapsing rows of biological effects is to combine similar biological features into composite classes, or to combine individual animal species into groups representing common impacts.

Screening reduces the number of cells that must be evaluated (for some specific question), without changing the structure of physical disturbances or biological features. Screening is accomplished either by selecting or eliminating cells that meet certain criteria established by the decision maker. For example, the decision maker may want to see only those cells in which impacts have been determined to be irreversible.

Integration is a process for producing a matrix of cells that satisfies a combination of assessment criteria. For example, an individual cross-impact cell may have impact characteristics that include a large area affected, a short duration of impact, significant importance to the population, and a high degree of mitigation potential. If these characteristics were the assessment criteria, the cell would be included in the integrated matrix, as would all other cells with the same four characteristics regardless of their other characteristics. But if the assessment criteria contained some additional characteristics not contained in the cell, the cell would not be included in the integrated matrix.

INFORMATION RETRIEVAL

As previously explained, information is stored in the system's physical and biological libraries in catalogs of names. The information in the libraries can represent single-feature subject matter or various cross-referenced or cross-impact subject matter. The IM's information retrieval system is designed so that information stored in any of the single feature or cross-referenced combinations may be retrieved and displayed by providing the IM's interactive program with catalog names in one of three combinations:

1. One name from either of the catalogs will retrieve pure information on the subject matter.
2. Two names (entered in sequence) from either the biological catalog or the physical catalog will retrieve cross-referenced information for the two physical or two biological subjects.
3. Two names (entered in sequence), one from the physical catalog and one from the biological catalog, will retrieve cross-referenced information for the physical and biological subjects.

The IM also contains an information storage and retrieval system that works as a name-structured library. Information in this system is stored under a coded name, with the coded character rigidly defined. The purpose of this library is to store massive amounts of data that have many characteristics in common and thus need to be rapidly retrieved and reviewed as a set. A wide variety of population characteristics can be accommodated.

Appendixes

A Assessment Techniques

LEOPOLD MATRIX

An interaction matrix is a simple means of identifying those environmental effects and impacts that are considered to be the most important by the people making the impact assessment.

METHOD DESCRIPTION

Typically, the interaction matrix is used to identify (to a limited extent) the cause-and-effect relationships between a list of human actions and a list of impact indicators.

An example is the Leopold matrix (Leopold *et al.*, 1971) which is intended as a guide for the evaluation and preparation of environmental impact reports (particularly those concerning construction projects) before the results of any environmental studies have been completed. The Leopold matrix lists 100 actions along the horizontal axis that might cause environmental impacts and 88 existing environmental conditions along the vertical axis that might be affected (Figure A.1). The impact associated with each intersection of an action and a factor of the environment is described in terms of its magnitude and importance. Magnitude is a measure of the general degree, extensiveness, or scale of the impact; thus, highway development will alter or affect the existing drainage pattern and so may have a large impact on drainage. Importance is a measure of the significance of the particular human action on the environmental factor in the specific instance under consideration. The importance of the impact of a particular highway on a particular drainage pattern may be small because the highway is very short or because in this particular case it will not interfere significantly with the drainage. It was hoped that factual data, more easily obtained in magnitude measurements, might be kept separate

PART 1: PROJECT ACTIONS

A. Modification of Regime

(a) Exotic flora or fauna introduction
(b) Biological controls
(c) Modification of habitat
(d) Alteration of ground cover
(e) Alteration of groundwater hydrology
(f) Alteration of drainage
(g) River control and flow codification
(h) Canalization
(i) Irrigation
(j) Weather modification
(k) Burning
(l) Surface or paving
(m) Noise and vibration

B. Land Transformation and Construction

(a) Urbanization
(b) Industrial sites and buildings
(c) Airports
(d) Highways and bridges
(e) Roads and trails
(f) Railroads
(g) Cables and lifts
(h) Transmission lines, pipelines and corridors
(i) Barriers including fencing
(j) Channel revetments
(k) Channel dredging and straightening
(l) Canals
(m) Dams and impoundments
(n) Piers, seawalls, marinas and sea terminals
(o) Offshore structures
(p) Recreational structures
(q) Blasting and drilling
(r) Cut and fill
(s) Tunnels and underground structures

C. Resource Extraction

(a) Blasting and drilling
(b) Surface excavation
(c) Subsurface excavation and retorting
(d) Well drilling and fluid removal
(e) Dredging
(f) Clear cutting and other lumbering
(g) Commercial fishing and hunting

D. Processing

(a) Farming
(b) Ranching and grazing
(c) Feed lots
(d) Dairying
(e) Energy generation
(f) Mineral processing
(g) Metallurgical industry
(h) Chemical industry
(i) Textile industry
(j) Automobile and aircraft
(k) Oil refining
(l) Food
(m) Lumbering
(n) Pulp and paper
(o) Product storage

E. Land Alteration

(a) Erosion control and terracing
(b) Mine sealing and waste control
(c) Strip mining rehabilitation
(d) Landscaping
(e) Harbor dredging
(f) Marsh fill and drainage

F. Resource Renewal

(a) Reforestation
(b) Wildlife stocking and management
(c) Groundwater recharge
(d) Fertilization application
(e) Waste recycling

G. Changes in Traffic

(a) Railway
(b) Automobile
(c) Trucking
(d) Shipping
(e) Aircraft
(f) River and canal traffic
(g) Pleasure boating
(h) Trails
(i) Cables and lifts
(j) Communication
(k) Pipeline

H. Waste Replacement and Treatment

(a) Ocean dumping
(b) Landfill
(c) Emplacement of tailings, spoil, and overburden
(d) Underground storage
(e) Junk disposal
(f) Oil well flooding
(g) Deep well emplacement
(h) Cooling water discharge
(i) Municipal waste discharge including spray irrigation
(j) Liquid effluent discharge
(k) Stabilization and oxidation ponds
(l) Septic tanks, commerical and domestic
(m) Stack and exhaust emission
(n) Spent lubricants

I. Chemical Treatment

(a) Fertilization
(b) Chemical de-icing of highways, etc.
(c) Chemical stabilization of soil
(d) Weed control
(e) Insect control (pesticides)

J. Accidents

(a) Explosions
(b) Spills and leaks
(c) Operational failure

K. Others

(a)
(b)

PART 2: ENVIRONMENTAL "CHARACTERISTICS" AND "CONDITIONS"

A. Physical and Chemical Characteristics

1. *Earth*
   (a) Mineral resources
   (b) Construction material
   (c) Soils
   (d) Land form
   (e) Force fields and background radiation
   (f) Unique physical features

2. *Water*
   (a) Surface
   (b) Ocean
   (c) Underground
   (d) Quality
   (e) Temperature
   (f) Recharge
   (g) Snow, ice, and permafrost

3. *Atmosphere*
   (a) Quality (gases, particulates)
   (b) Climate (micro, macro)
   (c) Temperature

4. *Processes*
   (a) Floods
   (b) Erosion
   (c) Deposition (sedimentation, precipitation)
   (d) Solution
   (e) Sorption (ion exchange, complexing)
   (f) Compaction and settling
   (g) Stability (slides, slumps)
   (h) Stress–strain (earthquake)
   (i) Air movements

B. Biological Conditions

1. *Flora*
   (a) Trees
   (b) Shrubs
   (c) Grass
   (d) Crops
   (e) Microflora
   (f) Aquatic plants
   (g) Endangered species
   (h) Barriers
   (i) Corridors

2. *Fauna*
   (a) Birds
   (b) Land animals including reptiles
   (c) Fish and shellfish
   (d) Benthic organisms
   (e) Insects
   (f) Microfauna
   (g) Endangered species
   (h) Barriers
   (i) Corridors

C. Cultural Factors

1. *Land use*
   (a) Wilderness and open spaces
   (b) Wetlands
   (c) Forestry
   (d) Grazing
   (e) Agriculture
   (f) Residential
   (g) Commercial
   (h) Industrial
   (i) Mining and quarrying

2. *Recreation*
   (a) Hunting
   (b) Fishing
   (c) Boating
   (d) Swimming
   (e) Camping and hiking
   (f) Picnicking
   (g) Resorts

3. *Aesthetics and human interest*
   (a) Scenic views and vistas
   (b) Wilderness qualities
   (c) Open space qualities
   (d) Landscape design
   (e) Unique physical features
   (f) Parks and reserves
   (g) Monuments
   (h) Rare and unique species or ecosystems
   (i) Historical or archaeological sites and objects
   (j) Presence of misfits

4. *Cultural status*
   (a) Cultural patterns (life style)
   (b) Health and safety
   (c) Employment
   (d) Population density

5. *Man-made facilities and activities*
   (a) Structures
   (b) Transportation network (movement, access)
   (c) Utility networks
   (d) Waste disposal
   (e) Barriers
   (f) Corridors

D. Ecological Relationships Such As:

   (a) Salinization of water resources
   (b) Eutrophication
   (c) Disease–insect vectors
   (d) Salinization of surficial material
   (f) Brush encroachment
   (g) Other

E. Others

   (a)
   (b)

FIGURE A.1 The Leopold matrix (Leopold *et al.*, 1971). Part 1 lists the project actions (arranged horizontally in the matrix); Part 2 lists the environmental "characteristics" and "conditions" (arranged vertically in the matrix).

from the more subjective value judgments of impact importance by having two measures for each relevant interaction.

Clearly, no two intersections on any one matrix can be precisely compared. The significance of the numerical values for any intersection indicates only the degree of impact one type of action may have on one part of the environment. When a separate matrix is prepared for each policy alternative under consideration, comparison of the identical matrix intersections indicates the relative environmental impacts of the alternative policies.

If more detailed information is needed, submatrices can be devised with specific data about an action (e.g., Mineral Processing can be subdivided into the specific actions of sulfuric acid use) or environmental condition (e.g., Atmospheric Quality can be subdivided into the specific conditions of particulates, sulfur oxides, and nitrous oxides).

INSTRUCTIONS

Specific instructions for use are given in Figure A.2.

DISCUSSION

Identification

The main problem with interaction matrices is that the action/single-effect format is unrealistic and leads to difficulties in identifying sequential impacts and causes. For example, highway cuts may initially cause soil erosion off slopes into rivers, and a subsequent increase in river turbidity and shoaling of the watercourse. These effects in turn may lead to an increase in river flood potential, or may block passage of and/or degrade river habitat for aquatic biota. To identify this succession of impacts, the two actions, "highway cut" and "alteration of drainage" must be separately identified on the matrix. Thus it is only through the prior knowledge of the assessor that secondary and multiple-order impacts will be identified.

Similarly, the reviewer of the impact assessment will not be able to recognize how the matrix relationships between actions and environmental condition changes were derived without an explanation.

The 8,800 intersections make the Leopold matrix cumbersome to use, and it still may not accurately reflect all the relevant environmental conditions. In addition, this list of environmental conditions (Figure A.1) is biased toward the physical–biological at the expense of the socioeconomic factors. Furthermore, this list lacks structural parallelism and balance (e.g., it includes both swimming, an activity, and temperature, an indicator of state).

Another problem with the Leopold matrix in particular is that categories of actions or types of indicators are mutually exclusive, whereas in reality they overlap considerably.

1. Identify all actions (located across the top of the matrix) that are part of the proposed project.

2. Under each of the proposed actions, place a slash at the intersection with each item on the side of the matrix if an impact is possible.

3. Having completed the matrix, in the upper left-hand corner of each box with a slash, place a number from 1 to 10 which indicates the MAGNITUDE of the possible impact; 10 represents the greater magnitude of impact and 1 the least (no zeroes). Before each number place a "+" if the impact would be beneficial. In the lower right-hand corner of the box place a number from 1 to 10 which indicates the IMPORTANCE of the possible impact (e.g. regional versus local); 10 represents the greatest importance and 1 the least (no zeroes).

4. The text which accompanies the matrix should be a discussion of the significant impacts, those columns and rows with large numbers of boxes marked and individual boxes with the larger numbers.

Sample Matrix

	a	b	c	d	e
a		2/1			8/5
b		7/2	8/8	3/1	9/7

FIGURE A.2 Instructions for using the Leopold Matrix (Leopold *et al.*, 1971).

Prediction

The Leopold matrix can accept both qualitative and quantitative data but fails to discriminate between them. It tends to be subjective because each assessor develops his own mental ranking system on the 1-to-10 numerical scale. The Leopold matrix fails to indicate uncertainty (arising from insufficient information) and environmental variability, including the possibility that extremes might present unacceptable hazards.

Interpretation

Because of its use of incommensurable measures (magnitude and importance) that cannot be totaled for comparison, the Leopald matrix is not explicit in indicating the most desirable of several alternatives. However, trade-offs between alternatives can be clearly defined in quantitative/qualitative terms.

Communication

Interaction matrices are effective as illustrative support in communicating the results of an environmental impact assessment, but alone they provide little or no guidance.

Inspection Procedures

Interaction matrices have no mechanism for recommending inspection procedures to monitor environmental quality after an action has been taken.

SUMMARY

Its ease of development makes the interaction matrix a useful tool for the initial stages of an environmental impact assessment despite numerous limitations. The prime value of an interaction matrix is illustrative rather than analytic.

KSIM-CROSS-IMPACT SIMULATION LANGUAGE

KSIM is a procedure that quickly and easily enables the user to structure a simulation of his perceptions of the nature of the interactions (structure and function) in the system under review. No concern need be given to the computer hardware or the mathematics of modeling. Thus the user can learn for himself the intricacies of the system and gain insight into the problems of systems management. KSIM's main advantage is the speed with which the user can structure a working model. However, as a consequence of its speed and simplicity, the model has embedded assumptions that limit its realism.

METHOD DESCRIPTION

The user first selects a set of variables x_i, which are believed to be relevant to the problem being analyzed. This selection is not restrictive, since additions and deletions can be easily made.

Next, the user must normalize the variables between zero and one by selecting upper and lower bounds for each of the x_i's. He also establishes the real-time unit that a model period is to represent and the total number of time periods to be simulated.

After selection and normalization of the variables, an interaction matrix (α-matrix) is prepared. The α-matrix lists each variable twice, once heading a column (j) and once a row (i). The matrix entry a_{ij} (interaction coefficients) in column j and row i represent the *first-order* effect x_j has upon x_i in a unit of time. This number will be positive, negative, or zero according to whether x_j increases the value of x_i, decreases it, or does not change it. Similarly, a second matrix (β-matrix) can be prepared in which the interaction coefficients b_{ij} represent the degree of a change in x_j on x_i (i.e., dx_i/dx_j). These matrices need not be square. Frequently, there are variables in the system that act on the other variables but are not themselves acted upon; such a variable appears only as a column in the matrix. Finally, the user designates the initial values for each of the variables. An example of a set of KSIM variables and an α-matrix is given in Table A.1.

TABLE A.1 Sample KSIM Matrix for Obergurgl

	Effect of			
Effect on	Population	Hotels	Tourism	Erosion
Population	1	.5	0	0
Hotels	0	0	1	0
Tourism	0	1	0	−1
Erosion	0	1	1	−.5

The effects summarized in this table are:

1. Population causes itself to go up.
2. Hotels cause population to increase.
3. Hotels cause tourism to increase.
4. Hotels cause erosion to increase.
5. Tourism causes the number of hotels to go up.
6. Tourism causes erosion to go up.
7. Erosion causes tourism to decrease.
8. Erosion causes erosion to decrease.

At this point, the model can be run and the results examined. The output is graphical, which permits easy visualization of the time path of selected variables. If the time paths do not agree with the user's perception of reality, the user can modify the choice of variables, initial values, bounds, or coefficients for the interaction matrices. Furthermore, he can consider the addition of constraints to the model or alternative representations for the interaction coefficients. The ease of interpretation of output and adjustment of input imposes certain restrictions on the system simulation. Primary among these are the bounded nature of the variables and the limitation, for the most part, to binary and first-order interactions.

INSTRUCTIONS

Implicit in a KSIM simulation are five basic rules of behavior:

1. All system variables are bounded.
2. Variables change according to the net impact of all the other variables.
3. The response of a variable to a given impact goes to zero as the variable approaches boundary, threshold, or saturation.
4. All else being equal, a variable produces greater effects on the system when it is larger.
5. Complex interactions are described by an array of binary interactions.

It is important to keep these in mind while structuring the simulation. Although the following steps summarize the basic strategy to be followed for a KSIM simulation, the reader is encouraged to read the various papers listed in the bibliography.

1. Select the variables x_i.
2. Choose minimum and maximum values for each of the x_i's and normalize them over the range (0,1).
3. Prepare an interaction matrix (α-matrix), listing each variable twice, once heading a column and once a row. The entry a_{ij} represents the effect x_j has upon x_i (j = column number; i = row number). This number will be positive, negative, or zero, according to whether x_j increases the value, decreases the value, or does not change x_i.
4. Prepare a second matrix (β-matrix) where the interaction coefficients b_{ij} represent the degree of a change x_j on x_i. (This matrix is optional and can be omitted if not considered relevant.)
5. Variables that act upon others but are not acted on, put in the matrix as columns only.
6. Select time increment, Δt and initial values for each of the x_i.
7. Input this information into KSIM according to the format described in the user's manual.
8. Run the simulation and view the graphics display.
9. Modify the model if results are unsatisfactory (i.e., add or delete variables; modify initial conditions, bounds, or matrix coefficients).
10. Repeat 8 and 9 iteratively until a satisfactory model is structured. If all alternatives are exhausted and a satisfactory model has not resulted, then abandon the model, rethink the structure, and start again.
11. Once a satisfactory model has been structured, it can be used for policy gaming and evaluation for impact assessments.

Numerous examples of KSIM are given in Kane (1972), Kane *et al.*, (1972, 1973), and Thompson *et al.*, (1973). Table A.1 gives a sample α-matrix for the Obergurgl problem (Chapter 13).

COMPUTATIONS

The formal mathematical calculations performed are as follows:

$$x_i(T + \Delta t) = x_i(T)^{\phi_i(T)}, \tag{A.1}$$

where $T = k\Delta t$ for some positive integer k and Δt represents one time period, and

$$\phi_i(T) = \frac{1 + \dfrac{\Delta t}{2} \sum_{j=1}^{m} [|a_{ij} + B_{ij}| - (a_{ij} + B_{ij})]\ x_j(T)}{1 + \dfrac{\Delta t}{2} \sum_{j=1}^{m} [|a_{ij} + B_{ij}| + (a_{ij} + B_{ij})]\ x_j(T)}, \tag{A.2}$$

where

$$B_{ij} = b_{ij} \frac{d(\ln x_i(t))}{dt}$$

m = number of column variables
a_{ij} = element from the interaction matrix giving the impact of x_j upon x_i
b_{ij} = element from the derivative interaction matrix giving the impact of $d(\ln x_i)/dt$ upon x_i

Inputting the logarithmic derivative reflects the tendency of people to react to percentage or relative change rather than absolute change.

The equation for $\phi_i(T)$ implies $\phi_i(T) > 0$, hence the transformation, Eq. (A.1), maps the interval (0,1) onto itself and preserves the boundedness of the state variables. Equation (A.2) can be made somewhat clearer if thought of as follows:

$$\phi_i(T) = \frac{1 + \Delta t|\text{ sum of negative impacts on } x_i\ |}{1 + \Delta t|\text{ sum of positive impacts on } x_i\ |}.$$

When negative impacts outweight positive ones, the exponent p_i is greater than unit and x_i decreases. When $p_i = 1$, x_i is unchanged. If the negative impacts are less than the positive ones, p_i is less than unity and x_i increases.

The remaining properties of this formulation become clearer if we examine the limiting system of differential equations implied by Eqs. (1) and (2) as $\Delta t \to 0$.

$$\frac{dx_i}{dt} = -\sum_{j=1}^{m} \left(a_{ij}x_j + b_{ij}\frac{dx_j}{dt} \right) x_i \ln x_i \qquad \text{i} = 1, \ldots, \text{n}. \tag{A.3}$$

Inspecting Eq. (A.3), we find that as $x_i \to 0$ or 1, the derivative $(dx_i/dt) \to 0$ and thus characterizes a bounded threshold response as the variable approaches its minimum or maximum. The expression $-x_i \ln x_i$ then appears to modulate the response of variable x_i to the impact given by the summed terms.

Consider the special case of a single independent variable without any derivative feedback: $b = 0$. For this situation, Eq. (A.3) becomes

$$\frac{dx}{dt} = -ax \ln (x). \tag{A.4}$$

This growth curve is sigmoidal in character – i.e., change near threshold ($x = 0$) and saturation ($x = 1$) approaches 0. Also, since Eq. (A.4) involves $x \ln (x)$, the behavior of the curves is not symmetric about $x = .5$. Note that as long as α is restricted to constant values, growth rates near threshold are not paralleled by similar positioning near saturation.

CONCLUSIONS

1. KSIM enables an environmental impact assessment team to structure a system simulation and view the results quickly without the need of sophisticated computer expertise. This technique provides an excellent workshop environment, allowing

experts from various disciplines to communicate their knowledge and view the consequences of various policies on the system as it is structured (i.e., the simulation). This permits the policymakers to take part in the modeling process and so can greatly increase the impact and meaning of the results. The model's credibility is increased and each participant has an opportunity to include the variables and other aspects considered important in his subsystem.

2. A computer with graphics capabilities is a necessary support for the use of KSIM.

3. The ease with which a simulation can be structured has some drawbacks. The assumptions imbedded in the language limit the applicability of the model. For example:

The sigmoidal growth curves describe one of a number of growth relationships that can be active in a system. In KSIM the user is restricted to this particular monotonic relation.

The maximum–minimum boundaries negate the possibility of experiencing the unexpected result that takes the system to previously unknown extremes.

Nonbinary interactions between the variables are difficult to program and, if not included, eliminate regions of system behavior resulting from such terms. It may be these nonbinary interactions that are the key determinants in the system.

The easy manipulation of the model to generate preconceived results permits the user to bias the model unconsciously. The user views the model as a whole, structures the α and β matrices within that framework, and compares the results with his "image of the whole." Other approaches have a more differential concept. The system is viewed as many working parts, all of them interrelated. The purpose of the simulation in this case is to model each of the subprocesses separately and then "integrate" them. In other words, the interpretation is performed more by the model, not so much by the modeler.

We feel, however, that if the user keeps this bias in mind, the KSIM simulation can improve his understanding of the system.

GSIM: QUALITATIVE SIMULATOR

GSIM is an approach that can easily be turned into the format of a simulation language and used for simple empirical models of complex systems (Gallopin, 1977). This approach is intended to be used in a situation in which the only previous knowledge about the real system is reduced to the identification of the relevant variables, to the very basic logical form of the relationships among variables, and to some general indication about the relative level or size of the variables. The principal advantage of this approach is that it allows one to consider the dynamics of the systems and the interactions among variables at an information level that usually does not permit the construction of a full simulation model. Other advantages are the speed with which the user can structure the model and the very low hardware requirements (desk-computer or even desk-calculator at a minimum). This kind of model can provide only rough qualitative trends of the variables and cannot handle situations dependent on precise numerical balances.

DESCRIPTION OF THE APPROACH

In general, the value of any variable in the system at a given time $t + 1$ is calculated according to

$$X_i^{t+1} = X_i^t + \Delta X_i^{t,t+1} \,.$$

However, the approach allows for algebraic relationships like $X_i^t = X_j^t * X_k^t$ where $*$ indicates an ordinary product.

The increment of any variable in the time interval $(t, t + 1)$ is defined as

$$\Delta X_i^{t,t+1} = \begin{cases} 1 \text{ if } X_i \text{ increases} \\ -1 \text{ if } X_i \text{ decreases} \\ 0 \text{ if } X_i \text{ does not change} \end{cases}$$

Therefore, the approach only considers whether a given variable is increasing, decreasing, or staying at about the same level, and the levels of the variables change only in unit steps. This is directly related to the low level of information that is assumed to be available, namely, that one knows only that some variables will increase, decrease, or not change through time, because of the effect of some other variables.

The range of values of the variable X_i is defined as a finite, small set of integer values. For instance, the range of X_k can be defined as $\{0, 1, 2\}$, where 0 can be viewed as a very small value, or nil, 1 as small, 2 as large.

The direction of change ΔX_i will depend, in general, upon the value of its own or other variables' rates of change at some time, upon the values of some variables (including itself) at some time, and also upon a set of constraints given by

$$\Delta X_i^{t,t+1} = \text{sg}[f(Z^{t-\tau}, \Delta Z^{t-\tau,t-\tau+1}, R)],$$

where "sg" denotes the sign function adopting the values $1, -1, 0$; τ is an integer-valued time lag; $Z^{t-\tau}$ is a set of variables (possibly including itself) affecting X_i; $\Delta Z^{t-\tau,t-\tau+1}$ is a set of directions of change of variables (possibly including ΔX_i) affecting X_i, and R is a set of constraints given by the problem. When no time lags are used, $\tau = 0$ and

$$\Delta X_i^{t,t+1} = \text{sg}[f(Z^t, \Delta Z^{t,t+1}, R)].$$

As an arbitrary example, the direction of change ΔX_i could be

$$\Delta X_i^{t,t+1} = \begin{cases} \text{sg}\,[Z_5^t * \Delta Z_4^{t-1;t} + Z_6^{t-2}] & \text{if } \Delta Z_4^{t-1,t} = -1 \\ 0 & \text{if } \Delta Z_4^{t-1,t} = -1 \end{cases}$$

when the constraints are related to the value of $\Delta Z_4^{t-1,t}$. The function f is in general just a useful combination of two basic operations: addition and multiplication, representing two elementary logical interactions. As an example, $f = \Delta Z_j^{t,t+1} + \Delta Z_k^{t,t+1}$ implies that opposite influences of Z_j and Z_k upon X_i will tend to cancel each other; X_i will increase whenever either Z_j or Z_k increases, provided the other does not decrease. The expression $f = \Delta Z_j^{t,t+1} * \Delta Z_k^{t,t+1}$ implies that the two variables affecting X_i must change simultaneously in order to force a change in X_i. The number of variables affecting X_i is not reduced to two. Other forms of f are allowed, but in most cases they will not be necessary at this low level of information.

The system is then specified by a set of equations of the type described, including a set of constraints, and those equations are solved sequentially starting from the initial state of the system.

RULES FOR USING THE APPROACH

1. Select the variables X_i.
2. Construct a variables-and-arrows diagram showing which variables are directly affecting X_i with X_j. For example, does ΔX_i depend upon ΔX_j or upon X_j (its variables appear in the rows and the columns.
3. Assign ranges of values of the variables.
4. For each variable X_i, decide the form of the function f connecting the variables affecting X_i with X_j. For example, does ΔX_i depend upon ΔX_j or upon X_j (its level)? If it depends on the increments of X_j, will X_i increase or decrease when X_j increases? If more than one variable is affecting X_i, is the effect additive or multiplicative? Does the function depend upon threshold values of some variables?
5. Identify constraints. Can a variable not be negative, or can its value not exceed some upper threshold, for example?
6. Assign initial values to the variables and increments.
7. Program the equation in a computer or solve sequentially with a hand calculator.
8. Run the simulation.
9. If unsatisfactory behavior is detected, modify the model by changing ranges or variables, forms of functions, constraints, initial conditions, the set of variables, time lags, and so on.
10. Repeat steps 8 and 9 until the model seems satisfactory. In this connection, the model will not provide quantitative predictions; only the broad qualitative features of the time trends in the variables are predicted (whether the variables increase, decrease, or do not vary over time).

EXAMPLE

The example offered here refers to the simulation of an agricultural production situation.

The potentially arable land available in a given year depends upon the potentially arable land in the previous year and the land degradation rate of potentially arable land during the year. It is assumed that control measures are taken in order to avoid soil erosion and fertility loss, and therefore the only significant reduction of arable land is due to urbanization. Thus the degradation rate of the potentially arable land is assumed to be proportional to the urbanization rate. The rate at which new land is put into production (land colonization rate) depends upon the unit cost of land colonization and the available economic resources for land colonization. The unit cost of land colonization increases as the potentially arable land not yet utilized is exhausted. Thus, the arable land in a given year depends upon the arable land the previous year and the land colonization rate, and cannot exceed the total available potentially arable land. The agricultural yield is assumed to increase with the agricultural inputs applied per hectare, up to a limit beyond which additional agricultural inputs do not increase yields. The total agricultural inputs available in any year are assumed to depend upon the agricultural inputs produced the previous year and the rate of increase in inputs production. If there is no increase in inputs production, it is assumed that in the current year the production will be the same as the previous year. The agricultural inputs per hectare are given by the total inputs produced in the year and the arable land to be cultivated. The rate of increase in the production of agricultural inputs depends upon the unit cost of production, assumed to be constant, and the economic resources available for agricultural inputs production.

Part of the economic resources for input production is assumed to be diverted toward erosion and soil fertility control measures. The total agricultural production is a function of the arable land cultivated with food crops (a proportion of the total cultivated land), the agricultural yield, and the processing losses. Every year, economic resources are allocated to land colonization and agricultural inputs production. The economic resources allocated to agriculture every year represent the net increase with input to the previous year and are used to increase land or agricultural inputs, but not to cover maintenance costs of existing land or current agricultural inputs production.

The condition to be explored represents a situation in which the total potentially arable land cannot increase even with technological advances; the economic resources allocated to agriculture grow at a fixed rate per year; and the urbanization of potentially arable land is stopped after the first year. The conceptual interaction diagram of this situation appears in Figure A.3.

From the qualitative point of view, many causal chains of variables can be collapsed because they do not affect the sign of the interactions. For instance, an increase in the economic resources allocated to agriculture will ultimately

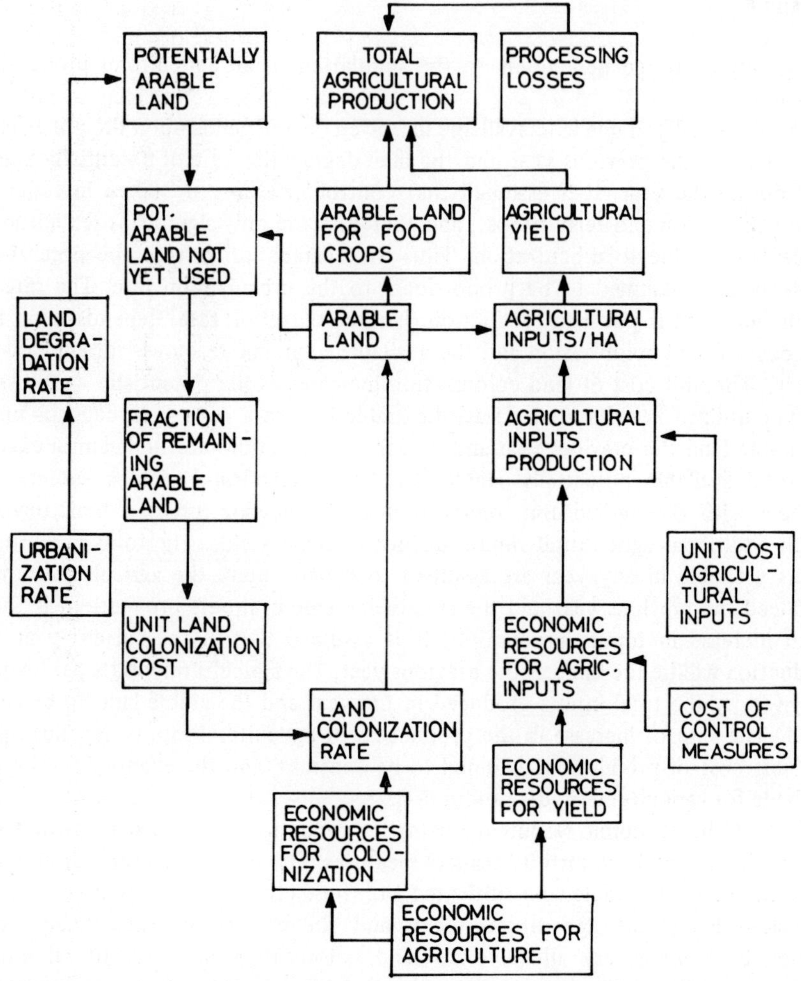

FIGURE A.3 Conceptual flow diagram of the agricultural system.

produce an increase in the agricultural yields, arable land being constant. Thus, the diagram of Figure A.3 can be greatly simplified, as seen in Figure A.4, where the variables are

CAAG = economic resources allocated to agriculture
YIELD = agricultural yield
LC = land colonization
AL = arable land
PALN = potentially arable land, not yet utilized
PAL = potentially arable land available

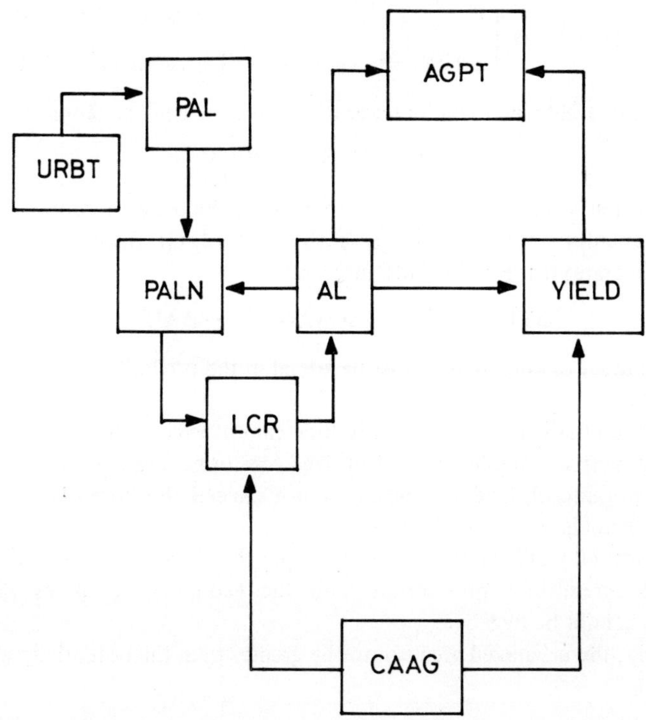

FIGURE A.4 Simplified flow diagram of the agricultural sector. CAAG = net increase in economic resources allocated to agriculture; YIELD = agricultural yield; ΔLC = land colonization rate; AL = arable land; PALN = potentially arable land, not yet utilized; PAL = potentially arable land available; URBT = urbanized area; AGPT = total agricultural production.

URBT = urbanized area
AGPT = total agricultural production

The GSIM structure can be as follows. If urbanization increases, the potentially arable land decreases. However, urbanization cannot decrease (it is assumed that an area built upon cannot be converted back to agricultural production). Thus

$$\Delta \mathrm{PAL}^{t,t+1} = -\Delta \mathrm{URBT}^{t,t+1} \; (\Delta \mathrm{URBT}^{t,t+1} \geqslant 0).$$

The stock of potentially arable land not yet utilized will increase if the total potentially arable land increases, and it will decrease if new land is colonized (the arable land increases):

$$\Delta \mathrm{PALN}^{t,t+1} = \Delta \mathrm{PAL}^{t-1,t} - \Delta \mathrm{AL}^{t-1,t}.$$

The colonized land will increase if the economic resources for agriculture increase, but only if the amount of potentially arable land not utilized is greater than zero. Otherwise, the colonization rate will be zero. A time lag of 1 year is assumed.

$$\Delta LC^{t,t+1} = \begin{cases} 0 & \text{if } \Delta CAAG^{t-1,t} < 0 \\ sg[PALN^{t} * \Delta CAAG^{t-1,t}] & \text{if } \Delta CAAG^{t-1,t} \geqslant 0 \end{cases}$$

The amount of arable land will increase whenever new land is colonized:

$$\Delta AL^{t,t+1} = \Delta LC^{t,t+1}.$$

The agricultural yield will increase if there is an increase in economic resources put into agriculture, and will increase (because of the lowering of agricultural inputs per hectare) if the arable land increases:

$$\Delta YIELD^{t,t+1} = \Delta CAAG^{t,t+1} - \Delta AL^{t,t+1}.$$

The following set of constraints must be added in the program:

- The potentially arable land at any time cannot exceed the initial stock.
- The potentially arable land not utilized cannot be negative.
- The amount of land colonized cannot exceed the potentially arable land, and the same holds for the arable land.
- Agricultural yield cannot exceed an upper threshold, here taken as 5.
- Total agricultural production, and the economic resources allocated to agriculture, cannot be negative.
- Finally, the urbanized area cannot be greater than the potentially arable land.

Therefore,

$$PAL^{t} \leqslant PAL^{\circ}$$

$$PALN^{t} \geqslant 0$$

$$LC^{t} \leqslant PAL^{\circ}$$

$$AL^{t} \leqslant PAL^{\circ}$$

$$YIELD^{t} \leqslant YIMAX = 5$$

$$AGPT^{t} \geqslant 0$$

$$CAAG^{t} \geqslant 0$$

$$URBT^{t} \leqslant PAL^{\circ}$$

The values of all of the variables are calculated according to

$$X_i^{t+1} = X_i^t + \Delta X_i^{t,t+1}$$

except for AGPT, because the value of the total agricultural production will depend upon the present value of the arable land and the yield:

$$AGPT^{t} = AL^{t} * YIELD^{t}.$$

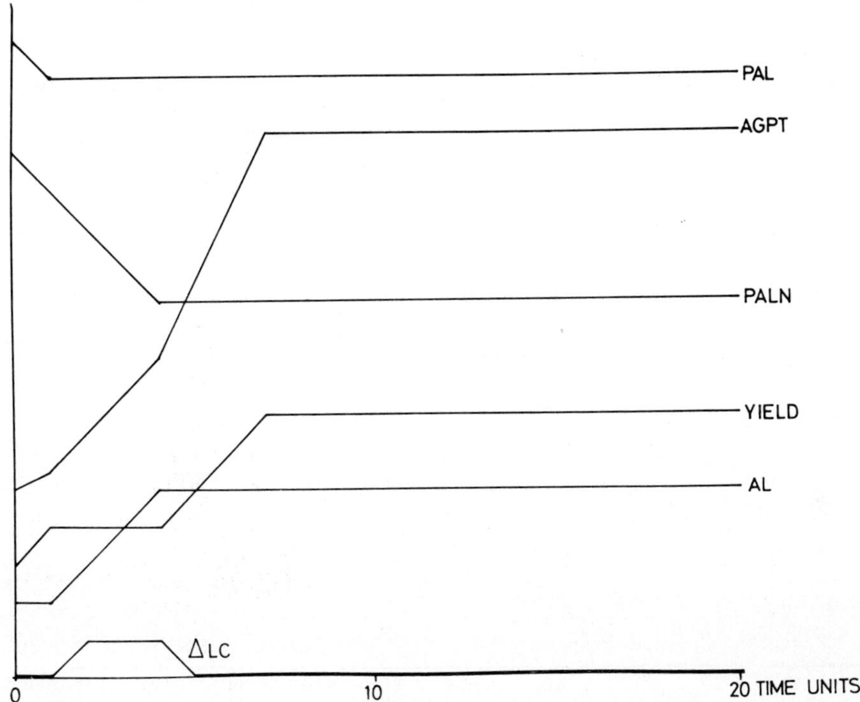

FIGURE A.5 Output of the simple agriculture model. The names of the variables are the same as in Figure A.4. Their minimum and maximum values in the simulation are AL (1–4); PALN (0–4); YIELD (1–5); PAL (4–5); AGPT (1–20); ΔLC (0–1).

The input conditions, according to the general description given earlier, are

$$\Delta \text{CAAG}^{t,t+1} = 1 \text{ for } t \geqslant 0$$

$$\Delta \text{URBT}^{0,1} = 1$$

$$\Delta \text{URBT}^{t,t+1} = 0 \text{ for } t \geqslant 1$$

One possible set of initial conditions is

$$\text{PAL}^\circ = 5; \text{PALN}^\circ = 4; \text{CAAG}^\circ = 4; \text{URBT}^\circ = 2; \text{LC}^\circ = 0;$$

$$\text{AL}^\circ = \text{YIELD}^\circ = \text{AGPT}^\circ = 1. \ \Delta \text{LC}^{0,1} = 0.$$

The time behavior of the variables resulting from the simulation appears in Figure A.5. The scale on the vertical axis is different for each variable because actual numbers are irrelevant; the important features are the qualitative trends of the variables.

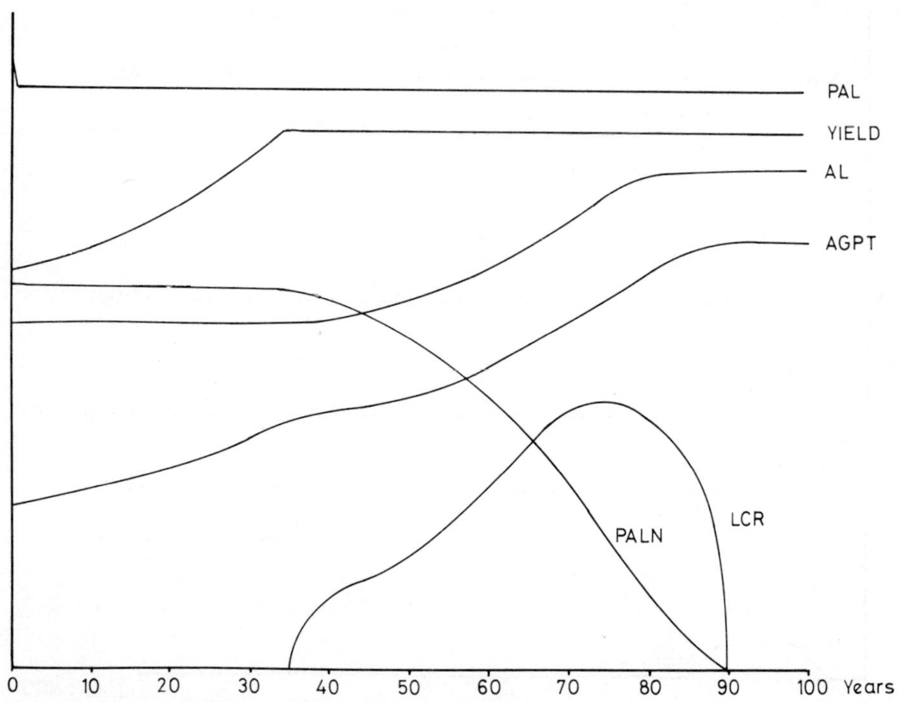

FIGURE A.6 Output of the full simulation model. The names of the variables are the same as in Figure A.4. Their ranges during the simulation are: AL (0.634E6 – 0.109E7); PALN (0 – 0.459E6); YIELD (0.65E1 – 0.10E2); PAL (0.10929E7 – 0.10930E7); AGPT (0.195E16 – 0.517E16); ΔLC (0. – 131E5).

For this particular example, a full numerical simulation model was available, composed of more than 20 equations with many parameters and including a process for allocating optimally the economic resources for agriculture into colonization of land and production of agricultural inputs (Herrera *et al.*, 1976). The results of the full model appear in Figure A.6. The numerical values of the variables are of no interest here; only the qualitative trends (increasing, decreasing, staying constant) are relevant to the purpose of the comparison. The parallelism in the behavior of the two models is evident. The qualitative model, with much lower information requirements, reproduces very well the behavior of the full simulation model. The shift in time in the curve of the land development rate, ΔLC, is due to the fact that in the full simulation model the optimization process acts in such a way that land is colonized only after the maximum yield is reached. In the qualitative model, no optimization is included, and land is colonized while yield is still increasing. On the other hand, the time units in the qualitative model bear no relation to the time units of the full simulation model. However, if one includes the constraint

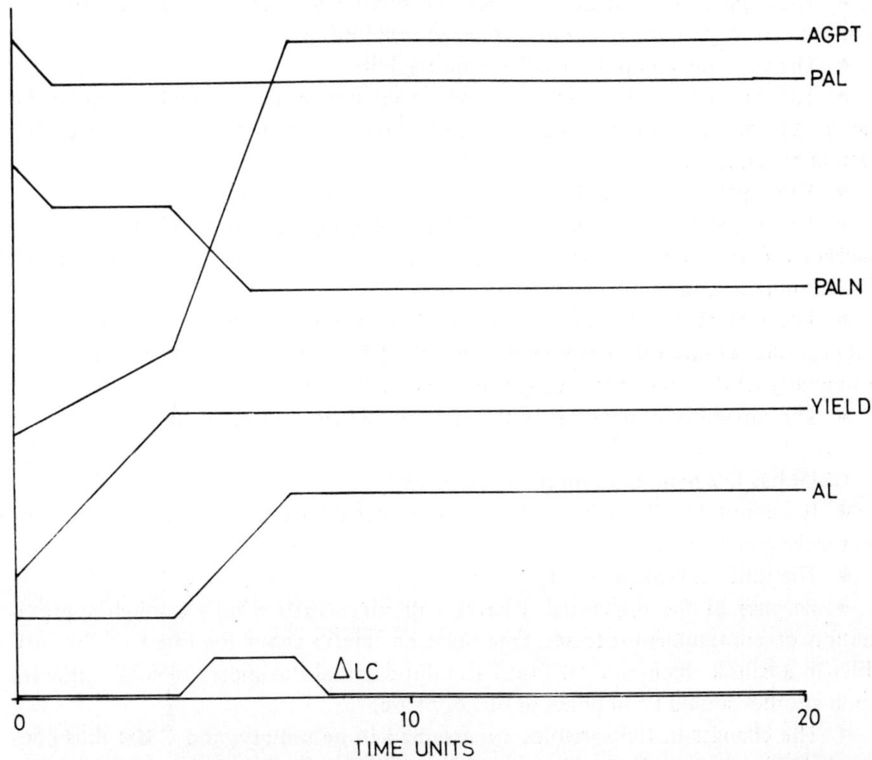

FIGURE A.7 Output of the simple agricultural model with the constraint that no land is colonized until maximum yield is reached. The names of the variables and their ranges are the same as in Figure A.5.

that no land is colonized until maximum yield is reached ($\Delta LC = 0$ if YIELD < YIMAX), the results of the qualitative model are still more similar to the numerical model (Figure A.7).

CONCLUSION

GSIM is strictly applicable to situations with discrete causes and effects, in which the only information available is about the positive, negative, or negligible effect of variables upon each other, the basic logical form of the relation, and some qualitative judgment about the relative size of the variables. The only output that can be expected is information about temporal qualitative trends of the variables and the overall behavior of the system. If the behavior of the system is strongly dependent upon precise numerical balances, the approach presented here in its present form will be of little use. The main advantages are as follows:

- The capability of handling very low information levels, imprecise or qualitative, without introducing too many unwarranted assumptions
- The very low computer facility requirements
- The ease of conceptualization and programming, and of understanding the causal determinants of the response, providing insight into the behavior of the system by using direct conceptual variables
- The capability of handling a large number of causal chains
- The capability of handling multiple relations, feedback relations, logical decisions ("IF" statements), time lags, basic nonlinearities, threshold effects, discontinuities, and so on
- The fact that it forces the user to think about very basic forms of causal connections within the user's own conceptual background and thus reduces the probability of the user's being caught in the details of the system
- The capability of handling both transient and steady-state behavior

GSIM has five main limitations:

- It cannot handle numerical effects or behavior modes directly dependent on precise numerical balances.
- The time units are arbitrary.
- Because of the sequential discrete structure, GSIM is only a rough approximation of continuous processes. One must be careful about the order of the variables in a causal chain, and take into account whether the impact of some variables upon another should be in phase or out of phase.
- The changes in the variables are assumed to be unitary, and GSIM thus does not differentiate among variables changing at numerically different rates.
- One should be careful in the assignment of ranges of values of the variables.

On balance, it can be said that GSIM, if used properly, is a valuable tool for improving the understanding of interacting environmental processes and is also useful as a way of simplifying complex numerical models. The technique is particularly designed for handling situations where information is poor.

SIMULATION MODELING[1]

INTRODUCTION

Ecological simulation is so new a tool that no generally accepted synthesis of its principles and limitations has yet been published. We present only one viewpoint here: other introductory discussions can be found in Watt (1968b), Patten (1971),

[1] This section has been reprinted from Walters *et al.* (1974). Reproduced by permission of the Minister of Supply and Services Canada.

Jeffers (1972), Forrester (1971), Holling (1972), and Walters (1971). Our discussion is for readers who are unfamiliar with mathematics and computers. We are mainly interested in dispelling commonly held misconceptions about model building.

The past few years have seen rising interest among resource managers in the tools of systems analysis and computer simulation. These tools seem to offer a powerful means of tackling large-scale problems of information synthesis and resource forecasting. However, a major problem has been that biologists are seldom trained in quantitative methodology, so mathematical techniques and computers have been viewed with fear and distrust. "Garbage in, garbage out" is an axiom of computer programming, expressing the fact that good biological input is essential for good resource simulation. Some attempts have been made to bridge the communication gap between biologists and formal systems analysts, but these attempts have not been particularly successful. It appears that resource people must learn to do their own model building. Recently attempts have been made to develop teaching programs that avoid the jargon and confusion of standard mathematics and computer training.

Simulation modeling can provide special benefits beyond information handling and forecasting. These benefits are often the best justification for modeling activity and arise from two characteristics of resource problems. First, these problems are large and require teamwork in data collection and interpretation; generally specialists from several disciplines must work together. Second, the problems are difficult to define and the goals of management activity are thus hard to identify. Model building enters the picture by providing a common language, a focus for mutual attention, and a concrete goal (the simulation model) for the team.

METHOD DESCRIPTION

In order to demonstrate some of the principles and steps of building simulation models, let us examine a typical set of calculations made by resource managers who are trying to predict sustainable yield from a duck population. The simplest estimate of sustainable yield would be

$$\text{sustainable yield} = \%\ \text{gain}/100 \times \text{population size}$$

where percent gain is estimated from an unhunted, growing population. This crude estimate requires little understanding of the dynamics of the duck population. A more accurate estimate breaks population gain into production and loss components:

$$\text{sustainable yield} = (\text{production per duck} - \text{loss per duck}) \times \text{population size}$$

This second calculation would require considerably more data, although it gives little increase in precision of the sustained yield estimate. Next, the time sequence of events in the population can be considered, and a series of calculations generated to describe the annual sequence of changes in population:

spring population next year = adult population this spring + production ×

survival rate to fall × survival rate through hunting × survival rate through winter

harvest = fall population × (1 − survival rate through hunting)

These relationships can be used to generate survival-through-hunting data and to evaluate sustainable harvest by trying out different values for harvest rates and noting their relationship to population next spring. This calculation would allow consideration of replacement mortality (those birds that are killed which would otherwise have died naturally). Given still more information, one might differentiate the age classes in the population by assigning to each its own survival and birth rates and vulnerability.

total production = new adults in spring × production rate for first breeding
+ old adults in spring × adult production rate (1)

fall adult population = new + old spring adults × adult summer survival rate (2)

fall juvenile population = total production × juvenile summer survival rate (3)

harvest = (fall juvenile population × juvenile kill rate)
+ (fall adult population × adult kill rate) (4)

new adults next spring = juvenile survival × winter survival rate for juveniles (5)

old adults next spring = adult survival × winter survival rate for adults (6)

This sequence of equations is about as complicated as would ever be attempted without resorting to a computer. An obvious extension would be to repeat Eqs. 3–6 over several years, while varying production and harvest rates over the time periods of the calculations. The rates appearing on the right sides of Eqs. 3–6 are called *driving variables*. The other quantities are called *system state variables*. The extended sequence of calculations we call a simulation model. Given considerable time, we can do the calculation sequence for several species, in several areas, and even account for migration movements between areas.

Each set of calculations like the one above is what we call a model. The basic principles which emerge from such a set are:

1. We can write down the calculations to be made without reference to any specific numbers, and some shorthand notation for the various variables would be useful.

2. Calculations about biological systems can be organized into hierarchies of complexity, but there is no objective way to decide when to stop increasing the complexity of the calculations.

3. As models become more detailed, we need more information, we have to make more assumptions and the possibility of errors in our predictions becomes more likely. In addition, we are likely to leave out some critical factor which may have a disproportionate effect.

4. As we add more detail, it becomes harder to see intuitively the consequences of the model.

5. More detailed models require that we define variables more accurately and pay more attention to logic and consistency.

The key point to be made is that there is no best way to describe a particular system; the value of each model or calculation sequence depends on the particular situation to which it is being applied.

A further important principle is that the boundaries of the system to be modeled are arbitrary; these boundaries must be carefully defined by the model builder. In Eqs. 1–6 we have implicitly set one system boundary by saying that harvest shall be described in terms of constant kill rates only. Instead, we could have extended the boundaries of the model to include calculations of potential and actual numbers of hunters and their kill by considering aspects of the human population and its growth. One way to define a driving variable is to say that it is some factor whose variation is determined by forces outside the arbitrary boundaries of the system under study, e.g., light conditions. When we change a model to include calculations or predictions about a factor that we have previously called a driving variable, then that factor is no longer called a driving variable but is instead part of the arbitrary system (a system or state variable).

Notation and Symbolism

Two steps are necessary to rewrite Eqs. 1–6 in order to condense them and make them easier to deal with:

1. We must assign symbols to variables and constants.
2. We must rewrite our basic sentences using the symbols.

Let us make a list of symbols to use in Eqs. 1–6.

P = total production
NAS = old adults in spring
NAF = fall adult population
NJS = new adults in spring
NJF = fall juvenile population
H = harvest
KA = adult kill rate
KJ = juvenile kill rate
PA = adult production rate
PJ = production rate for first breeding
SAS = adult summer survival rate
SJS = juvenile summer survival rate
SWJ = winter survival rate for juveniles
SWA = winter survival rate for adults

With these symbols, we can rewrite Eqs. 1–6 as Eqs. 7–12, respectively:

$$P = NJS \cdot PJ + NAS \cdot PA \tag{7}$$

$$NAF = (NJS + NAS) \cdot SAS \tag{8}$$

$$NJF = P \cdot SJS \tag{9}$$

$$H = NJF \cdot KJ + NAF \cdot KA \tag{10}$$

$$NJS = NJF \cdot (1 - KJ) \cdot SWJ \tag{11}$$

$$NAS = NAF \cdot (1 - KA) \cdot SWA \tag{12}$$

This is simply a condensed way of writing the series of rules for calculations and has the same biological meaning as the original sentences. Difficulty in understanding papers that contain equations is usually a problem of understanding the definitions that authors choose for their symbols. Notice also that the equations and symbols shown are meaningful only if presented in the proper order; this is often true of models.

Key Components of Models

We classify the elements in any calculation sequence or model as:

1. system state variables – the entities which the model tries to predict; indices of the state of the biological system;
2. parameters – constants, such as survival rates, which are necessary in the predictions;
3. equations – those shorthand sentences which say how system state variables and parameters are related and state the basic rules for the calculation;
4. driving variables – the factors, such as kill rates, that we want to manipulate or vary over time but that are not to be predicted within the basic calculation sequence.

The system state vector is the list of all the system state variables. Dynamic models are calculation sequences that try to predict change over time. The basic structure of any dynamic model can be shown as:

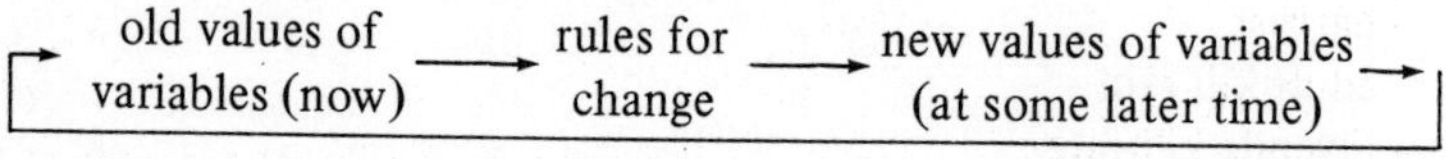

old values of variables (now) → rules for change → new values of variables (at some later time) → (back to old values of variables)

We usually try to make the rules for change (the model) fairly general so that we can have the new values of the variables become old values in a repeated sequence. The application of this repeated sequence is called a simulation.

Rules for change can be specified in a variety of ways that fall into three classes: continuous, event-oriented, and state-oriented.

We specify rules for continuous change in terms of differential equations that indicate how fast each variable is changing over every moment of time. We usually try to avoid continuous system models because they are often hard to formulate and solve.

In setting up event-oriented rules, we first specify how much variable change is to occur (e.g., loss of one animal); the rules are then stated in terms of the amount of time required before the change should occur. Event-oriented models are especially useful in describing processes like predation, where we want to calculate the amount of time between successive attacks by a predator.

State-oriented rules are usually the easiest to specify and form the basis for most biological simulation schemes. Here we start with the list of variables describing the state of a system at some time, and specify our rules so as to give the system state at a fixed later time directly in terms of the starting state. The population harvest models given above are state-oriented models.

Steps in Model Building

Decide purpose and scope of model. The first step in model building is to decide exactly why the model is being built. We cannot go ahead until the following questions are answered. What predictions are wanted? How precise should these predictions be? Over what range of situations and for how long should the predictions be applicable? What information is available for inclusion in the calculation sequence? It is obvious that we could continue to build models of increasing detail and complexity, without knowing when to stop, what to include or what to leave out. There are no formal rules or guidelines to help the model builder at this stage.

Choose variables to be included. Simulation models are always based on a set of numerical indices of system condition (just as we always measure indices of system condition in field or laboratory studies). Commonly used indices are numbers of animals in a population, numbers of hunters in an area, and numbers of ponds available for breeding birds. Indices or variables used in a simulation model need not necessarily be the best measures of the condition of the system to be simulated. To decide whether or not it is useful to include a particular variable, we have to know the specific purpose for which the model is being built.

How detailed should the model be? Again, this depends on the circumstances to which the model is applied, and the kinds of questions being asked. One of the factors which will influence our choice of variables is the fact that predictions are always conditional. Of necessity every prediction we make assumes certain regularities about the circumstances surrounding the study. For example, in developing duck population models we must assume regularities about recreational demand and about genetic composition of the duck population. Thus, our predictions are always in the form, "If the following circumstances occur, then we expect the following factors to change in such and such a way."

There are some criteria for choosing the variables. First, for highly correlated biological factors, only one factor need be represented in a model. For example, if survival rates for two age classes of animals are approximately equal, then a single survival rate parameter will suffice. As another example, if pond drying rates are correlated with initial numbers of spring ponds, we need only include the latter (because it is easier to measure) for predicting potential production. Second, we can watch for factors which, when taken together, may qualify one another. For example, hunters vary in individual success, but statistically they may act as a unit whose success rate remains constant. Also, increasing the number of hunters may simultaneously lead both to interference in hunting activities and to their facilitation (due to increased numbers of birds in the air at any time). When the effects of two variables are expected to cancel one another, we can treat the total effect as being constant. In this example, we may be able to treat hunter success as constant and independent of the numbers of hunters. Third, we can ask what factors will have constant effects over all ranges of possible model application. We can treat these factors as parameters or determinants of parameters, and estimate their effects empirically. For example, we usually assume that populations will have constant genetic composition over periods of a few years; we can consider the effects of genetic factors on production in terms of empirical production rates that can be estimated from field data (for short predictions only).

In choosing variables we must be careful to distinguish between system state variables and driving variables. For example, in building a waterfowl harvest model we have the choice of trying to simulate recreational demand as a system state variable or treating demand as a driving variable. If demand is treated as a driving variable, then different demand patterns can be tested for their effects, giving a series of conditional predictions about population change. In general, more and more driving variables must be treated as system state variables as one increases the time span over which the model is to apply.

State basic relationships among variables. Once a basic set of variables or factors has been chosen for simulation, one must decide what factors interact with one another, and in what time sequence and pattern these relationships occur. While stating basic relationships, we may discover other variables which should be included in the model.

A useful device for helping to identify basic relationships is the interaction table, a cross-listing of the factors to be included in the model (Table A.2). By checking each row against each column in the table, we can look at all possible interactions between system variables, and decide which interactions to include in the model. Such tables are particularly useful in designing models that describe flows of materials or individuals between different parts of a system or between spatial areas.

Once the basic lists of variables and their interactions have been established, we can concentrate on specific parts of the model, confident that a coherent picture is being maintained. This is one of the primary values of model building in resource

TABLE A.2 Interaction Table Providing a Format for Systematically Identifying Factors and Relationships

	Effect on			
Effect of	Total Production	Number of Adults	Effort Level	Harvest
Total production			X[a]	X
Number of adults	X	X	X	X
Effort level		X	X	X
Harvest		X	X	X

[a] X indicates direct effect of row variable on column variable.

management: with simulation schemes we can look very carefully at each part of a system while building a description of how the parts fit together.

In order to describe basic relationships among variables, we must concentrate on one variable at a time, and be precise in its definition. When we are certain of the biological factor or event that is represented by the variable, we can state how the variable will change, considering the degree of resolution desired of the model. For example, if it is clear that production is to mean the number of newborn Mallards in Manitoba that survive to their first autumn, then we may describe production as the product of

spring breeding population × eggs produced per adult

× survival rate of eggs to hatching × survival rate of chicks to fledging

× survival rate through early flight period

Each of these factors can then be broken down into subfactors, treated as constant, or related to other variables or factors in the model. As an example of this last method, we can describe by means of a graph the egg production per adult in terms of size of breeding population (Figure A.8). Then the population size beyond which production drops may in turn be described in terms of the availability of ponds or other factors. In this example, we are using breeding population size as an index to the conditions which birds will encounter in terms of factors such as competition for nesting sites or food supply.

If simple linear equations will not adequately describe a relationship, it is often best to express the relationship in terms of a graph. There are computer techniques for entering graphical relationships directly into models. Suppose we are studying waterfowl production, and we have information to support the following assumptions: that production is proportional to numbers of breeding adults for low population densities; that there is a maximum production, set by availability of ponds and by territorial characteristics of breeding birds; and that production will drop off at very high population densities, due to competition between breeding birds and failure of food supplies for the young. We can represent all these

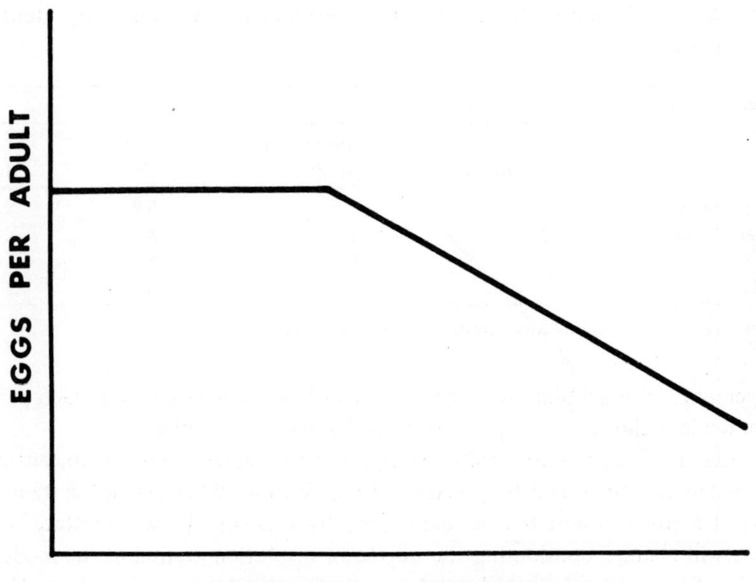

FIGURE A.8 Functional relationships may be used in models to represent the action of various biological mechanisms.

assumptions at once by means of a simple graph of production versus breeding population size (Figure A.9). Specific data can then be used to scale the graph axes to give proper maximum production rates and breeding population sizes. In graphical representation no biological content is lost by stating a relationship in that form. Several different biological relationships may result in the same graph. When this happens, the behavior of the model is invariant to certain assumptions.

Frequently a particular relationship is not well understood or supported by data. For example, suppose we are trying to describe kill rates for a population in terms of the numbers of hunters. The problem is that increased numbers of hunters might result in decreased individual success, increased success, or no effect on individual success. Although more data might help to resolve this problem, decisions and predictions must be made in the meantime. Rather than ignore the problem, or use a simpler model, it seems best to develop the model, and test it with several alternative assumptions. Sensitivity analysis is the term used for the process of testing the effects of different assumptions and parameter values on model predictions.

Illustrate the basic relationships. A useful tool for illustrating relationships among variables is a flow chart (Figure A.10) showing the calculation sequence with boxes and arrows. This sequence will usually follow the real sequence of events that is to be simulated. Each box, in itself, may represent a whole series

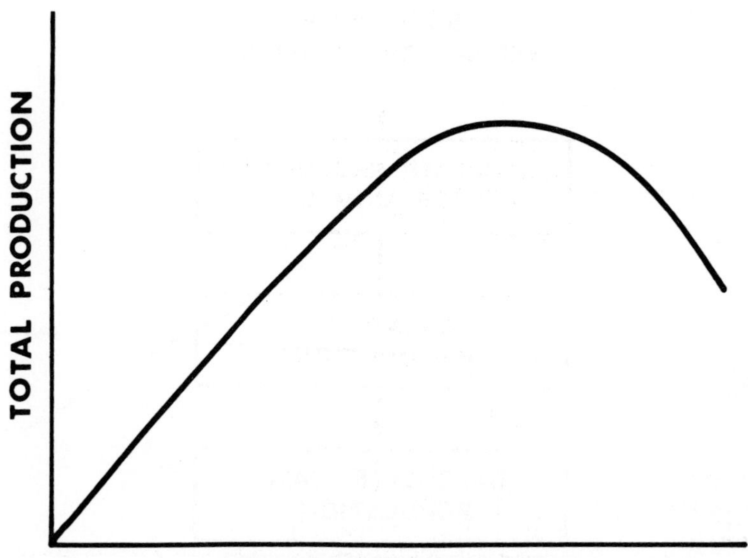

FIGURE A.9 Another way of representing the relationship shown in Figure A.8. With appropriate units, either relationship could be used in a model to give the same prediction.

of calculations (e.g., "total production") that could be shown in another, more detailed, flow chart.

Program the model for the computer. Writing the computer program is relatively simple once basic relationships have been clearly stated and flow charts have been designed. A number of computer languages have been designed expressly for simulation (DYNAMO, GASP, SIMULA, etc.), but experience has shown that standard FORTRAN or ALGOL usually give the best results.

Most simulation programs have three basic parts: parameter and initial variable input; the simulation sequence; and variable output (Figure A.11). No special programming tricks are needed to develop simulation models. Repeated use of the same variable names in time sequences of calculations and simple looping and branching operations are the only essential programming conventions. For more complicated simulation models, such output devices as plotters and cathode ray displays are useful.

Models and Data

A major problem in model building is estimation of parameters, initial values of state variables, and driving variables. In some situations we avoid the problem

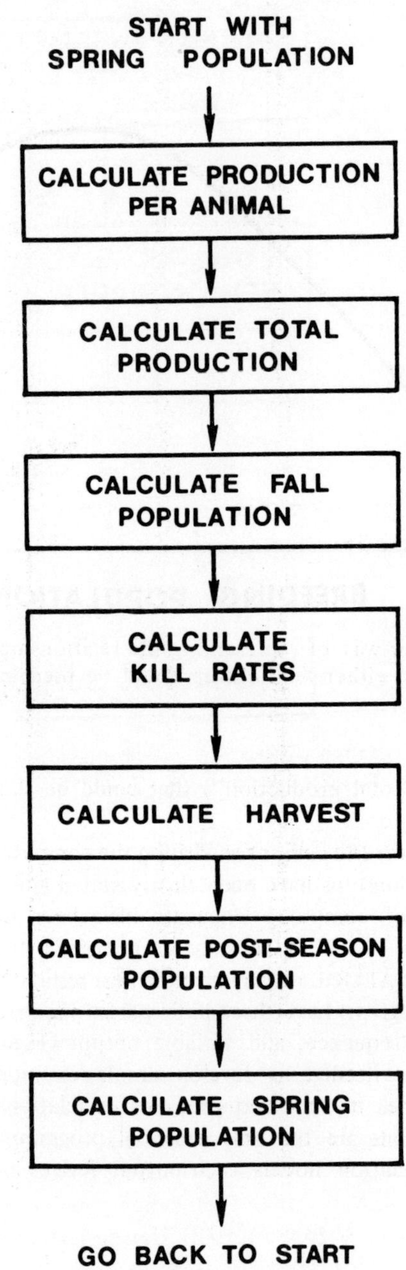

FIGURE A.10 Sequence of calculations that might be performed in the simple duck population model given in Eqs. 7–12.

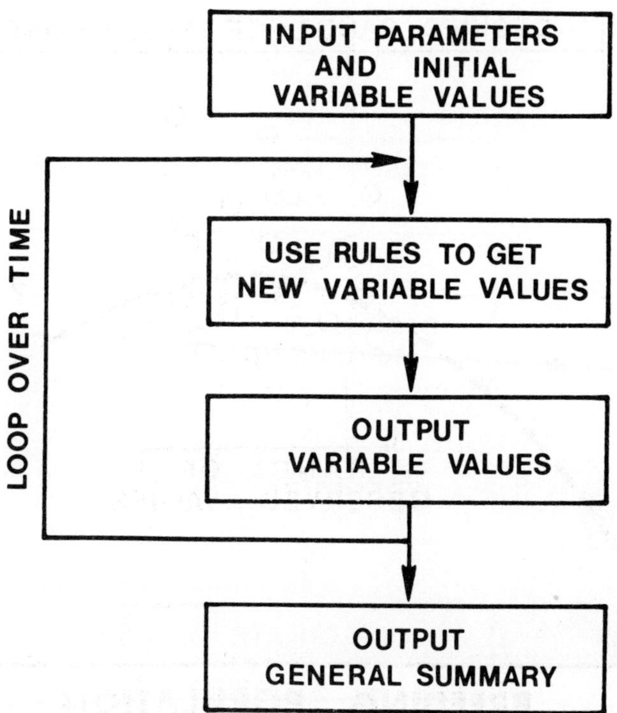

FIGURE A.11 Most dynamic simulation models have the same basic format: rules for change that can be applied repeatedly.

by making only broad conditional predictions of the form: if parameter A is in the range X_1 to X_2, then pattern Q will occur if parameter B is in the range Y_1 to Y_2. For example, we may say that if production rate is in the range 0.9 to 1.3, then if each hunter kills between 0 and 3 birds when there are 30 birds available, then the duck–hunter predation system will remain self-regulating. However, unless most of the parameters are well-established, conditional predictions are almost meaningless in complicated models.

Most field data are of limited value in parameter estimation. This is because when left alone, natural systems usually do not vary over the full range of conditions that we might like to examine with a model. For example, in the problem of predicting production of ducks in terms of breeding population size, we may want to predict production for a wide range of breeding population sizes, although past data do not cover such a range (Figure A.12). However, resource systems that have experienced great changes in exploitation rates and management policies do give a wide range of past data. Studies of population response to progressive changes in exploitation have formed the basis for the few successful models that now exist, for example, in commercial fisheries management.

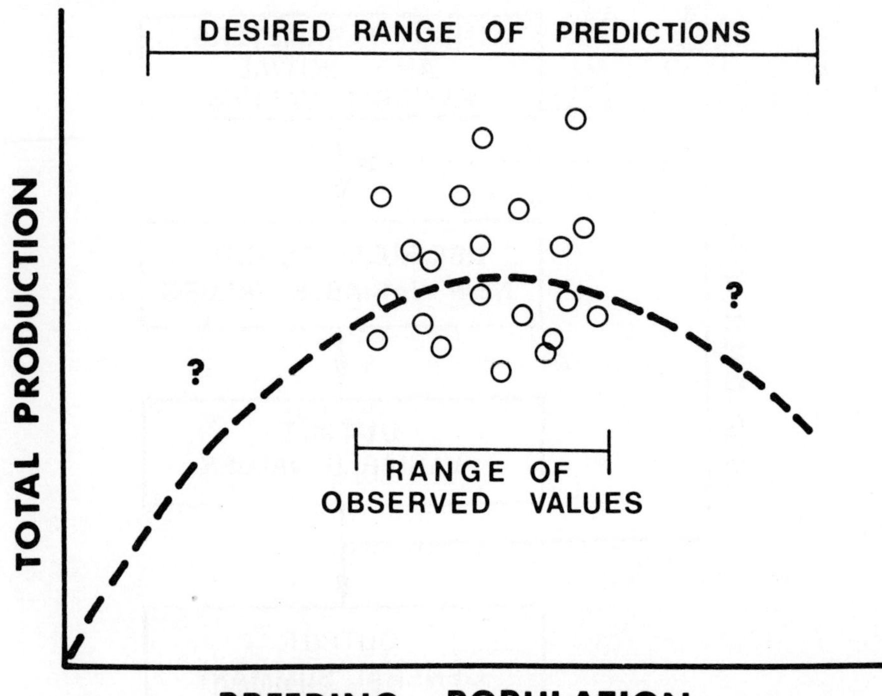

FIGURE A.12 Field data are usually not adequate to estimate functional relationships in models. Field experiments involving deliberate manipulation of populations are necessary to fill in the gaps.

We can take three courses of action when dealing with a narrow range of field data on a particular relationship:

1. restrict our predictions to those situations for which data are available;
2. use our biological intuition to extrapolate beyond observed data;
3. try to resolve the overall relationship into simpler experimental components (Holling, 1972) for which better data may be available.

The first course of action is safest, but may defeat the purpose of the model. The second alternative is risky, but may prove best in many situations. Some relationships can be extrapolated with fair confidence, given some basic biological understanding about the system of study. For example, we know that total production in the graph in Figure A.12 must eventually fall off as breeding population decreases; if our predictions need not be too precise, we may assume that this drop will begin to occur at breeding populations just below those observed. A danger would be that in reality production might fall off very rapidly for low breeding populations, due to failures in mating or lack of social facilitation. Alternatively, we can use conditional predictions and base management policies on "least optimistic" assumptions.

The third course of action, experimental components analysis, is not necessarily best. It can greatly increase the number of assumptions in the model, without ensuring that model behavior will not depend critically on just a few of these assumptions. In more complex models, the odds are greater that any one assumption will be incorrect; at the same time, there is no assurance that model predictions will not depend strongly on such erroneous assumptions. For example, in the problem of calculating total production for a duck population, our first step in an experimental components analysis would be to identify a series of time stages:

Mating → selection of nest area → egg laying → hatching → . . . .

Each of these stages will provide a gain or loss factor. These factors, when multiplied together, give a final production rate of premating adults. If any one stage is inaccurately estimated, and if compensatory mechanisms do not operate in successive stages, then the resulting production calculation will be equally inaccurate. Luckily, nature seems to provide for compensation between life history stages. For example, low survival in one period may be followed by higher survival in later stages, so that overall survival is nearly constant. A good experimental components' analysis will reveal these compensatory mechanisms when they exist.

Judging the Performance of Models

We can never say that a model has been validated; its rules are always simplifications. Likewise, models should not be judged solely on their ability to fit past data and predict new observations. Models are intended to apply to situations that are in some respects novel (otherwise we would need no model and could rely for decision-making on past data), and model predictions may fail in some but not all of these novel situations.

A model is not necessarily a bad one because it lacks numerical precision in fitting past data. For example, a waterfowl model should not be considered useless if it predicts a kill of 20,000 when the actual kill is 100,000. We make this assertion for two reasons. First, failure of the model may give us clues to errors in the formulation of the rules for change. If these rules embody our biological understanding, then the model is helping us to find errors in that understanding. Second, the model may predict the correct basic pattern of responses even if particular numerical results are in error. We can always rescale or change the units of the model.

The model can be particularly useful if the patterns it predicts are counter to our intuitions. For example, consider a model of flyway harvest patterns in waterfowl management. Intuitively we may predict that some harvest pattern in one flyway will have a particular effect on subsequent yields in other flyways (e.g., through breeding populations) that we have omitted from intuitive consideration.

A classic example of counterintuitive model behavior comes from aquatic biology. Limnologists have fertilized many lakes on the intuitive assumption that the effects of fertilization should include increases in phytoplankton standing crops. Often these increases are not seen, so fertilization is discounted as a management tool for many situations. Recently, aquatic models have predicted that phytoplankton crops should rarely increase under fertilization and instead that only zooplankton standing crops should change (McAllister *et al*., 1972). The reason is that potential increases in plant standing crop are quickly transmitted to zooplankton populations, and mean plant standing crop is determined by feeding and energetic characteristics of individual zooplankters rather than by phytoplankton productivity.

With these thoughts in mind, we should ask where models can go seriously wrong. Major errors seem to come when we badly misstate key rules of change or omit important factors from consideration. Minor errors (10–30 percent) in most parameter values usually have little effect on the patterns predicted by a model, although they may change the numerical results. Usually there are only a few critical parameters. Basing the model on the wrong factors is not necessarily bad, if these factors are strongly correlated with whatever variables are really important in the system. The biggest danger is that of omission. Suppose we are trying to predict recreational demand for a game population. We assume this demand is determined by the potential number of users and by past hunting success. We then get good correlation between these factors considering past data. But suppose that demand can be strongly influenced by communication and publicity, and when developing the model we assume these factors will remain constant. An unexpected series of newspaper articles or game management bulletins could make our predictions much too low.

Finally, there is no absolute standard for judging the merit of a particular model or decision-making method; there are only relative standards. One has to compare the predictions of one method against other, perhaps more intuitive ones.

GRAPHICAL EVALUATION OF ENVIRONMENTAL MANAGEMENT OPTIONS: EXAMPLES FROM A FOREST–INSECT PEST SYSTEM[1]

INTRODUCTION

In recent years there has been a proliferation of simulation models applied to several areas of renewable resource management (e.g., Paulik and Greenough, 1966; Watt, 1968; Walters and Bunnell, 1971; Walters and Gross, 1972; Gross *et al*., 1973; Clark and Lackey, 1974; Walters *et al*., 1975). However, few of these attempts to infuse systems techniques into resource management have met with wide acceptance

[1] This section is reprinted from Peterman (1977a) with the permission of Elsevier Scientific Publishing Company, Amsterdam.

among the decision-makers who were the potential clients. There are several reasons for these failures. First, management questions were rarely addressed at the outset of the modelling project; such management considerations usually appeared only as an "afterthought" – a means to make a purely scientific modelling exercise "relevant." This has inevitably led to dissatisfaction among managers with the spatial, temporal or disciplinary boundaries of the modelled system, variables considered, or output produced. The obvious solution to this set of problems is to include management people at the start of the model development. This will reap the additional benefits of enabling the managers to gain some confidence in the model by understanding how it is put together and to instill in them a healthy skepticism toward the model by making the model's assumptions clear.

The second major reason many natural resource modelling efforts have failed to step successfully into the domain of decision-making is that uncertainties are often ignored altogether or are only crudely handled (by putting in some variance term). And yet uncertainties about the future are a major part of any decision-maker's world (e.g., through changes in management goals, environmental conditions, harvesting technology, or system structure). Still, explicit inclusion of uncertainties in an analysis cannot eliminate management risks or even reveal the path of lowest risk; it can only help the decision-maker to evaluate management options, given that the assumptions used in the exercise are valid.

However, even if managers take part in the modelling exercise and uncertainties are handled in a comprehensive way, a third issue often arises – the credibility gap. After the manager specifies some objective that he wishes to achieve, the model (which he supposedly understands) is used in combination with some relatively sophisticated optimization procedure such as dynamic programming (which most managers do not understand) to produce some management "rules" which will achieve the objective (e.g., Watt, 1963). However, it is this "black-box" nature of the optimization which often leads to the credibility problem, especially if the optimization answer is quite different from the one the manager intuitively thought would be right.

This paper mainly addresses this credibility issue. A technique is presented which fills a serious gap in the spectrum of present policy evaluation tools, which ranges from very qualitative and credible approaches to highly quantitative and esoteric methods which are rarely understood by resource managers. This technique graphically provides the manager with a comprehensive array of information on the state of the system under various management regimes and permits him to perform relatively complicated optimizations in an easily understood way without the aid of a computer. It should be emphasized that the purpose of this paper is *not* to present *the* solution to the example forest–insect pest problem, but to illustrate an approach to analyzing management options.

THE SPRUCE BUDWORM–BALSAM FIR SYSTEM

The technique for exploring management options which will be illustrated uses examples from the spruce budworm–balsam fir system in eastern Canada, perhaps one of the most thoroughly studied forest–insect systems in existence (e.g., Morris, 1963). A preliminary model was put together in 1972 to simulate the dynamics of the interaction between this defoliating insect and its host trees in New Brunswick (Walters and Peterman, 1974). This initial model has been extensively modified and it is now much more detailed, realistic and useful (Holling, 1974; Holling *et al.*, 1975; Jones 1976).

The following description of the behavior of the spruce budworm–forest system is taken from Morris (1963), Holling (1974), Holling *et al.*, (1975) and the papers in *Forestry Chronicle*, 51 (4), 1975. The budworm population causes widespread tree mortality owing to defoliation as it goes through outbreaks every 35–70 years. Not all tree species are susceptible, however; balsam fir is most affected, followed by white and red spruce, while black spruce is essentially unaffected. Susceptibility of balsam fir to budworm damage is positively correlated with age. The interest in budworm defoliation is not purely academic; loss of potentially harvestable timber can be enormous (Marshall, 1975). Since the New Brunswick forest and tourist industries constitute a significant portion of that province's economy, the insect problem is a very real concern.

There are at present two favored classes of management options for controlling the budworm; one is to kill insects by insecticide application, and the other is to harvest potentially susceptible trees before the insects get to them. Various biological control and integrated management approaches are under study but these are not yet operational on a large scale. The spraying option has been in use more than the cutting option and after about 25 years of spraying at about 80% larval mortality, the insect problem has become a chronic one instead of an occasional one. Large amounts of timber have been saved, but the threat potential is still present because the insects have had ample food supply upon which to feed; they have not been permitted to go through a full outbreak cycle and to thereby deplete their food supply.

By looking at the state-dependent biological processes involved in the dynamics of this forest–insect system (e.g., bird predation on insects, insect survival at different life stages, tree growth and response to defoliation, etc.), the present model has been able to adequately represent the behavior of the real-world system, over both space and time (Holling, 1974; Holling *et al.*, 1975). The basic growth, survival and reproduction processes for insects and trees are represented for a site of about 65 miles^2. To simulate what goes on over a large part of the whole province, 265 of these sites are linked together in a grid by insect dispersal. In the examples that follow, however, only a single "site" model was used and dispersal parameters were adjusted to make that site behave as if it were embedded in the full-province model.

EVALUATION OF MANAGEMENT OPTIONS

Now that this systems model is available, how can it be used to explore management questions? The first step is to ensure that the model produces information normally used by managers as well as other potentially usable indices. These indicators may be merely state variables, or combinations of them (e.g., mean and maximum insect density, tree age-class diversity, mean period between outbreaks, amount of timber harvested annually). These indicators are essentially performance measures (Gross, 1972) which, when combined in certain ways, can quantitatively compare the benefits of different management options.

There are two basic kinds of management questions that can be asked by using simulation models. First: "If certain management options were chosen, what would be the results?" Second, and conversely: "If certain results or objectives were desired, which management options should be chosen?"

Spraying and tree harvesting are the two primary management options present for the budworm–forest system. In this example, we will explore two "rules" for enacting these options, the age above which trees are harvested in the 65 mile^2 site, and the "threat state" above which insecticide is applied (at 80% larval mortality dosage). "Threat state" is measured by the hazard index used in New Brunswick which is dependent upon egg density and amount of defoliation of both old and new foliage. The higher the hazard index, the more susceptible the forest.

Let us examine the behavior of the site model over a 125-year period (long enough to encompass at least one full outbreak cycle) as the two above management options are varied. Fig. A.13 shows the values of one indicator, average third larval instar density, which resulted from 30 different model runs. Each model run used different combinations of the two management options. This figure shows that if the age of tree harvest is low, the average insect density is also low, independent of how much spraying is done. This is because there is very little food available for the insects. On the other hand, if tree cutting age is high and the hazard index threshold above which spraying is done is about six, then very high average insect densities result over the 125-year period.

A set of isopleths or contours can be drawn through this grid of indicator values to create a topographic map of that indicator (Fig. A.14). This surface gives a useful graphical picture of how rapidly the indicator values change when management options are varied. These types of graphs are called "nomograms" (Gross *et al.*, 1973; Peterman, 1975) or response surfaces (Maguire, 1974, 1975). For any given set of simulation runs, nomograms or response surfaces can be generated for any number of indicators. Fig. A.15 shows a set of six indicators which were judged particularly relevant by the management people taking part in this project. There are actually over 30 different indicator surfaces to be displayed but these six will be used to illustrate the application of nomograms to the two types of management questions posed earlier. Note that on all the graphs the two management options are identical; only the indicator surfaces differ.

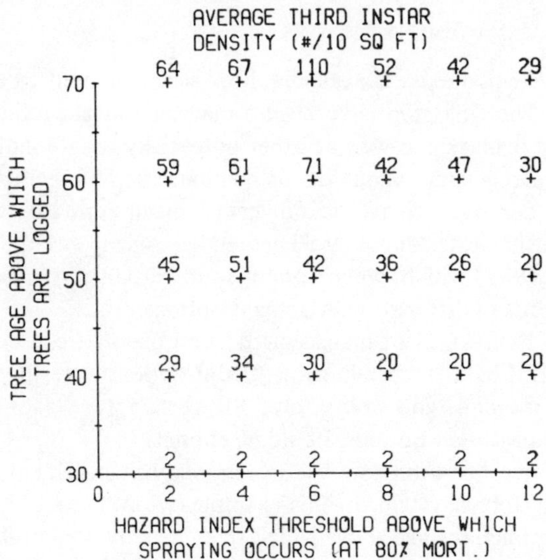

FIGURE A.13 The simulation model was run 30 different times, and each time different combinations of the management options (tree logging age and hazard index threshold) were used. For each of these 125-year runs, a value was calculated for the indicator, average third larval instar density during that period. This indicator is measured in terms of number per 10 ft^2 of foliage because this is the unit used by New Brunswick forest entomologists.

First, we address the question concerning what results would be obtained if certain management options were chosen. The set of nomograms shown is, in part, a graphical information retrieval system which contains much information in a compact, easily understood form. Also, the graphs show what limits there are in the system; for example, it is not possible to annually harvest more than an average of 9000 cunits (cunit = 100 ft^3) of host species from the 65 mile^2 block, given the two management options shown. Next, pointers which show identical coordinate locations on all six nomograms can be put on a separate clear sheet of plastic, and this overlay can be used to "experiment" with different options. For example, Fig. A.15 shows the pointer set at a tree cutting age of 50 and a hazard index threshold of 4. One can easily read off the values from the various indicator surfaces using the pointers (proportion of years spraying done = 0.25, average cunits harvested per year = 6500, etc.). In this way, nomograms which are nothing more than summaries of numerous simulations, are a powerful way of answering the type of question posed earlier.

These nomograms have proven their value as pedagogic tools during several workshops with forest researchers and managers. This has been true particularly because unavoidable tradeoffs between indicators are made apparent. For example,

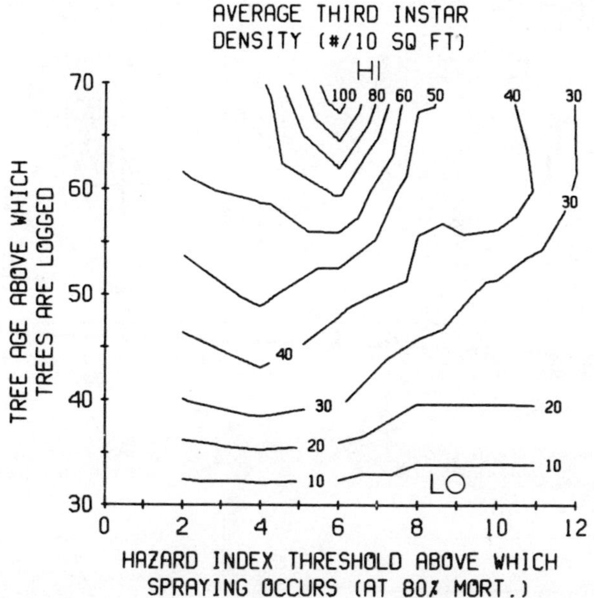

FIGURE A.14 Contour lines can be drawn through the "heights" of the indicator shown in Fig. A.13 to yield a "nomogram," or response surface.

by inspecting the shapes of the indicator surfaces, it is clear that if one desires to keep the proportion of years in which spraying is done very low, then one will have to accept a decrease in the possible cunits yielded from the forest. Tradeoffs such as this, which may not be intuitively obvious, are an important part of the value of nomograms. Note that all of the benefits of nomograms mentioned so far do not require the user to interact with a computer at all. If he has any confidence in the model which produced the nomograms, he can explore management alternatives at his desk.

DERIVATION OF "OPTIMAL" SOLUTIONS

We now turn to the second type of management question which nomograms can address, "If certain objectives are desired, which management options should be chosen?" The first step in this process is to define quantitatively the objective which is sought. This can be done in the budworm–forest case by choosing which indicators are to be considered, and by assigning a relative importance weighting to each of them. For example, let us assume for the moment that we as provincial forest managers are only considering a simple objective which simultaneously seeks to reduce the proportion of years in which spraying is done (to satisfy environmentalists) and to increase the profit of the forest industry (Fig. A.16). In addition, the forest industry profit indicator is considered to be about

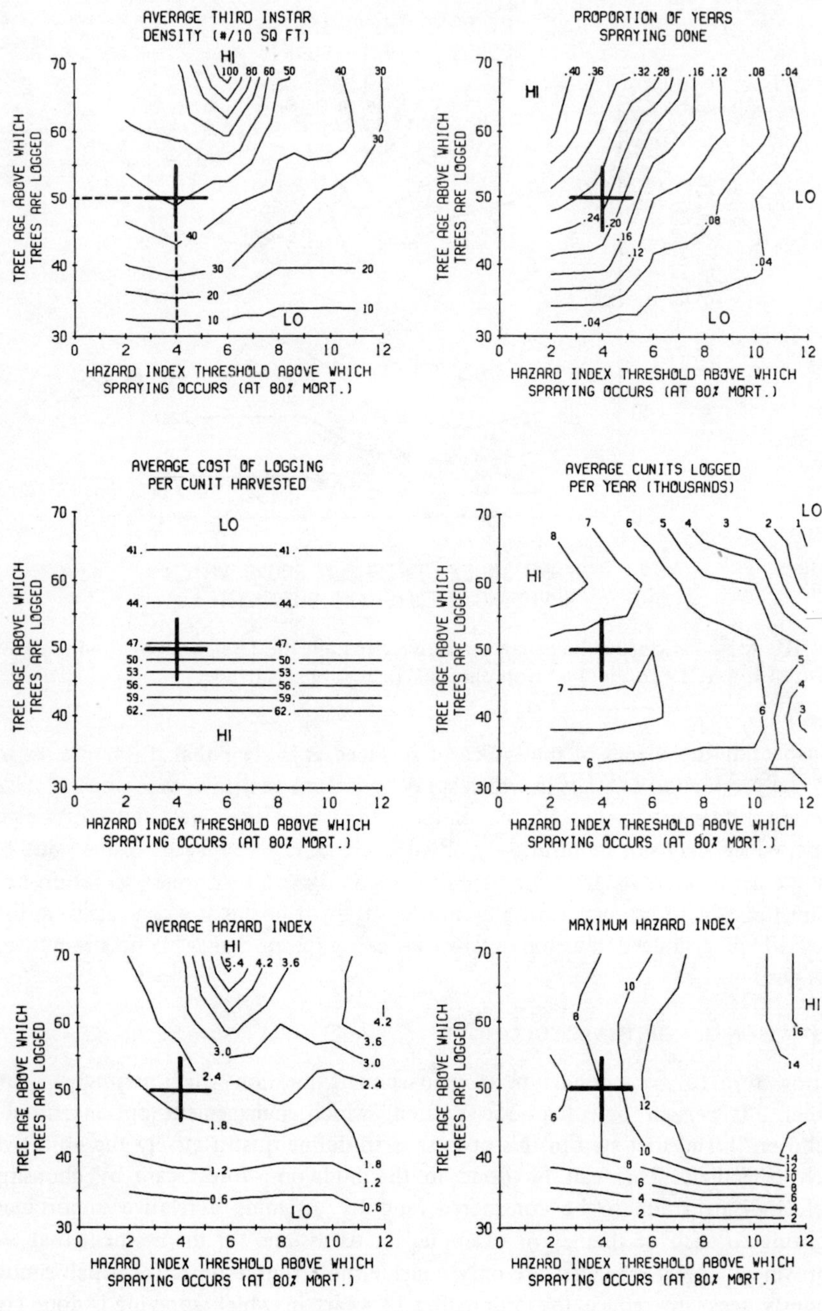

AVERAGE THIRD INSTAR DENSITY (#/10 SQ FT)
PROPORTION OF YEARS SPRAYING DONE
AVERAGE COST OF LOGGING PER CUNIT HARVESTED
AVERAGE CUNITS LOGGED PER YEAR (THOUSANDS)
AVERAGE HAZARD INDEX
MAXIMUM HAZARD INDEX
TREE AGE ABOVE WHICH TREES ARE LOGGED
HAZARD INDEX THRESHOLD ABOVE WHICH SPRAYING OCCURS (AT 80% MORT.)
HI
LO

$2\frac{1}{3}$ times as important as the spraying indicator (i.e., their relative importance weightings on a scale from 0 to 1 are 0.3 (spraying) and 0.7 (profit). Given this objective function (or quantitative expression of the objective), what is the best tree cutting age and hazard index threshold for spraying?

To find the answer, we need to convert the indicator surfaces which are components of the objective to the same units (say 0 to 1) and then do a weighted summation of the surfaces, where the weights are the relative importance weightings assigned by the user. The weighted summation could be done in either of two ways, either by a mathematical summation of the points across the surface using a computer or by a visual summation using shaded overlays of the indicator surfaces. The shades of grey would represent the heights on any one surface, and the range of shades of grey on any one surface would be darker the higher the relative importance weighting of that indicator.

This shaded overlay technique has been used in some salmon management nomograms (Peterman, 1975) and has been preferred only in those cases where it was important, for reasons of credibility, to avoid the computer. However, by using either method of weighted summation, an objective function surface results which has peaks and valleys. The best set of management options for achieving the specified objective are the ones which put the system on the high points of this surface, in this example, tree cutting age of 70 and hazard index threshold of 10 (Fig. A.17).

Management constraints based on factors not explicitly considered in the model can also be easily incorporated into the use of the nomograms. For the New Brunswick situation, for instance, it might be reasoned that at least 6000 cunits should be harvested from a site each year in order to maintain full employment in the forest industry. Thus, a non-feasible region can be illustrated by shading out all the area on the cunits harvested surface below 6000 cunits. When this constraint region is overlaid on the final objective function surface just shown, we find that the optimal solution of cutting at 70 years and using a hazard index threshold of 10 is no longer feasible, as it entails harvesting only 2600 cunits of wood (see Fig. A.15). The best solution thus lies somewhere else (Fig. A.18). Any number of additional constraints could also be applied in the same way, such as

FIGURE A.15 Six different indicator nomograms selected from the 32 produced by the simulation model. Note that axes on all the graphs are identical, only the indicator surfaces are different. Definitions of some indicators: (a) "Proportion of years spraying done" is the proportion of the 125 years that the site was sprayed. (b) "Average cost of logging per cunit harvested" gives the average dollar cost to the logging operation of delivering one cunit (100 ft^3) of lumber to the mill. In this case, it is strictly dependent upon the age of the forest harvested and certain fixed costs. (c) "Average hazard index" is merely the average value, over the 125 years, of the New Brunswick hazard index (see text). (d) "Maximum hazard index" is the largest value of that index which occurred during the 125 years. The crosshairs are on a moveable, transparent sheet of plastic which has been overlaid. These pointers indicate identical coordinate locations on the six graphs. Values of the two management options are read off the pointer in the upper left corner.

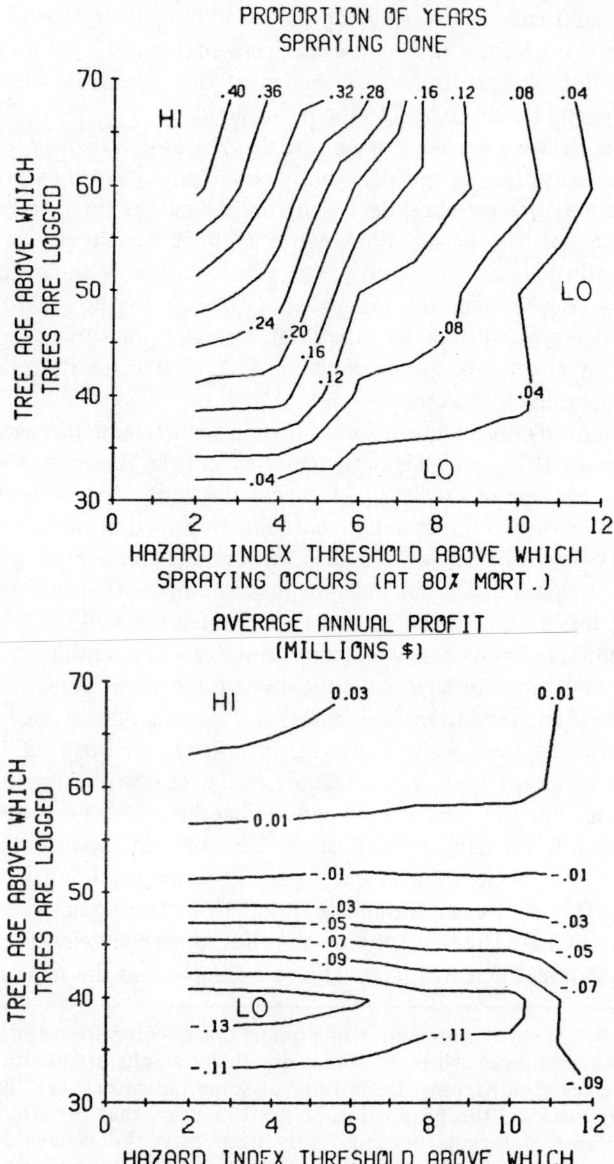

FIGURE A.16 Two component indicators of a simple, hypothetical objective. The profits indicator only shows the total dollars profit to the forest industry where the sale price is $45 per cunit and the costs of logging are as shown by that indicator in Fig. A.15. Note that if "proportion of years spraying done" should be minimized and profits maximized, there will have to be some compromise, as the optimal regions for these two indicators are at different corners of the graphs.

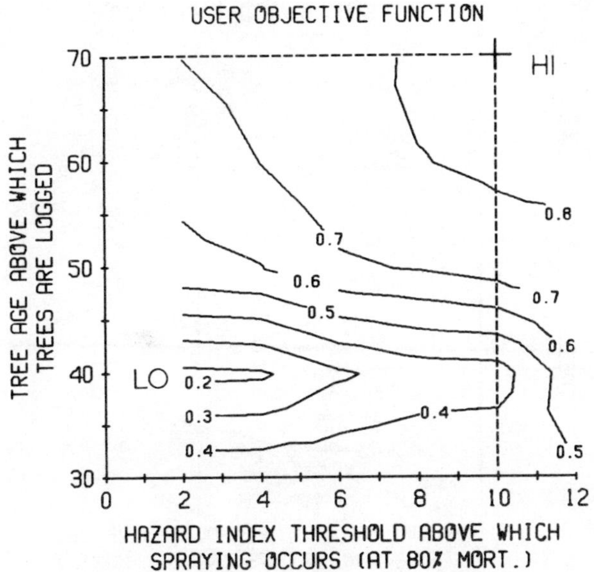

FIGURE A.17 The hypothetical objective function surface derived by giving a relative importance weighting of 0.3 to minimization of years spraying done and 0.7 to maximization of profits (see text). The general form of the objective function is $U = \Sigma_i W_i . I_i$, where W_i is the relative importance weighting of the i-th indicator ($\Sigma_i W_i = 1.0$) and I_i is the value of the i-th indicator scaled from 0 to 1 (1.0 is the lowest value of I_i if that indicator is being minimized or the highest value if it is being maximized). The "best" management option, given the specified objective, is to cut trees above age 70 and to spray the site when the hazard index gets above 10.

ensuring cost of harvesting is below some amount. Thus, a fairly narrow range of feasible options might be delineated, a range which probably would not have been intuitively obvious.

An important issue must be discussed at this point. Given that any particular management option produces, with the model, a complicated fluctuating time stream perhaps 125 years long for each indicator and since there are several indicators of interest, how can different management options be compared? We have seen that the nomogram approach compresses these time series into useful indicators (such as means, maxima or minima, coefficients of variation, minimum 3-year running averages, etc.) and then assigns each indicator a relative importance weighting which is used in a linear weighted summation to evaluate an objective. However, this nomogram approach to indicator compression and weighting is different from the "utility analysis" approach (e.g., Bell, 1975; Clark and Bell, 1976; Keeney, 1976; Keeney and Raiffa, 1976). In order to clarify some simplifying assumptions made by the nomogram technique, let us compare it with the more sophisticated "utility" approach.

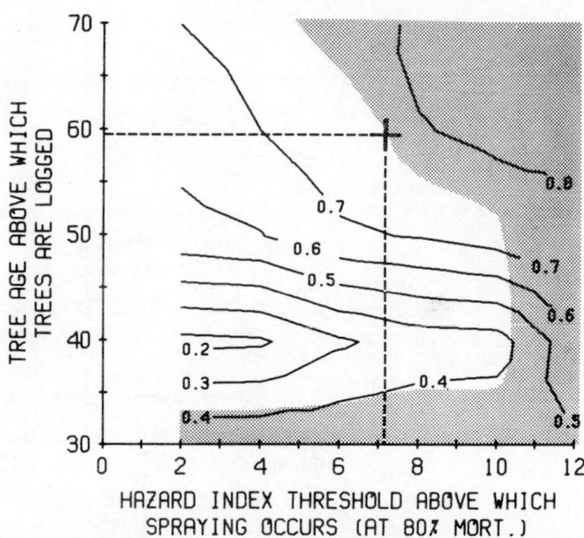

FIGURE A.18 When a constraint is applied to the objective of Fig. A.17, by requiring more than 6000 cunits to be harvested annually, a non-feasible set of management options (in the shaded area) are delineated. This constraint region shifts the "best" management option to cutting age of 59 years and hazard index threshold of a little over 7. This particular constraint region is derived from the location of the 6000 cunit contour on the "average annual cunits harvested" nomogram shown in Fig. A.15.

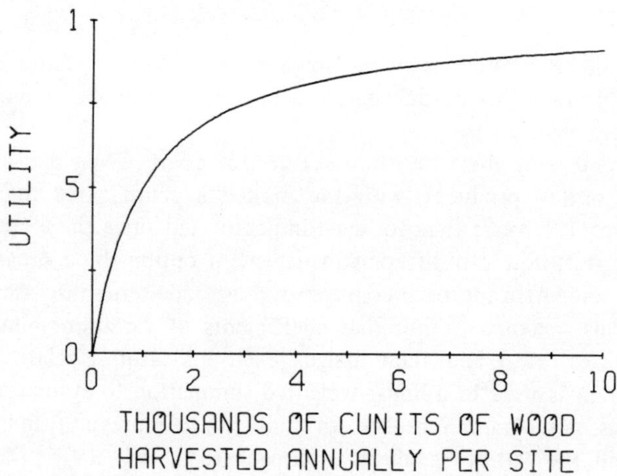

FIGURE A.19 A hypothetical example of the utility, or "satisfaction gained" by having different amounts of wood harvested in New Brunswick each year.

Utility analysis permits the value, or utility, of any indicator to be a non-linear function of that indicator's level (e.g. Fig. A.19). This non-linearity is apparently rather common (Hilborn and Walters, 1976; Keeney, 1976) because there are limits, for example, to how much wood can be used on the market. In contrast, the described nomogram approach assumes a linear relation between the level of some indicator and its "value," e.g., three times more wood harvested is worth three times as much.

The second difference between nomograms and utility analysis is that the former technique assumes a linear objective function by using the relative importance weightings of different indicators in a weighted summation to evaluate an objective. Utility analysis permits evaluation of non-linear objectives, which may be uncommon (Slovic and Lichtenstein, 1971) but which nevertheless occur (e.g., Bell, 1975; Keeney, 1976).

The above simplifying assumptions of the nomogram approach have not detracted from its value; in fact, they have permitted nomograms to be an effective way of getting management people to explore the implications of their options and to compare optimal solutions when different objectives are used. The key to the tool's effectiveness has been its easily comprehended graphical nature and the fact that people can, if desired, manipulate it without using the computer and without doing complex analyses of their objectives.

COPING WITH UNCERTAINTIES

No matter how much basic research is done on the natural system, any resource manager will still be faced with a large number of uncertainties. It is necessary to analyze how any "optimal policies" which are derived by use of nomograms, formal optimization or plain intuition would be modified if these uncertainties were taken explicitly into account. There are several sources of uncertainty, each of which can be handled in its own way.

1. There are certain processes in the natural (and model) world about which we know very little, for instance, tree response to defoliation. We need to ask how different our "optimal policies" would be if we were to make different assumptions about the structure of the natural system dynamics. This is essentially a classical sensitivity analysis, but one which can be handled in a unique way with nomograms. The new assumption can be incorporated into the model, the nomograms can be regenerated, and the shape of the new objective function surface can be compared with the original one. If the optimal solution were on a steeply sloping peak in the original case, then the value of the objective function might have dropped more when the new assumption was put in than if an equally high, but more gently sloping peak had been chosen for the original "optimal solution."

2. Another source of uncertainty is in the objectives which managers use when deciding upon the best options. Even if a suitable quantification of today's objectives

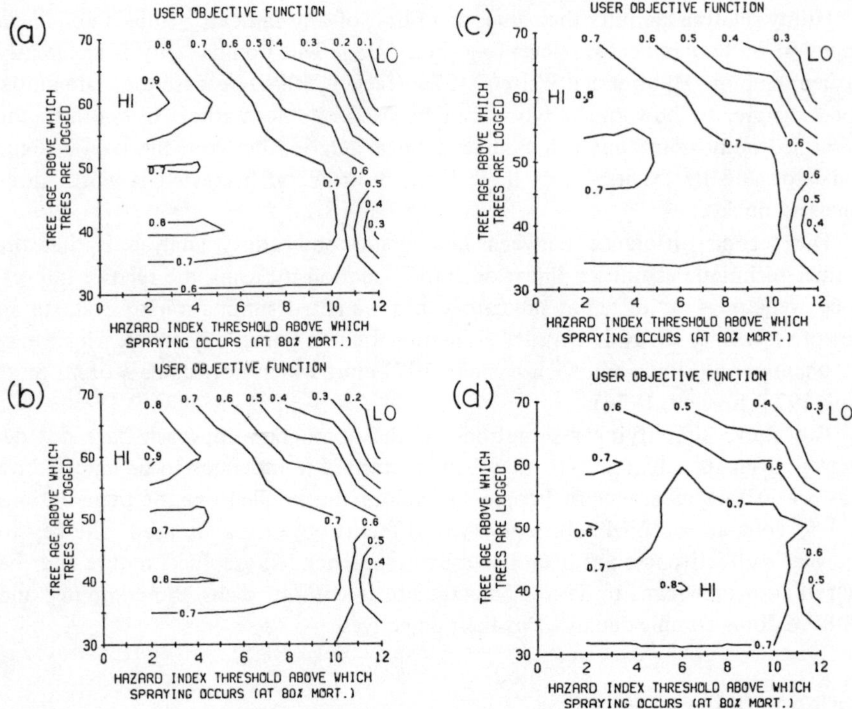

FIGURE A.20 An example of how shifts in relative importances of indicators can change the "best" management options (see text). The areas marked "HI" are the high points on the objective function surfaces. (a) – relative importance weightings are 0.05 on proportion of years sprayed and 0.95 on average annual cunits logged (denoted 0.05/0.95); optimum is at (2, 60). (b) – weightings are 0.1/0.9 and optimum is also at (2, 60). (c) – weightings are 0.2/0.8 and optimum is still (2, 60). (d) – weightings are 0.3/0.7 and optimum now changes to (6, 40).

is obtained, there is no guarantee that these objectives won't shift dramatically within the next several years (Holling and Clark, 1975). The manager must ask how sensitive his optimal solution is to changes in the objective. A very simple example of this type of analysis is shown in Fig. A.20. Here, the objective was simply composed of minimization of proportion of years sprayed and maximization of average annual cunits logged. The weights started out as 0.05 and 0.95, respectively. The best tree cutting age was 60 years and the best hazard index threshold was 2 [symbolized as (2, 60)] , This optimal solution remained the same as the relative importance weightings changed from 0.05 and 0.95 to 0.1 and 0.9 and then to 0.2 and 0.8 (Figs. A.20 a, b, and c). Thus, that one set of management options could satisfy a wide range of objectives, where timber harvest ranged from 19 times to only four times as important as amount of spraying. However, when a further incremental change in weights was made, to 0.3 and 0.7, the optimal solution shifted clear over to a hazard index threshold of 6 and a tree cutting age of 40 (Fig. A.20 d). Thus, the optimal solution for a present objective may become totally inadequate if the objective changes in certain ways.

A manager can explore ranges of objectives for these shifts by using an interactive computer program which allows him to enter a new objective function and see the resulting surface immediately (or he can use the set of shaded nomogram overlays as described earlier). Changes in objectives can involve altering the indicators included, as well as their weightings.

This interactive objective function program has been used successfully in several workshops with forest managers, where the objectives of several different interest groups were compared. These interest groups, chosen to represent extremes in viewpoints, were forest industry, environmentalist, and provincial forest management. In some cases, the optimal policies for these groups were quite different, but in other cases, the solutions were surprisingly similar. When objectives with more than one or two indicators are considered it becomes very difficult to ascertain sensitivity of policies to changes in goals without quantitative techniques such as those described here.

3. Management acts often fail to give desired results because of the occurrence of some unexpected event, such as a series of unusually warm summers which lead to unprecedented insect survival, or high winds which blow insecticides off target. Each management option can be tested through simulation for its sensitivity to such "failures." New nomograms can be created and the cost associated with such failures can be assessed by comparison with the previous "optimal solution." Detailed policy failure analysis would involve an estimation of both the probabilities of certain events occurring and their costs (biological, economic). Ideally, some management options would be less sensitive to failures than others, and would therefore be "safe-fail" as opposed to "fail-safe" (Holling and Clark, 1975).

4. Another type of failure to be considered is the "control error" type. This results from being unable to actually achieve the proper tree cutting age, or being unable to use the desired hazard index threshold. This will result in the existence of some probability distribution around the desired location of the pointer which will describe where the system can actually be. Again, as for many of the previous sensitivity questions, those "optimal solutions" which put the system on a peak with flatter surrounding regions are more desirable than those which put the system on an equally high, but steeply sloping peak. This notion is just the opposite of the classical optimization approach, which is to prefer a steeply sloped peak because any deviation from the optimum can be quickly detected and corrective action can be taken to get the system back on the peak. However, this approach assumes there is little lag time in acquisition of deviation information and that corrective actions will always give desired results. Neither of these assumptions is particularly valid for ecological systems where lags are characteristic and management actions are not very precise.

The importance of this type of sensitivity analysis is indicated by the example

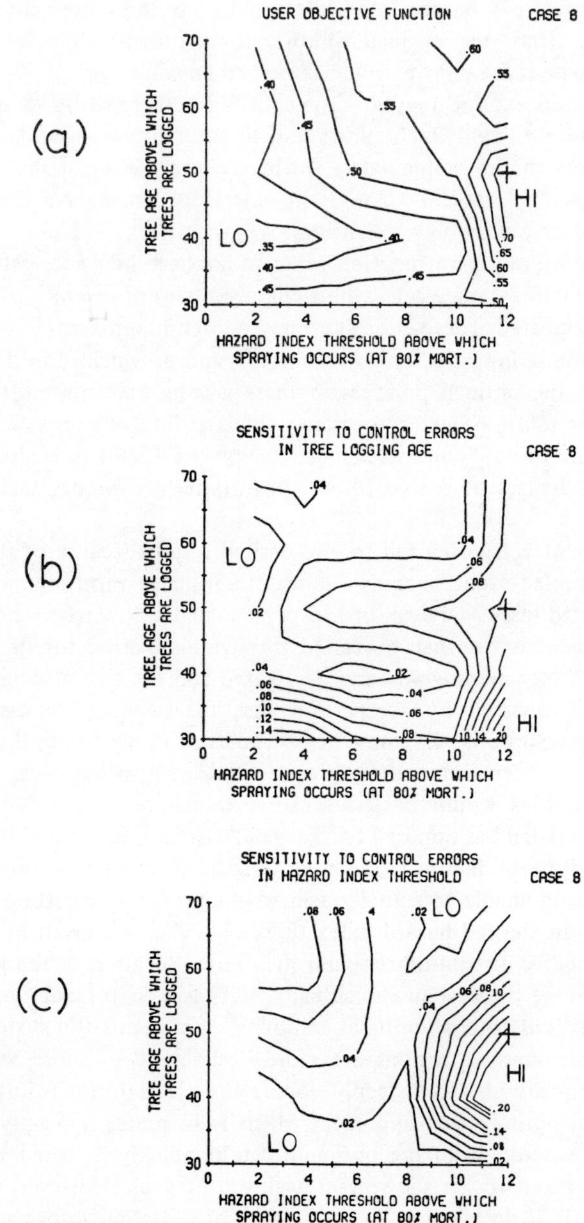

FIGURE A.21 The values of an example objective function are shown in graph (a), and the cross-hairs indicate the high point for this objective. Sensitivity to "control errors" (see text) can be analyzed by measuring the slopes of the objective function surface in both the vertical and horizontal directions, corresponding respectively to errors in tree logging age and the hazard index threshold (b) and (c).

shown in Fig. A.21. Here, the objective function investigated is one described at a workshop by a group representing the environmentalist's viewpoint. The highest value for this objective is given by a hazard index threshold of 12 and tree cutting age of 50 (12, 50). However, it can be seen from Figs. A.21b and A.21c that the objective function surface is fairly steep at this "optimum" point of (12, 50). "Control errors" such as harvesting trees younger than 50 years or using a hazard index threshold different than 12 will result in rapidly changing and much lower values of the objective function, i.e., "suboptimal" conditions. Based upon his relevant uncertainties and his willingness to take risks, a manager might be better off choosing the option of (10, 70), which yields a lower value of the objective but which is in a flatter region, much less sensitive to "control errors."

An interesting question arises from this discussion of uncertainties and how to deal with them. How much higher would the *steeply* sloping objective function peak have to be before one would choose it over the peak with the *gently* sloped surrounding area? Clearly the answer would depend upon some probability estimates of the occurrence of the various uncertain events (wrong assumptions, changing objectives, control errors).

5. The final type of uncertainty managers should consider derives from changes in the internal workings of the biological system which in turn arise from natural evolution or response to management regimes. An example of the latter is the alteration of bird predation effects through spray-induced bird mortality. The simulation model could be used to explore the importance of these types of effects in changing "optimal solutions."

If the above five classes of uncertainty are analyzed as described, the decision maker will have a better assessment of the risks involved with any particular set of actions than might have been available with other existing techniques of policy evaluation. However, one should not be left with the impression that simulation models, nomograms, or any other quantitative devices are a replacement for the experienced decision maker. On the contrary, such techniques are only intended to *supplement* the normal intuitive decision-making processes (Walters and Bunnell, 1971). Drucker (1970) has stated this case eloquently when writing about the general use of long-range planning:

> Long-range planning does not "substitute facts for judgement," does not "substitute science for the manager." It does not even lessen the importance and role of managerial ability, courage, experience, intuition, or even hunch – just as scientific biology and systematic medicine have not lessened the importance of these qualities in the individual physician.

ACKNOWLEDGEMENTS

C.S. Holling, D.D. Jones and W.C. Clark provided the data and model used for generating the nomograms. G. Baskerville and W.C. Clark suggested changes in nomogram indicators. The whole approach of model use in policy evaluation has benefited from numerous discussions with the policy analysis group at the Institute of Resource Ecology, University of British Columbia, and W.C. Clark commented on the manuscript. Financial support for this work was provided by Environment Canada.

REFERENCES

Bell, D.E., 1975. A Decision Analysis of Objectives for a Forest Pest Problem. Int. Inst. Appl. Syst. Anal., Laxenburg, Austria, RR-75-43, 46 pp.

Clark, W.C. and Bell, D.E., 1976. Intertemporal Indicator Evaluation: A Preliminary Note on Problems of Evaluating Time Stream Data for Environmental Policy Analysis. Inst. Resourc. Ecol., Univ. British Columbia, Vancouver, B.C., W-7, 27 pp.

Clark, R.D. and Lackey, R.T., 1974. Managing trends in angler consumption in freshwater recreational fisheries. Proc. 28th Annu. Conf. Southeastern Assoc. Game and Fish Comm., pp. 367–377.

Drucker, P.F., 1970. Technology, Management and Society. Harper and Row, New York, N.Y., 209 pp.

Gross, J.E., 1972. Criteria for game planning: Performance measures vs. intuition. Trans. 37th North Am. Wildl. Nat. Resourc. Conf., Mexico City, March 1972, pp. 246–259.

Gross, J.E., Roelle, J.E. and Williams, G.L., 1973. Progress Report: Program Onepop and Information Processor: A System Modeling and Communications Project. Colo. Coop. Fish. Wildl. Res. Unit, Colorado State Univ., Fort Collins, Colo., 327 pp.

Hilborn, R. and Walters, C.J., 1976. Differing goals of salmon management on the Skeena River. J. Fish. Res. Board Can., in press.

Holling, C.S. (Editor), 1974. Project Status Report: Ecology and Environment Project. Int. Inst. Appl. Syst. Anal. Laxenburg, Austria, SR-74-2-EC, 88 pp.

Holling, C.S. and Clark, W.C., 1975. Notes towards a science of ecological management. In: W.H. van Dobben and R.H. Lowe-McConnell (Editors), Unifying Concepts in Ecology. W. Junk, The Hague, pp. 247–251.

Holling, C.S., Dantzig, G.B., Baskerville, G., Jones, D.D. and Clark, W.C., 1975. A case study of forest ecosystem/pest management. Proc. Int. Can. Conf. Appl. Syst. Anal., Ottawa, Ont., May 1975, in press.

Jones, D.D., 1976. The budworm site model. W-13, Inst. Resourc. Ecol., Univ. British Columbia, Vancouver, B.C., 66 pp.

Keeney, R.L., 1976. A utility function for examining policy affecting salmon in the Skeena River. J. Fish. Res. Board Can., in press.

Keeney, R.L. and Raiffa, H., 1976. Decisions with Multiple Objectives. John Wiley, New York, N.Y., in press.

Maguire Jr, B., 1974. Ecosystem simulation through use of models of subsystem response structures. Simulation, 23 (5): 149–158.

Maguire Jr, B., 1975. Analysis and prediction of ecological and ecosystem dynamics with response structure models. Ecol. Modelling, 1 (4): 269–287.

Marshall, K.B., 1975. The spruce budworm and the dollar in New Brunswick, For. Chron. 51 (4): 143–146.

Morris, R.F. (Editor), 1963. The dynamics of Epidemic Spruce Budworm Populations. Mem. Entomol. Soc. Can., No. 31, 332 pp.

Paulik, G.J. and Greenough Jr, J.W., 1966. Management analysis for a salmon resource system. In: K.E.F. Watt (Editor), Systems Analysis in Ecology. McGraw-Hill, New York, N.Y., pp. 215–252.

Peterman, R.M., 1975. New techniques for policy evaluation in ecological systems: Methodology for a case study of Pacific salmon fisheries. J. Fish. Res. Board Can., 32 (11): 2179–2188.

Slovic, P. and Lichtenstein, S., 1971. Comparison of Bayesian and regression approaches to the study of information processing in judgement. Organ. Behav. Hum. Performance, 6: 649–744.

Walters, C.J. and Bunnell, F., 1971. A computer management game of land use in British Columbia. J. Wildl. Manage., 35: 644–657.

Walters, C.J. and Gross, J.E., 1972. Development of big game management plans through simulation modelling. J. Wildl. Manage., 36 (1): 119–128.

Walters, C.J. and Peterman, R.M., 1974. A systems approach to the dynamics of spruce budworm in New Brunswick. Proc. 23rd Meet. Entomol. Soc. Can. Quaest. Entomol., 10: 177–186.

Walters, C.J., Hilborn, R. and Peterman, R.M., 1975. Computer simulation of barren-ground caribou dynamics. Ecol. Modelling, 1 (4): 303–315.

Watt, K.E.F., 1963. Dynamic programming, "Look-Ahead Programming", and the strategy of insect pest control. Can. Entomol., 95: 525–536.

Watt, K.E.F., 1968. Ecology and Resource Management: A Quantitative Approach. McGraw-Hill, New York, N.Y., 450 pp.

B Participants in Workshop on Adaptive Assessment of Ecological Policies

International Institute for Applied Systems Analysis, Laxenburg, Austria, 13-17 June 1977

W. EVAN ARMSTRONG
Assistant Deputy Minister
Environment Canada
Planning and Finance
Ottawa
Canada

ASIT K. BISWAS
Biswas and Associates
Ottawa
Canada

JOHN BUSTERUD
Executive Office of the President
Council on Environmental Quality
Washington, D.C.
USA

GORDON CONWAY
Imperial College Field Station
Silwood Park
Ascot, Berkshire
England

J.K. EGUNJOBI
Department of Agricultural Biology
University of Ibadan
Ibadan
Nigeria

WILLIAM E. FELLING
Oak Ridge Association of Universities Inc.
Oak Ridge, Tennessee
USA

DAVID FISCHER
International Institute for Applied Systems Analysis
Laxenburg
Austria

GILBERTO GALLOPIN
Departmento de Recursos Naturales y Energia
Fundacion Bariloche
San Carlos de Bariloche
Rio Negro
Argentina

BRANISLAV GOSOVIC
United Nations Environment Program
Nairobi
Kenya

JACK GROSS
Office of Biological Services
U.S. Fish and Wildlife Service
Ft. Collins, Colorado
USA

ARTHUR J. HANSON
Project Specialist, Resources and Environment
The Ford Foundation
Jakarta
Indonesia

RAY HILBORN
Institute of Resource Ecology
University of British Columbia
Vancouver
Canada

ALAN HIRSCH
Office of Biological Services
Fish and Wildlife Service
U.S. Department of the Interior
Washington, D.C.
USA

M.W. HOLDGATE
Director General of Research
Department of the Environment
London
England

C.S. HOLLING
Institute of Resource Ecology
University of British Columbia
Vancouver
Canada

JAIME HURTUBIA
UNEP Regional Office
Mexico City
Mexico

DIXON D. JONES
Institute of Resource Ecology
University of British Columbia
Vancouver
Canada

A. KHOSLA
International Referral System
United Nations Environmental Program
Nairobi
Kenya

JOHN C. MARR
Director General
ICLARM
Makati, Metro Manila
Philippines

WILLIAM H. MATTHEWS
International Institute for Applied Systems Analysis
Laxenburg
Austria

R.W. MUNN
Air Quality Research Branch
Atmospheric Environment Service
Environment Canada
Downsview, Ontario
Canada

MICHAEL NELSON
Economic Commission for Latin America
Santiago, Chile

J. PEACHEY
Department of the Environment
London
England

WILLIAM PENDLETON
Resources and Environment
The Ford Foundation
New York, NY
USA

RANDALL M. PETERMAN
Institute of Animal Resource Ecology
University of British Columbia
Vancouver, B.C.
Canada

JORGE E. RABINOVICH
Instituto Venezolano de Investigaciones Cientificas
Centro de Ecologia
Caracas
Venezuela

JORGE SABATO
Capital Federal
Argentina

OTTO SOEMARWOTO
Institute of Ecology
Padjadjaran University
Bandung
Indonesia

JOHN WIEBE
Environmental Management Service
Ontario Region
Burlington, Ontario
Canada

References[1]

Ackerman, B.A., S. Rose-Ackerman, J.W. Sawyer, Jr., and D.W. Henderson. 1974. *The Uncertain Search for Environmental Quality*. The Free Press, New York.

Baskerville, G.L. (ed.). 1976. Report of the task-force for evaluation of budworm control alternatives. Department of Natural Resources, Fredericton, New Brunswick, Canada.

Baumol, W.J. 1968. On the social rate of discount. *Am. Econ. Rev.*, September 1968: 788–802.

Bazykin, A.D. 1974. Volterra's system and the Michaelis–Menten equation. (In Russian). In: V.A. Ratner (ed.), *Problems in Mathematical Genetics.* USSR Academy of Science, Novosibirsk. pp. 103–143. (Available in English as Structural and dynamic stability of model predator–prey systems. 1976. IIASA RM-76-8).*

Beard, J.S. 1953. The Savanna vegetation of the northern tropical America. *Biol. Monogr.* 23 (2): 149–215.

Beeton, A.D. 1969. Changes in the environment and biota of the Great Lakes. In: *Eutrophication: Causes, Consequences, Correctives.* National Academy of Sciences, Washington, D.C. pp. 150–187.

Bell, D.E. 1977a. A utility function for time streams having interperiod dependencies. *Oper. Res.* (in press).

Bell, D.E. 1977b. A decision analysis of objectives for a forest pest problem. In: D.E. Bell, R. Keeney, and H. Raiffa (eds.), *Conflicting Objectives in Decisions.* Wiley, Chichester. pp. 389–421.

Bellman, R. 1961. *Adaptive Control Processes: A Guided Tour.* Princeton University Press, Princeton, New Jersey.

Belyea, R., *et al.* 1975. The spruce budworm. *For. Chron.* 51: 135–160.

---

[1] In an effort to make the bibliography as current as possible, we have cited many works presently available only as publications of the International Institute for Applied Systems Analysis and the Institute of Animal Resource Ecology. These may be obtained from the following addresses:

* Documents and Publications
International Institute for
Applied Systems Analysis
Schloss Laxenburg
A-2361 Laxenburg
Austria

† Publications (attn. Ralf Yorque)
Institute of Animal Resource Ecology
University of British Columbia
Vancouver, British Columbia
V6T 1W5
Canada

Beverton, R.G.H., and S.J. Holt. 1957. *On the Dynamics of Exploited Fish Population.* Her Majesty's Stationery Office, London.

Blais, J.R. 1968. Regional variation in susceptibility of eastern North American forests to budworm attack based on history of outbreaks. *For. Chron.* 44: 17–23.

Bretsky, P.W., and D.M. Lorenz. 1969. Adaptive response to environmental stability: an unifying concept in paleoecology. *Proc. North Am. Paleontol. Conv. Pt. E:* 522–550.

Brewer, G.D. 1975. An analyst's view of the uses and abuses of modeling for decision making. Rand Corp. Paper P-5395.

Branscomb, L.M. 1977. Science in the White House: a new slant. *Science* 196: 848–852.

Bunnell, P. 1976. The spruce budworm: an ecosystem problem and modeling approach to managment. An eight-part slide–tape presentation (80 min.). Available from IRE.†

Bunnell, P., and D. Tait. 1974. A primer on models: why and how. A five-part slide-tape presentation (50 min.). Available from IRE.†

CTV, MAC, NPS. 1974. Parque Nacional Canaima. La Gran Sabana/Plan Rector. R. Gondelles A. (ed.), Caracas.

CVG. 1974. Informe Anual. Electrificacion del Caroni, C.A. Edit. Cromotip, Caracas.

Caughley, G. 1970. Eruption of ungulate populations, with emphasis on Himalayan thar in New Zealand. *Ecology* 51: 53–72.

Chambers, A. 1971. Simulation of Cottage Lot Subdivision: A Synthesis of Social, Economic and Environmental Concerns. Ph.D. Thesis, Univ. of British Columbia, Vancouver, Canada.

Christie, W.J. 1974. Changes in fish species composition of the Great Lakes. *J. Fish. Res. Board Canada* 31: 827–854.

Clark, W.C., and D.E. Bell. 1976. Intertemporal indicator evaluation. IRE W-7.†

Clark, W.C., D.D. Jones, and C.S. Holling. 1977. Lessons for ecological policy design: a case study of ecosystem management. IRE R-10-B.† (Also *Ecol. Modeling,* in press.)

Council on Environmental Quality. 1976. Environmental impact statements, an analysis of six years' experience by seventy federal agencies. President's Council on Environmental Quality, Washington, D.C.

Crozier, M. 1964. *The Bureaucratic Phenomena.* University of Chicago Press, Chicago.

Crutchfield, J.A. 1977. The fishery: economic maximization. In: D.V. Ellis (ed.), *Pacific Salmon: Management for People,* University of Victoria Press, Victoria, British Columbia, pp. 1–33.

Cyert, R.M. and J.G. March. 1963. *A Behavioral Theory of the Firm.* Prentice-Hall Inc., Englewood Cliffs, New Jersey, 332 pp.

Dasmann, R.E., J.P. Milton, and P.H. Freeman, 1973. *Ecological Principles for Economic Development.* Wiley, New York.

Etzioni, A. 1968. *The Active Society.* Free Press, New York.

Evans, G., G. Kullenberg, and J.H. Steele. 1976. A shear-diffusion model of plankton populations. International Council for Exploration of the Sea, Plankton Committee, CM 1976/L24.

Ewel, J.J., and A. Madriz. 1968. Zonas de vida de Venezuela. Memoria explicativa sobre el mapa ecologico. Editorial Sucre, Caracas.

Feldstein, M.S. 1964. The social time preference discount rate in cost–benefit analysis. *Econ. J.* 74: 360–379.

Fiering, M.B. 1974. Compressed policy analysis. In: Project status report: ecology and environment project. IIASA SR-74-2-EC.*

Fiering, M.B., and C.S. Holling. 1974. Management and standards for perturbed ecosystems. *Agro-ecosystems* 1: 301–321.

Foerster, R.E. 1968. The sockeye salmon. *Fish. Res. Board Can., Bull.* 162.

Ford Foundation. 1974. *The art of managing the environment.* New York.

Forrester, J. 1971. *Principles of Systems.* Wright-Allen Press, Cambridge, Massachusetts. 178pp.

Fox, I.K., and O.C. Herfindahl. 1964. Attainment of efficiency in satisfying demands for water resources. *Am. Econ. Rev.* 1964: 198–206.

Gallopin, G.C. 1977. Modelling Incompletely Specified Complex Systems. Third International Symposium on Trends in Mathematical Modelling. S.C. Bariloche, December 1976. UNESCO-Fundacion Bariloche.

Gilbert, N., A.P. Gutierrez, B.D. Fraser, and R.E. Jones. 1976. *Ecological Relationships.* W.H. Freeman, Reading, England.

Glendening, G. 1952. Some quantitative data on the increase of mesquite and cactus on a desert grassland range in southern Arizona. *Ecology* 33: 319–328.

Gomez-Pompa, A., C. Vazquez-Yanes, and S. Guevara. 1972. The tropical rain forest: a non-renewable resource. *Science* 177:762–765.

Goodall, D.W. 1972. Building and testing ecosystem models. In: J.N.R. Jeffers (ed.). *Mathematical Models in Ecology,* Blackwell, Oxford. pp. 173–194.

Goodman, D. 1975. The theory of diversity–stability relationships in ecology. *Q. Rev. Biol.* 50: 237–266.

Gross, J.E., J.E. Roelle, and G.L. Williams. 1973. Progress report: program onepop and information processor: a systems modelling and communication project. Colorado Cooperative Fish. Wildl. Res. Unit, Colorado State University, Fort Collins, Colorado.

Gulf Oil Corporation and Standard Oil Company of Indiana. 1976. Rio Blanco Oil Shale Project – Detailed Development Plan. 4 volumes.

Häfele, W. and R. Bürk. 1976. An attempt of long-range macroeconomic modeling in view of structural and technological change. IIASA RM-76-32.*

Hamilton, H.R., S.E. Goldstone, J.W. Milliman, A.L. Pugh, E.B. Roberts, and A. Zellner. 1969. Systems simulation for regional analysis: an application to river-basin planning. M.I.T. Press, Cambridge, Massachusetts.

Hardy, F. 1970. *Edafologia Tropical.* Herrero Hnos., Scus., S.A. Mexico.

Herrera, A.O., H.D. Scolnik, G. Chichilnisky, G.C. Gallopin, J.E. Hardoy, D. Mosovich, E. Oteiza, G.L. de Romero Brest, C.E. Saurez, and L. Talavera. 1976. Catastrophe or new society? A Latin American World Model. International Development Research Centre, Ottawa, Canada IDRC-064e.

Hidalgo, A. 1971. *Metodos Modernos de Riego de Superficie.* Aguilar, S.A. de Ediciones, Madrid.

Hilborn, R. 1973. A control system for FORTRAN simulation programming. *Simulation* 20: 172–175.

Hilborn, R. 1976. Optimal exploitation of multiple stocks by a common fishery: a new methodology. *J. Fish. Res. Board Can.* 33: 1–5.

Hilborn, R., C.S. Holling, and C.J. Walters. 1977. Managing the unknown, approaches to ecological policy design. In: J.J. Reisa (ed.), *Biological Analysis of Environmental Impacts.*

Hilborn, R., and R.M. Peterman. 1977. Changing management objectives. In: D.V. Ellis (ed.), *Pacific Salmon: Management for People.* University of Victoria Press, Victoria, British Columbia, pp. 68–98.

Hilborn, R. and C.J. Walters. 1977. Differing goals of salmon management on the Skeena River. *J. Fish. Res. Board Can.* 34: 64–72.

Himamowa, B. 1975. The Obergurgl model: a microcosm of economic growth in relation to limited ecological resources. *Nat. Resour.* 2: 10–21.

Holcomb Research Institute. 1976. *Environmental Modeling and Decision making: the United States Experience.* Praeger, New York.

Holling, C.S. 1965. The functional response of predators to prey density and its role in mimicry and population regulation. *Mem. Entomol. Soc. Can.* 45: 1–60.

Holling, C.S. 1969. Stability in ecological and social systems. In: *Diversity and Stability in Ecological Systems.* Brookhaven Symposium in Biology, Vol. 22, pp. 128–141.

Holling, C.S. 1972. Ecological models; a status report. In: A.K. Biswas (ed.), Proceedings of the International Symposium on Modelling Techniques in Water Resources Systems. Environment Canada, Ottawa 1: 3–20.

Holling, C.S. 1973. Resilience and stability of ecological systems. *Ann. Rev. Ecol. Syst.* 4: 1–23.

Holling, C.S. 1976. Resilience and stability of ecosystems. In: E. Jantsch and C.H. Waddington (eds.), *Evolution and Consciousness: Human Systems in Transition.* Addison-Wesley, Reading, Massachusetts. pp. 73–92.

Holling, C.S., 1976. Myths of ecology and energy. *In* Proceedings of a Conference on Future Strategies for Energy Development: *A Question of Scale*. Oak Ridge Associated Universities, Oak Ridge, Tennessee. pp. 34–49.

Holling, C.S., *et al.*, Forthcoming. *Ecological Policy Design: A Case Study of Forests, Insects, and Managers.* Wiley, Chichester.

Holling, C.S., and S. Buckingham. 1976. A behavioral model of predator–prey functional responses. *Behav. Sci.* 3: 183–195.

Holling, C.S., and A.D. Chambers. 1973. Resource science: the nurture of an infant. *BioScience* 23: 13–20.

Holling, C.S., and W.C. Clark. 1975. Notes towards a science of ecological management. In: W.H. van Dobben and R.H. Lowe-McConnell (eds.), *Unifying Concepts in Ecology*. Dr. W. Junk B.V. Publ., The Hague, pp. 247–251.

Holling, C.S., and G.B. Dantzig. 1976. Determining optimal policies for ecosystems. IRE-R-7-B.†

Holling, C.S., and M.A. Goldberg. 1971. Ecology and planning. *J. Am. Inst. Planners.* 37 (4): 221–230.

Holling, C.S., C.C. Huang, and I. Vertinsky. 1976. Technological change and resource flow alignments: an investigation of systems growth under alternative funding/feedback. In: R. Trappl (ed.), *Progress in Cybernetics and Systems Research*. Hemisphere, Washington, D.C.

Holling, C.S., D.D. Jones, and W.C. Clark. 1975. Spruce budworm/forest management. IRE PR-5.†

Hornbeck, J.W., R.S. Pierce, and C.A. Federer, 1970. Streamflow changes after forest clearing in New England. *Water Resour. Res.*, 6: 1124–1132.

Hueck, K., 1968. Mapa de la vegetacion de la Repulica de Venezuela. Inst. For.

Huffaker, C.B. 1958. Experimental studies on predation: dispersion factors and predator–prey oscillations. *Hilgardia* 27: 343–383.

Hutchinson, G.E. 1970. Ianula: an account of the history and development of the Lago di Monterosi, Latium, Italy. *Trans. Am. Philos. Soc.* 16: 1–178.

Isaev, A.S., and R.G. Khlebopros. 1977. Inertial and noninertial factors regulating forest insect population density. In: G. Norton, and C.S. Holling (eds.), *Proceedings of a Conference on Pest Management.* IIASA, Laxenburg, Austria. pp. 317–339.

Jeffers, J.N.R. (ed.). 1972. *Mathematical Models in Ecology.* Blackwell, Oxford.

Joint Economic Committee. 1969. *The Analysis and Evaluation of Public Expenditures: The PPB System.* U.S. Congress, 91st Congress, 1st Session.

Jones, D.D. 1975. The application of catastrophe theory to ecological systems. In: G.S. Innis (ed.), *New Directions in the Analysis of Ecological Systems. Part 2.* Simulation Councils, Inc. La Jolla, California. pp. 133–148. (Also appeared in *Simulation* 29 (1): 1–15, 1977.)

Jones, D.D., and C.J. Walters. 1976. Catastrophe theory and fisheries regulation. *J. Fish. Res. Board Can.* 33 (12): 2829–2833.

Kane, J. 1972. A primer for a new cross-impact language – KSIM. *Tech. Forecasting Soc. Change,* 4: 129–142.

Kane, J., W. Thompson, and I. Vertinsky. 1972. Health care delivery: a policy simulator. *Socio-Econ. Plan. Sci.* 6: 283–293.

Kane, J., I. Vertinsky, and W. Thompson. 1973. KSIM: a methodology for interactive resource policy simulation. *Water Resour. Res.* 9: 65–79.

Keeney, R.L. 1977. A utility function for examining policy affecting salmon in the Skeena River. *J. Fish. Res. Board Can.* 34: 49–63.

Keeney, R.L., and H. Raiffa. 1976. *Decisions with Multiple Objectives.* Wiley, New York.

Koopmans, T.C. 1974. Proof for a case where discounting advances the doomsday. *Rev. Econ. Stud.* 1974: 117–120.

Krutilla, J.V. 1969. Efficiency goals, market failure, and substitute of public for private action. In: Joint Economic Committee, *The Analysis and Evaluation of Public Expenditures: the PPB System.* Joint Economic Committee, 91st Congress, 1st Session, pp. 277–290.

Larkin, P.A. and W.E. Ricker. 1964. Further information on sustained yields from fluctuating environments. *J. Fish. Res. Board Can.* 21: 1–7.

Layard, R. (ed.). 1972. *Cost–Benefit Analysis.* Penguin Books, Harmondsworth, Middlesex, England.

Lee, D.B., Jr. 1973. Requiem for large-scale models. *J. Am. Inst. Planners,* 34: 163–177.

Leopold, L.B., F.E. Clarke, B.B. Hanshaw, and J.R. Balsley. 1971. A procedure for evaluating environmental impact. Geol. Survey Circ. 645. U.S. Government Printing Office, Washington, D.C.

Lind, R., and M. Greenburger (eds.). (In press.) *Rate of Discount: Its Meaning and Appropriateness in Energy Investment and R & D Decision Making.* Resources for the Future, Washington, D.C.

Lipset, S.M. 1976. The wavering polls. *Public Interest,* 43: 70–89.

Liska, A.E. (ed.). 1975. *The Consistency Controversy: Readings on the Impact of Attitude on Behavior.* Halsted Press, New York.

Ludwig, D., D.D. Jones, and C.S. Holling. 1977. Qualitative analysis of an insect outbreak system: the spruce budworm and forest. *J. Anim. Ecol.*

Mar, B.W. 1974. Problems encountered in multidisciplinary resources and environmental simulation models development. *J. Environ. Manage.* 2: 83–100.

MacLeod, J.R. 1976. Salmonid enhancement program – framework of strategies: a discussion paper. Internal Fisheries and Marine Service document, 17 pp.

MacLeod, J.R. 1977. Enhancement technology: a positive statement. In: D.V. Ellis (ed.), *Pacific Salmon: Management for People.* University of Victoria Press, Victoria, British Columbia. pp. 137–147.

McAllister, C.S., R.J. LeBrasseur, and T.R. Parsons. 1972. Stability of enriched aquatic ecosystems. *Science* 175: 562–565.

Meadows, D.H., D.L. Meadows, J. Randers, and W.W. Behrems. 1972. *The Limits to Growth.* Universe Books, New York.

Miller, D.R. 1974. Sensitivity analysis and validation of simulation models. *J. Theor. Biol.* 48: 345–360.

Mitchell, R., R.A. Mayer, and J. Downhower. 1976. An evaluation of three biome programs. *Science* 192: 859–865.

Moore, P.G., and H. Thomas. 1976. *The Anatomy of Decisions.* Penguin Books, Harmondsworth, Middlesex, England.

Morris, R.F. (ed.). 1963. The dynamics of epidemic spruce budworm populations. *Mem. Entomol. Soc. Con.* No. 31.

Munn, R.E. (ed.). 1975. Environmental impact assessment: principles and procedures. SCOPE Report 5. SCOPE Secretariat, Paris, 160 pp.

Niering, W.A., and R.H. Goodwin. 1974. Creation of relatively stable shrublands with herbicides: arresting "succession" on rights-of-way and pastureland. *Ecology* 55: 784–795.

Northcote, T.G. (ed.). 1969. *Symposium on Salmon and Trout in Streams.* H. R. MacMillan Lectures in Fisheries, Institute of Fisheries, University of British Columbia, Vancouver.

Noy-Meir, I. 1975. Stability of grazing systems: an application of predator–prey graphs. *J. Ecol.* 63: 459–481.

Nye, P.H., and D.J. Greenland. 1965. The soil under shifting cultivation. Technical Communication No. 51. Commonwealth Bureau of Soils, Commonwealth Agricultural Bureau, Franham Royal, Bucks, England.

Ogawa, H., K. Yoda, K. Ogino, and T. Kira, 1965. Comparative ecological studies on three main types of forest vegetation in Thailand. II. Plant Biomass. *Nat. Life Southeast Asia* 6: 49–81.

O'Neill, R.V. 1973. Error analysis of ecological models. In: D.J. Nelson (ed.), *Radionuclides in Ecosystems,* Proc. 3rd Nat. Symp. on Radioecology, USAEC-CONF-71501.

O'Neill, R.V. 1975. Management of large-scale environmental modeling projects. In: C.S. Russell (ed.), *Ecological Modeling in a Resource Management Framework.* Resources for the Future Inc., Washington, D.C., and Johns Hopkins University Press, Baltimore, Maryland. pp. 251–282.

Ovington, J.D. 1965. *Woodlands.* The English University Press Ltd., London.

Patten, B.C. (ed.). 1971. *Systems Analysis and Simulation in Ecology.* Vol. I. Academic Press, New York.

Patten, B.C. 1971. A primer for ecological modelling and simulation with analog and digital computers. In: B.C. Patten (ed.), *Systems Analysis and Simulation in Ecology,* Vol. 1. Academic Press, New York. pp. 3–121.

Paulik, G.J., A.S. Hourston, and P.A. Larkin. 1967. Exploitation of multiple stocks by a common fishery. *J. Fish. Res. Board Can.* 24: 2527–2537.

Peterman, R.M. 1975. New techniques for policy evaluation in ecological systems: methodology for a case study of Pacific salmon fisheries. *J. Fish. Res. Board Can.* 32: 2179–2188.

Peterman, R.M. 1977a. Graphical evaluation of environmental management options: examples from a forest–insect pest system. *Ecol. Model.* 3: 133–148.

Peterman, R.M. 1977b. A simple mechanism that causes collapsing stability regions in exploited salmonid populations. *J. Fish. Res. Board Can.* 34 (8): 1130–1142.

Peterson, R.W. 1976. The impact statement – Part II. *Science* 193: 193.

Popper, K.R. 1959. *The Logic of Scientific Discovery.* Basic Books, New York.

Raiffa, H. 1968. *Decision Analysis.* Addison-Wesley, Reading, Massachusetts.

Ricker, W.E. 1954. Stock and recruitment. *J. Fish. Res. Board Can.* 11: 559–623.

Ricker, W.E. 1958. Maximum sustained yields from fluctuating environments and mixed stocks. *J. Fish. Res. Board Can.* 15: 991–1006.

Ricker, W.E. 1975. Computation and interpretation of biological statistics of fish populations. *Fish. Res. Board Can. Bull.* 191.

Roedel, P.M. (ed.). 1975. Optimum sustainable yield as a concept in fisheries management. Spec. Pub. No. 9. American Fisheries Society, Washington, D.C.

Rosenzweig, M.L., and R.H. MacArthur. 1963. Graphical representation and stability conditions of predator–prey interactions. *Am. Nat.* 97: 209–223.

Ross, G.J.S. 1972. Stochastic model fitting by evolutionary operation. In: J.N.R. Jeffers (ed.), *Mathematical Models in Ecology,* Blackwell, Oxford. pp. 297–308.

Rutter, A.J. 1963. Studies in the water relations of *Pinus silvestris* in plantation conditions. I. Measurements of rainfall and interception. *J. Ecol.* 51: 191–203.

Salazar, L.C. 1962. Fenomeno de sedimentacion del Rio Caroni con relacion a la vida util de la Represa Guri. Informe Interno, EDELCA, Venezuela. 24 pp.

Sasaba, T., and K. Kiritani. 1975. A systems model and computer simulation of the green rice leafhopper populations in control programs. *Res. Pop. Ecol.* 16: 231–244.

Schindler, D.W. 1976. The impact statement boondoggle. *Science* 192: 509.

Scolnik, H.D. 1973. On a methodological criticism of the Meadows World 3 Model. Tech. Rep. Dept. Math., Fundacion Bariloche, Argentina, 10 pp.

Simon, H.A. 1962. The architecture of complexity. *Proc. Am. Philos. Soc.* 106: 467–482.

Slovic, P., and S. Lichtenstein. 1971. Comparison of Bayesian and regression approaches to the study of information processing in judgement. *Organ. Behav. Hum. Performance,* 6: 649–744.

Smith, R.F., and R. van den Bosch. 1967. Integrated control. In: W.E. Kilgore and R.L. Doutt (eds.), *Pest Control.* Academic Press, New York. pp. 295–340.

Southwood, T.R.E., and H.N. Comins. 1976. A Synoptic population model. *J. Anim. Ecol.* 45: 949–965.

Stedinger, J. 1977. Spruce budworm management models. Ph.D. thesis. Harvard University, Cambridge, Massachusetts.

Steele, J.H. and E.W. Henderson. 1977. Plankton patches in the northern North Sea. *Fish. Math.* (in press).

Thom, R. 1975. *Structural Stability and Morphogenesis.* (Transl. from French by D.H. Fowler). Benjamin, Reading, Massachusetts.

Thompson, W., I. Vertinsky, and J. Kane. 1973. Canadian industrial policy – simulation and analysis. *Long Range Planning* 6: 66–73.

Tribus, M. 1969. *Rational Descriptions, Decisions, and Designs.* Pergamon Press, New York.

Vila, P. 1960. *Geografia de Venezuela.* Vol. I. Direccion de Cultura y Bellas Artes, Departamento de Publicaciones. Ministerio de Educacion. Tipografia Vargas, S.A. Caracas.

Walters, C.J. 1971. Systems ecology: the systems approach and mathematical models in ecology. In: E.P. Odum (ed.), *Fundamentals of Ecology.* 3rd ed. Saunders, Philadelphia. pp. 276–292.

Walters, C.J. 1974. An interdisciplinary approach to development of watershed simulation models. *Technol. Forecast. Soc. Change* 6: 299–323.

Walters, C.J. 1975a. Foreclosure of options in sequential resource development decisions. IIASA RR-75-12.*

Walters, C.J. 1975b. Optimal harvest strategies for salmon in relation to environmental variability and uncertain production parameters. *J. Fish. Res. Board Can.* 32: 1777–1784.

Walters, C.J. 1977. Confronting uncertainty. In: D.V. Ellis (ed.), *Pacific Salmon: Management for People.* University of Victoria Press, Victoria, British Columbia. pp. 261–297.

Walters, C.J., and S. Buckingham. 1975. A control system for intraseason salmon management. In: *Proceedings of a Workshop on Salmon Management,* IIASA CP-75-2. pp. 105–137.*

Walters, C.J., and R. Hilborn. 1976. Adaptive control of fishing systems. *J. Fish Res. Board Can.* 33: 145–159.

Walters, C.J., and R.M. Peterman. 1974. A systems approach to the dynamics of spruce budworm in New Brunswick. Proc. 23rd Mtg. Entomol. Soc. Can. *Quaest. Entomol.* 10: 177–186.

Walters, C.J., R. Hilborn, E. Oguss, R.M. Peterman, and J.M. Stander. 1974. Development of a simulation model of Mallard duck populations. Canadian Wildlife Service, Occas. Paper No. 20.

Walters, C.J., R. Hilborn, and R.M. Peterman. 1975. Computer simulation of barren-ground caribou dynamics. *Ecol. Model.* 1: 303–315.

Watt, K.E.F. 1968a. A computer approach to analysis of data on weather, population fluctuation and disease. In: W.P. Lowry (ed.), *Biometeorology.* Oregon State University Press, Corvallis. pp. 145–159.

Watt, K.E.F. 1968b. *Ecology and Resource Management: a Quantitative Approach.* McGraw-Hill, New York.

Watt, K.E.F. 1974. *The* Titanic *Effect.* Sinauer, Stamford, Connecticut.

Watt, K.E.F. 1977. Why won't anyone believe us? *Simulation* 28: 1–3.

Wilimovsky, N.J. (ed.). 1962. *Symposium on Pink Salmon.* H. R. MacMillan Lectures in Fisheries, Institute of Fisheries, University of British Columbia, Vancouver.

Winkler, C. 1975. An optimization technique for the budworm forest–pest model. IIASA RM-75-11.*

Zeeman, E.C. 1976. Catastrophe theory. *Sci. Am.* 234: 65–83.

Index

Page numbers in italic indicate illustrations; a lowercase *t* following the page number indicates a table.